From
the
Ground
Up

From the Ground Up

**The Autobiography
of an
Aeronautical Engineer**

Fred E. Weick and James R. Hansen

Smithsonian Institution Press

Washington and London

Library of Congress Cataloging-in-Publication Data

Weick, Fred E.
    From the ground up, the autobiography of an aeronautical engineer.
    Includes index.
    1. Weick, Fred E.   2. Aeronautical engineers—United States—
Biography.   I. Hansen, James R.   II. Title.
TL540.W36A3   1987   629.13'0092'4[B]   87-23414
ISBN 0-87474-950-6

British Library Cataloguing-in-Publication data available

∞ The paper used in this publication meets the minimum requirements
of the American National Standard for Performance of Paper for Printed
Library Materials Z39.48—1984

Cover: *Ercoupe equipped with Edo floats, 1946. The seaplane is flying over
the East River near Manhattan. Photo from the collection of Fred E. Weick*

Frontispiece: *Fred Weick is shown during flight tests in 1945 of the Ercoupe
with an Everell automatic variable-pitch propeller made by Koppers. Photo
from the collection of Fred E. Weick*

Edited by Virginia Wageman

Contents

Foreword

Arriving at Langley Field, Virginia, in 1934 I had the great good fortune of being put to work under the supervision of Fred E. Weick. Working with Fred I had the feeling that the airplane was being reinvented, as indeed it was. Never mind that the general form and arrangement of the airplane had been well established for many years, Fred felt strongly that every function of the airplane needed to be studied from a logical point of view, without prejudice, so that designers and operators could make whatever changes were necessary to improve those functions.

Occasionally, Fred's strictly rational approach came up against deep-seated human resistance. Thus, it was difficult for Fred to show many members of the aviation community that both hands and both feet were not needed to control the airplane. Two controls, elevator and ailerons with one hand, the throttle with the other, were adequate and, actually, safer—unless one wanted to do crazy things like snap rolls and spins. Fred, as always, wanted this intuitive result quantified, a desire that led me, as a new employee of the National Advisory Committee for Aeronautics at Langley

Field, to make dynamical studies of maneuvers. Naturally, my own Fred Weick–designed Ercoupe airplane (N94378), now forty-two years old, has these innovative control features, and it flies perfectly. I would not trade it for any other airplane.

Those who worked with Fred Weick were privileged to work with one of the great people in American aviation. One tended to lose sight of that fact in everyday contacts. His humility and unassuming nature played down his accomplishments, but history shows that the accomplishments are there and that they are indeed significant. Though his name is not well known to the public, Fred has made as many contributions to the field of general aviation as anyone I can think of.

Some of Fred's most important contributions were in the area of improved safety. In flying, nothing is more important than safety, particularly in general aviation where the pilots often have little experience. So it was awfully important that designers like Fred did everything they could to improve the safety record of their small airplanes.

The reader of this book will have a dual reward: learning how engineering should be done, and making the intimate acquaintance of two wonderful human beings, Fred Weick and his beautiful and gracious wife, Dorothy.

Robert T. Jones
Los Altos Hills, California

Preface

When we think of a pioneer, we usually picture someone in the mold of Daniel Boone or Davy Crockett, wearing buckskins, fighting off Indians, and opening the way to settlements in our western frontier lands. But the English word "pioneer" has a more ancient history. It derives from the French word *pied*, meaning "foot," which in turn comes from the Latin word *pedis* (as in our English word "pedestrian"). In the legions of the Roman Empire, a *pedonis* was a foot soldier whose job was to build and repair roads. The *pedoni* were in fact engineers, members of a special construction corps who prepared the way for the main body of the Roman army. Etymologically, then, it is appropriate to equate pioneering activities with engineering.

The subject and co-author of this book, Fred E. Weick (pronounced Wyke), is an aeronautical pioneer. He meets and exceeds all the criteria for such. First, he is an engineer, and an extraordinarily talented one. He is in fact one of the first graduates of an American engineering school (the University of Illinois) to have pursued a career in aeronautics.

Second, he is one of the first engineers employed by the original U.S. Air Mail Service. This was during the early 1920s, and one of Fred Weick's assignments was to locate and establish a series of emergency flying fields for the first night flying of mail through the central United States, from Chicago to Omaha. This was pioneering work in the literal sense.

Third, over the years Fred Weick made many significant contributions to the advancement of aeronautical technology. In 1925/26, after becoming an employee of the National Advisory Committee for Aeronautics (NACA)—the agency that preceded the National Aeronautics and Space Administration (NASA)—he helped to design a major new wind tunnel for full-scale propeller research that would not have been built if he had not suggested the need for such research. This wind tunnel, which was built by the NACA at its Langley Aeronautical Laboratory in Virginia—the United States government's first and, until 1941, only aeronautical research center—was the first facility of its kind anywhere in the world. In this pioneering tunnel, Fred and his Langley associates designed the original NACA low-drag engine cowling, for which the NACA won its first Robert J. Collier Trophy in 1929, a prestigious award given annually by the National Aeronautic Association for the "greatest achievement in aviation in America, the value of which has been thoroughly demonstrated by use during the preceding year." During the same period Fred wrote one of the first textbooks on the design of aircraft propellers, a book (published by McGraw-Hill in 1930) that is now considered a classic.

Fred's lifelong dream was to build a low-cost and simple-to-fly airplane that was so inherently safe and inexpensive to operate and maintain that air travel in it could, for certain purposes, compete with automobiles as a mode of private and family transportation. He pursued his dream in earnest beginning in the early 1930s, when he and a small group of colleagues from Langley in a private venture designed the W-1. This home-built experimental airplane had several unique features, including an elevator whose upward travel was limited to the point where the airplane could not be forced into a spin. Another innovative feature of the W-1 was its coordinated control system. Fred's idea here was to reduce the number of controls from three to two by connecting the ailerons and rudder, thus eliminating the possibility of crossing these two controls and thereby simplifying the process of learning to fly.

In order to make it easier both to taxi and land the plane, Fred also equipped the W-1 with what was then an unconventional undercarriage: he moved the two main wheels a short distance *behind* the plane's center of gravity, took away the tail wheel, and added a nose wheel that could be steered. Fred dubbed this new undercarriage a "tricycle gear," and it was a name that stuck. Soon, starting with the Douglas DC-4, all American airliners were designed with a version of the tricycle landing gear designed by Fred. This, as we know, was a lasting and substantial contribution—just take a look at the landing gear on the Space Shuttle, which also uses the tricycle arrangement.

In the late 1930s, after leaving Langley, Fred began designing the now-famous Ercoupe, a two-seat, all-metal, low-wing cantilever monoplane that incorporated the W-1's tricycle gear arrangement as well as an improved version of the W-1's coordinated control system. The Ercoupe had no rudder pedals—as produced before World War II, the airplane was available with or without rudder pedals—but instead was flown entirely by the control wheel. The plane was first manufactured by the Engineering and Research Corporation (ERCO) of Washington, D.C. (thus the name Ercoupe), a firm that later moved a short distance to the Maryland suburb of Riverdale.

For its day the Ercoupe was a very clean design. With its original 65-horsepower engine, the little plane cruised at 100 miles per hour (and a top speed of 118 MPH) on only four or five gallons of fuel an hour. But its popular appeal was its safety and simplicity. It was so easy to fly that many student pilots mastered the Ercoupe in five hours or less.

Fred eventually earned two major awards for his Ercoupe design: the Sylvanus Albert Reed Award, which was presented to him by Dr. George W. Lewis, director of research for the NACA, in 1945, for the year's most "notable contribution to the aeronautical sciences . . . the beneficial influence of which on the development of practical aeronautics is apparent"; and the W. H. Fawcett Award, in 1946, "for the greatest scientific contribution to the advancement of aviation as a public service." This second award was presented to him by World War I flying ace Eddie Rickenbacker on the CBS radio program "We the People."

But perhaps the greatest tribute to Fred is that some 3,000 of the 6,000 or so Ercoupes that were manufactured are still flying today.

Subsequent to the Ercoupe, Fred moved on in the late 1940s to Texas A&M College, where he designed a revolutionary agricultural airplane known as the Ag-1 and, without any previous experience in the field, quickly became a national expert on the many problems of agricultural aviation. The basic features of the Texas A&M Ag-1 airplane were eventually incorporated into the Piper Pawnee, which Fred helped to build when he went to work for Piper at Vero Beach, Florida, in the late 1950s. Both the Ag-1 and the Pawnee set life-saving standards for agricultural airplanes.

In the early 1960s Fred became chief designer for the Piper Cherokee, a series of popular, low-cost general aviation aircraft. He remained with Piper at Vero Beach until his retirement at age seventy in 1969.

Since that time Fred has remained active as a consultant to aviation firms and as a member of various aeronautical associations. Although he is now nearly ninety years old, he still attends the Experimental Aircraft Association's annual fly-in at Oshkosh, Wisconsin, a pilgrimage he has made for the past several years. At Oshkosh he meets with old and new friends, many of whom are Ercoupe owners, and he presents technical and historical forums to large and appreciative audiences.

It has been a great honor and joy for me to get to know Fred Weick. Over the course of my short professional career as an aerospace historian, it has been my pleasure to meet and interview a number of leading figures in American aviation, past and present. But no one that I have met has impressed me more than Fred Weick. It is not just his record as an aeronautical engineer that is remarkable; it is his ingenuity and diligence and drive as a researcher and his thoughtfulness and concern and fair-mindedness as a human being. The thing that pleases me most about the publication of this book is that people who have never heard the name Fred Weick will get to know him for the great man that he is.

I advise the reader to be on the lookout for two special features of Fred Weick's personality. The first is his ability to change from one field of aeronautical engineering to another quickly, easily, and with great success. Fred changed jobs several times during his long career, especially in the 1920s and 1930s, and he was equally productive after each change. His general training as an engineer was so solid, and his mind so open to challenges, that new and different tasks caused him no great difficulty. This was particularly evident when he moved from ERCO to Texas A&M in the late 1940s. Before the move Fred had had virtually no experience whatsoever with the problems of agricultural aviation. Within a few years, however, no one in the country knew more about mesquite control, aerial spraying systems, nozzle sizes and arrangements, and chemical fertilizers and insecticides than did Fred Weick. In other words, in the span of two or three years he went from knowing nothing about aerial application to being one of the most respected and influential national experts on the subject.

In the 1940s and 1950s Fred had various opportunities to pursue different fields of aeronautical research and development, and personally I am a little sorry that Fred did not return to the National Advisory Committee for Aeronautics, where he might have become a director of one of its national laboratories and eventually might have played a leading role in NASA and the space program. Fred had a chance to do this, but he chose not to because he was happiest as a researcher and developer, a hands-on doer, not as an administrator.

I am also a little sorry that he did not choose to go to work for a major manufacturer of commercial airliners like Boeing or Douglas or for a company like Northrop or McDonnell that was involved in building high performance aircraft for the military services. I am sure that Fred would have made significant contributions with such a company.

But Fred Weick's dream was to build small and safe airplanes at reasonable cost for private owners, and thereby make the joys and conveniences of aviation directly accessible to middle-class Americans. Surely he would have become better known if he had moved out of the field of general aviation, but he would not have been pursuing his dream. Today's incarnation of Fred Weick, Burt Rutan, could be working at NASA, too, or he could be applying his design genius directly to the next-generation fighter plane or bomber, but who then would have built the Voyager? Historians like myself can ask "what if" questions as much as they like and wonder like I do what would have happened if Weick had gone in 1936 not to ERCO but to Douglas, or in 1948 to McDonnell or back to the NACA Langley instead of to Texas A&M, or in 1957 to NASA instead of to Piper, but the fact of the matter is that Fred Weick went where he could keep his dream of the W-1 alive.

We should all be glad that he chose the course he did. It is too bad, however, that the general aviation industry today is in such miserable shape. That is one of Fred's greatest disappointments.

The second outstanding feature of Fred's personality that the reader might want to keep an eye out for is his unbelievable diligence. Only a few hours after his first child was born in the 1920s, for instance, he went to work at Langley expecting to put in a full day. It took some strong urging from his fellow workers and from his boss to get him to take the day off. Another illustration involves his writing of the propeller textbook. In order to complete the book, Fred got up for weeks on end before the sun came up in order to put in two or three quiet hours of writing before breakfast and time to leave for work. And Fred was as careful and organized as he was hard-working. During his visit to the Schwarz propeller plant in Germany in 1937, he filled twelve notebooks with information about what he was seeing. On the ocean voyage home, despite rough seas, he sorted all of these notes by subject. All of these incidents are remembered by Fred in this book, but he does not give himself the credit for hard work that is his due.

While working with him on this book, I stayed for a very pleasurable week at the Weick home in Vero Beach and was thus able to observe Fred's energetic work habits firsthand. Fred (he turned eighty-seven one of the days of my visit) woke up at 6:30 each morning, and before he came to the breakfast table, he swam twenty-five brisk laps in his unheated pool. (I dragged myself out of bed, fifty-three years his junior, usually just in time to see Fred drying himself off.) After dressing, he ate a hearty breakfast, usually a dish of whole grain and nut cereal with milk, two poached eggs, toasted muffins, orange juice, and black coffee. (Though I never have more than coffee so early in the morning, I could tell that Dorothy, Fred's wife, was not going to let me get away with that, so I ate the same thing Fred did. I can't tell you how much better it made me feel; I was certain that I had the answer to Fred's long and incredibly vital life. After I said that out loud, Dorothy made me take a box of Fred's cereal home in my suitcase!)

One morning while I was with the Weicks I slept in ten or fifteen minutes later than usual. Fred was worried that something was wrong with me (something was, I was lazy), and he tapped on my door to ask if anything was wrong. His concern was sincere, but I also think he wanted to make sure that we didn't waste time. We had a lot of work to do that day if we were going to get certain things about the book decided before I returned to my home in Virginia.

After working a steady nine hours that day, with a forty-five-minute break for a substantial lunch, the Weicks took me out for a marvelous seafood dinner at a restaurant right on the oceanfront. (I'm tempted to relate what Fred had for dinner, but I think the reader already appreciates his appetite.) When we returned home two hours later, I was prepared for a soft armchair, perhaps a drink, relaxed small talk, maybe even a little television. After all, it was Saturday night. But Fred, eighty-seven years old, wanted to work—which we did, until just before midnight. The man is amazing. No wonder he has accomplished as much as he did.

I could go on and on, but it's time for the reader to meet Fred up close and personal and to let Fred speak for himself. I guarantee one thing: you won't be sorry you've met him. No one ever has been.

James R. Hansen

Acknowledgments

This book would not have been written except for the fact that my son Donald and his wife, Emily, gave me a tape recorder for Christmas in 1975, and I started to amuse myself by taping my aeronautical reminiscences. It might have stopped there but for my niece and daughter-in-law, Jean Church Weick, who, after historians became interested in certain aspects of my life story, volunteered to transcribe the tapes and spent many hours putting them on paper. Again it would have rested there except that Dr. James Hansen, NASA historian and professor of history at Auburn University in Alabama, became interested in reworking the transcripts, adding new material, and creating a real book.

Much of the activity described in our book would not have occurred without the cooperation of my "infinitely better half," Dorothy (this is our friend George Haddaway's term for my wife). Dorothy not only sewed the fabric covering of the experimental W-1 airplane and allowed me to dope the control surfaces in our bedroom in 1933, but she has been a great support and help all through the years. And by my side she has also enjoyed flying light airplanes all over the United States and parts of Mexico and Canada.

F.E.W.

1.

Fancy for Flight
(1903–1923)

This photo was taken in 1903. I was four years old.

1.

From Model Planes
to the Air Mail Service

When the Wright brothers made their first powered flight in 1903, I was four years old. Of course, news of that history-making performance went right by me at my home in Berwyn, Illinois, a western suburb of Chicago, just as it passed practically unnoticed by the rest of the world. I did not have the slightest inkling that this event hundreds of miles away, which had no immediate effect on me or anyone around me, would point the direction for my entire life.

The Wrights were far ahead of their contemporaries at that time, and I believe that the secret of their success was that they learned to fly and control the airplane in glider form before they put power into it. They learned a great deal about the use of aerodynamic surfaces to control the airplane in a satisfactory manner, and together with the experience they had had as pilots, they were able to fly the plane without difficulty when they did put power into it. After their first flights they worked in Dayton for several years to perfect both the machine, "the Flyer," as they called it, and their own techniques in handling it. Five years later, in 1908, they gained great public notice when they obtained a contract to furnish an airplane to the army; Orville Wright demonstrated this airplane in Fort Myer, Virginia, just across the Potomac River from Washington, D.C., at about the same time that his brother, Wilbur, was demonstrating another model in France. Wilbur's flying created a sensation in Europe because, as one Frenchman said, the French were as children compared to the Wrights in their aeronautical capabilities. The progress in aeronautics was so rapid after this time that by 1910 more than 1,000 airplanes had been built and flown in Europe and America. Companies such as Wright and Curtiss in this country and Blériot, Farman, and others in Europe were producing airplanes on a regular basis. Louis Blériot himself had produced more than 300 flying machines. When he flew across the English Channel in 1909, Blériot destroyed the isolation of England from a military standpoint.

It was not until 1911 that I became interested in flying. I got my dad, an artist who made his living by painting family portraits, to take me to an air meet at Grant Park in downtown Chicago. There on the lakefront I saw my first airplanes, including ones built by the Wrights, by Glenn Curtiss, and by the French pioneer Blériot. During this air meet I found out about a little flying field in nearby Cicero, Illinois, which was only about five miles east toward Chicago from where we lived in Berwyn. This field was run under the auspices of the Aero Club of Illinois, an affiliate of the Aero Club of America. I was soon spending my spare time in Cicero watching the flying. Some of the same types of airplanes that I had seen at the Grant Park meet were on hand all of the time in Cicero and others came in to the field occasionally. I remember particularly that a man by the name of Max Lilly flew a Wright Model B airplane and a "Baby Wright" airplane much of the time and even gave some lessons in them. I learned later that Matty Laird and Kathryn Stinson had learned to fly there during the particular period of my visits, but I did not meet Matty until later. At a Cicero Field air meet I also saw Lincoln Beachey, one of the most famous early exhibition fliers, loop-the-loop. I believe Beachey was the first to loop-the-loop in this country.

Some unusual experimental airplanes came to Cicero. One that I remember in particular was a tandem wing affair much like the original Langley aerodrome but with sliding "window" openings in the wings that would open up for lateral control when the pilot wanted one wing to go down. This airplane was actually built in

While in grade school I made models of various boats and airplanes, including a stick model of the 1910 Curtiss Pusher, the canard design I am holding in my left hand. Notice the dihedral on its main wing. My sailboat is plainly visible to the left of the photo, but my motorboat is hard to make out.

both model and full-scale forms but, so far as I know, neither one ever flew. I remember that the inventor would harangue the public on Saturday afternoons, using his model to show how the sliding "windows" would open and close.

The Illinois Model Aero Club was operating under the sponsorship of the Aero Club of Illinois, and before long I was making models and competing in their Saturday afternoon contests. Our flying models were mostly what we called stick models; we made them by having two sticks come together at the front and then spread out like a *V* at the rear. Along each stick there was a rubberband motor with a propeller at the rear, and across the sticks were two "main planes"—what we would now call wings, a small one in front in canard form. These models flew rather well, and we could have flights of many hundred feet—even up to about half a mile.

On September 9, 1912, I got a day off from the seventh grade to see the Gordon Bennett Cup Race, which was being held at a place called Clearing, west of Chicago near where the present Midway Airport is located. I took a streetcar from Berwyn into California Avenue in Chicago, then south to Sixty-third Street and then an-

I saw Jules Vedrines fly this sleek Deperdussin airplane to victory in the Gordon Bennett Cup Race in Chicago in 1912.

other one west on Sixty-third to the end of the line. Then I had to walk a couple of miles. Now, of course, the area is entirely built up, an industrial district full of railroad yards, but at that time it consisted of large open fields.

Only three airplanes—all French—were ready for the race. Curtiss and Wright were busy manufacturing commercially by then and did not furnish racers, and the only other American racers were not ready. I was able to get up close to the racing planes and examine them in detail. I was greatly impressed by the two Deperdussin planes in particular: they were not only far better streamlined but also had an innovative control system (basically the same as the system that is generally used today) with a wheel that was moved fore and aft for longitudinal or elevator control and a foot-operated rudder. (Turning the wheel did not operate ailerons, as it typically does today; rather, it warped the wings in the manner of the control system used by the Wrights.) During the race my admiration for the Deperdussins grew even greater. As was the custom at the time, the airplanes were flown one at a time, and their time to cover the course was taken. Both Deperdussin racers exceeded 100 miles per hour, the first time this had ever been achieved by a plane in a closed course. The winning plane, a Deperdussin flown by Jules Vedrines, which was powered by a 14-cylinder Gnome rotary engine delivering 160 horsepower, clocked 105.5 miles per hour and broke the world's straightaway speed record also.

While the racing planes were making their runs, Max Lilly from Cicero Field circled his Wright Model B way up about 600 to 800 feet above the ground; he seemed to be almost standing still at his speed of something less than 40 miles per hour. For the first time, airplanes were shown to be faster than steamships or railroads, and I was quite inspired by the future possibilities.

During 1912, 1913, and the early part of 1914 I continued to go to Cicero Field to watch the flying and engage in the model plane competitions. In this period I made a number of models, not only airplanes but also two motorboats, a sailboat, and some other items. My prize models, however, were a Blériot monoplane and a Curtiss biplane. I completed the Blériot monoplane just before my folks' fifteenth wedding anniversary in 1912; it was 32 inches long, had a 36-inch wing spread and a 12-inch propeller, with shellacked silk stretched over one-eighth-inch-square ribs for planes. I had taken it down into the basement and hidden it away so that no one would be bothered by it during the festivities. However, some of the guests found out about it and insisted that I fly it for the party. I had not yet tried to fly it, I said, and moreover it was barely dry from its last varnishing. But everyone insisted.

The people lined up on both sides of the sidewalk and I, in my innocence, wound up the rubber-band propeller and started it off down the sidewalk on the assumption that it would go straight along the sidewalk and take off and make a flight. I hoped all that would happen at any rate. What did happen, though, was that it started off all right down the sidewalk and began to lift off slightly but curved off to the right. An elderly, portly gentleman named Mr. Seabrook, an old friend of the family, found it coming right toward him. He lifted up his feet and tried to get out of the way but brought one of them down right smack on one wing. That ended the life of that model.

The Curtiss model, which in fact I was a little happier with than the Blériot because it had complete control of its vertical and horizontal movements with just one lever, also came to a tragic end—if not quite in such a humorous manner. My folks were proud of it and insisted on hanging it up in a space in a doorway between our living room (or what we called the sitting room) and parlor. The model was hanging high between two sliding doors, and one time my mother, in getting ready to clean the parlor, closed them right on the model, crushing it. My poor mother was more disturbed than I was.

When I entered high school in the autumn of 1914 I was very fortunate in that an advisory system (instituted by my high school principal and future father-in-law, Harry V. Church) was in effect in which each pupil had an advisor, and in that my advisor was Ray Denslow, the science teacher. He soon found that I had no plans, that I knew only that high school was supposed to be harder than grade school and that in addition you had to take some of your studies home, which we hadn't had to do in grade school. Mr. Denslow asked me if I planned to go to college, and when he found I had no idea in that direction he started in asking me what my interests outside of school had been. When he found that I liked to make things and draw them and build them and fly airplanes, model airplanes that is, he finally asked me if I would like to make a living by designing things of that nature. I had no idea that one could be paid for having that sort of fun and was interested to learn that if I went into that sort of thing, which was called engineering, I would need further education beyond high school. My idea of an engineer at that time was the man at the throttle of a railway locomotive. He counseled me that while engineering could be learned outside of formal school, it was much easier and quicker to learn it in a regular accredited university or college. He therefore arranged my courses throughout the entire four-year period so that I should be able to get into any regular technical college or university in the country. I've been thankful ever since that I was immediately guided directly into the field for which I was probably best suited.

The Cicero flying field was closed before I started high school in 1914, and I spent most of my spare time working on a "cycle car." Before I got it finished at the end of my junior year, I had rebuilt the

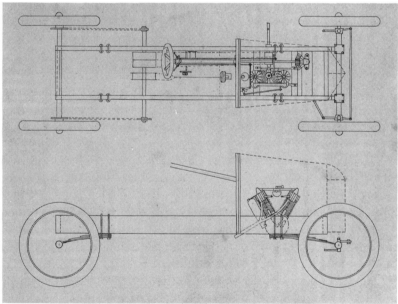

Two views of my cycle car, the **Baby Bullet,** *in various stages of completion. I made a garage by lengthening an old chicken coop. Ultimately I avoided the need for a differential by giving the car a single rear-wheel drive.*

entire thing a couple of times, and there was not a single part in it that had been in the original car. The original was made with two wheels in front and one wheel in the rear to avoid a differential. I purchased an old Indian motorcycle that gave me the seven-horsepower air-cooled V-engine, the rear wheel for a drive wheel, and the front wheel for one of the others. One other motorcycle wheel then fixed up my running gear. However, I had some knuckle joints made in downtown Chicago for the purpose of front steering. Unfortunately, the man welded them with cast iron, and I didn't know any better. When I was just carrying the front axle with the wheels all mounted on it to Mr. Clark's blacksmith shop at the corner of Home and Ogden avenues (fortunately, he allowed me to use his shop and work in metal there), one of the knuckle joints supporting a front wheel failed and the wheel dropped clear off; so I decided that was not the way to go. I did start with a metal frame for which Mr. Clark indicated the necessary size, because I didn't have any idea how strong it should be, but it turned out that we finally selected a mild steel-channel iron an inch and a half deep and with one-half-inch flanges. When we got the car assembled and sat on it, though, the car bent down. We reinforced it with trussing as Mr. Clark said was the way they do with railroad cars, but even with the trussing the steel channel bent locally where the attachments were made. I finally changed the design.

At this point I should say I wanted to put two people side-by-side in the car, but the seats were so close to the rear single wheel that when you had just one person sitting in them and turned in the wrong direction the car tended to tip over. So I changed gradually and step-by-step to a four-wheel arrangement but drove only one rear wheel to avoid the complexity of a differential. Inasmuch as the car had a narrow 36-inch tread and a 100-inch wheel base (which incidentally was 4 inches longer than a Model T and therefore made it look very sleek), I found that a single-wheel drive was quite satisfactory and in some ways was better than using a differential. In those days we had lots of mud to go through, and with a differential if you got either wheel in a slippery spot, the car just wouldn't go; whereas with one, I knew which wheel did the driving and could put it on the good terrain when there was any choice. I also followed the design practice of the Franklin automobile by changing to an all-wood and overstrength birch frame. With it I could whack away here and there where I wanted to get something

Dorothy Church in high school.

through without worrying about the strength; this made it much easier to attach other items to the frame.

I also bought a new 12-horsepower air-cooled V-engine from a cycle car company in Oswego, New York, that had gone broke, and this worked very much better than the previous 7-horsepower job. The new engine cost $27.50, which was a lot of money for me at that time. After the car was in running shape, I built a body for it in my Uncle Ernest's tin shop, which was behind his hardware store at the corner of Armitage Avenue and Hancock Street in Chicago. I filed and smoothed off the body to the best of my ability and then made use of some help I got from a friend, Al Knuepfer, who worked for a Chicago company that rebuilt and made special bodies for custom automobiles. Mr. Knuepfer gave me a seventeen-step paint scheme, which I followed religiously all the way through with seventeen different coats of paint, all rubbed down. I finally came out with what I thought was a very nice looking job. It was light French gray with maroon trimmings, and when it was clean you could see your face reflected in it. I used the car, which I dubbed the *Baby Bullet,* during my senior year and gave rides to various selected friends. One of those friends was my next-door neighbor Miss Dorothy Church, my future wife. Doro made the mistake of letting me talk her into taking her first car ride right after she had finished drying her beautiful red hair; when we got back her hair was so full of dust—because few streets were paved at that time, outside of major roads in big cities—that she had to wash it all over again!

Immediately after graduating from high school I drove the *Baby Bullet* with a friend and classmate, Walter Chamberlain, down about 100 miles from Chicago into the farm country of Indiana where we both got jobs on farms. It happened that a cowboy with his young son was working for the same farmer I was. He wanted to buy the car. I sold it to him for $70 and was rather glad to get rid of it because I was afraid it would be costing me too much and would hinder my progress going through college. Actually I got $35 cash and never got the rest, so the cycle car not only taught me my lessons in design the hard way, but it also gave me my first business lessons.

World War I started in August 1914, a month before I entered high school and by April of my junior year, 1917, the United States was in the war. Some of my friends joined the services immediately, but our neighbor Mr. Church talked me out of it on the basis that the country really needed educated men more and would call me when they needed me. This line worked for a while, but ultimately I did apply to both the army and navy air services, but in both cases was turned down and told to come back when I was twenty years old. Apparently, by the time I applied they had enough pilot applications.

In September 1918 I joined the army and was assigned to the student army training corps at Armour Institute of Technology (later the Illinois Institute of Technology) in Chicago. Within a couple of months the war was over and we were discharged, and I spent the rest of that school year at Armour Institute. The next three years were spent at the University of Illinois in Champaign-Urbana where I took a mechanical engineering course, which was as close as I could get to aeronautical engineering at the time. I also took special courses in civil engineering that involved bridge structures, and in my senior year got two elective courses in aeronautics, one in aerodynamics and one in structures. During all this time I had very little aeronautical activity except for keeping up with things through the aviation magazines. I did give a paper on "Variable

With my college roommate, Franklin Myers, at the University of Illinois during my junior year.

Pitch Propellers" before the student branch of the American Society of Mechanical Engineers, and for this I won a first-edition copy of Lionel S. Mark's *Mechanical Engineers' Handbook* (New York: McGraw-Hill, 1916) for the best student talk of academic year 1920/21. It is now worn to pieces but I still have it sixty-seven years later.

At the time I was about to graduate from the university in 1922, there was almost no aeronautical engineering activity in this country. Very few new airplanes were being manufactured because the surplus planes from World War I filled all the needs. In 1918, however, the United States Post Office Department had established an air-mail service in a meager way between New York and Washington. By 1922 it was flying mail planes daily in both directions from New York to San Francisco via Cleveland and Chicago. Surplus army DeHavilland DH-4 airplanes were being used, and they were being converted to mail planes at the Maywood Illinois Station of the air-mail system at Checkerboard Field west of Chicago, near present-day O'Hare International Airport.

During Easter vacation of my senior year in 1922, I visited the air-mail installation at Maywood and applied for a job there. I talked to Randolph Page, superintendant at the time, and he arranged for me to have a job starting July 1, which prior to the early 1970s marked the beginning of a new fiscal year. My first job was in the drafting room helping to remake the drawings to change the

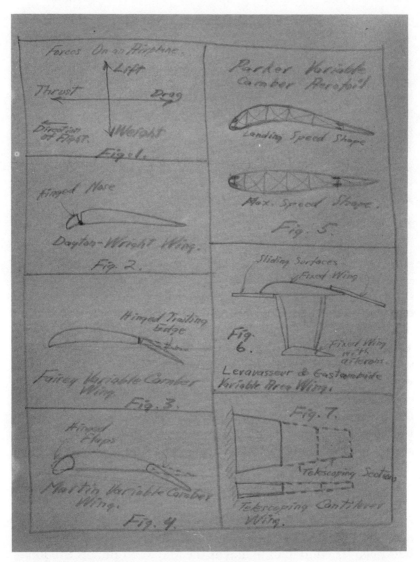

Drawings of wing airfoil sections and arrangements from a college paper I wrote at the University of Illinois on the problems of aeronautical engineering.

DH mailplane used by the U.S. Post Office air-mail system in 1922. The forward cockpit was changed into a mail compartment.

DH-4s to the air-mail configuration. The front cockpit was changed to a mail compartment, and many improvements were made, such as replacing the old wooden landing gear with a new steel one, to improve the planes' serviceability. My first assignment was to spend two weeks in the stockroom so as to get familiar with the parts. Not only were new drawings made, but they had to be traced in ink on tracing cloth so as to make a permanent record.

It wasn't long before I wangled my first airplane ride when a plane needed a flight check. We went up to 3,000 feet, and I still recall my first view from the air: how beautiful was the landscape that seemed to unfold, and how small the items on the ground appeared to be. I remember particularly the layout of a river nearby and the orderly layout of a cemetery with all the gravestones, two of them commemorating my grandfathers. In a nearby field a Buffalo Bill Wild West show was being set up, and I later went to see the performance.

At that time the Air Mail Service was operating only by day, but night flying was being contemplated because it would save a great deal in the overall mail delivery time. The first night flights were to be made in the flat country between Chicago and Omaha and were then extended to Cheyenne, Wyoming. The plan was to put a flashing acetylene beacon every 3 miles along the course and provide an emergency landing field every 25 miles. This was actually done. The emergency fields were equipped with rotating electric beacons. I found out a few years ago from my friend Ed Boots, who lives in Vero Beach, Florida, as I do, that he was associated with the design and provision of the small acetylene beacon lights.

In November 1922 a team of three of us started out west from Chicago to establish the emergency fields. One of the other men was a lawyer by the name of Hines. The other was a mechanic by the name of Kline. We started in a twelve-passenger White touring car, which was also surplus from World War I. Every 25 miles we scouted the area and selected two or three of the most likely pastures or hayfields for this purpose. The lawyer then made contact with the owners and arranged to rent the land if possible. My job as an engineer was to survey the fields and make maps showing the elevations, obstructions, drainage, and so forth. The surveying was done with a transit and a stadia rod (which had ruled lines across the lens of a telescope, as in a theodolite) to determine distances; Kline, the mechanic, helped me with the rod. The information was all sent to Washington, D.C., where the final selection of an emergency landing site for each place was made. By mid-December we met another team in the middle of Iowa that had been working eastward from Omaha. Incidentally, it was very cold in the Midwest that December, and it was no fun running a transit and trying to make charts and obtain figures out in zero-degree weather. We were mighty glad to get home for Christmas. The night-flying preparations went on from there, and the actual scheduled night flights were first made starting July 1, 1924.

The old air-mail hangar at Checkerboard Field was a corrugated sheet-metal shell on a steel framework. The front portion of the hangar held a dozen DHs. The rear portion had two floors. On the first floor the Liberty engines were overhauled, on the second floor the wings were doped, and ahead of that there was a balcony on which some fuselage work was done. In the winter time it was rather cold, and the engine overhaul area was heated by an old warm-air-type furnace that was in the center of the room and that had had its air ducts cut off short. Nearby there was a large hole in

Hines and Kline with the transit used in making maps of proposed air-mail emergency fields in 1922. Though Hines is looking through the transit, in all of the regular work I actually did all of the transit sightings and he held a stadia rod for me.

the ceiling to the second story so that the warm air would go up and heat the place where the wings were being doped.

One day I was up on the balcony taking measurements on a fuselage frame, adjacent to the wall separating the balcony from the dope room. This wall was made up of one-by-six-inch tongue-and-groove boards that had dried out and left cracks between most of the boards. All of a sudden there was a deep boom as if a great log had dropped and hit the earth. I looked up and saw that every crack in the wall was red. A 30-gallon drum of highly flammable dope had been too close to the furnace underneath on the floor below, and it had exploded.

The men in the dope room dived through the second-story windows onto the roof of a lean-to and were saved. Only one older man who got down through the hole in the floor was burned, but he recovered. A few of us got the airplanes out of the front part of the hangar, and then we tried to use the ordinary hand fire extinguishers, but we might as well have been spitting on it—nothing happened.

By the time the fire department got there a few minutes later, the entire building was destroyed, and the steel girders were nothing but a twisted red mass on the ground. The fire was so intense that even most of the sheet-iron roofing burned. Shortly thereafter a fine new brick hangar and maintenance building was constructed with another air strip on the land of the Hines Veterans Hospital about a mile away.

Some of the air-mail pilots that I knew were E. Hamilton Lee, the senior pilot of the group, Jack Knight, Rube Wagner, Tony Yackey, and later Tex Marshall. Jack Knight had become famous the year before, 1921, by making an epic night flight. An experimental flight had been planned carrying the mail from coast to coast without stopping except for the necessary deliveries. Starting from San Francisco early in the morning, four separate daylight flights were made with changes of plane and pilot at Reno, Salt Lake City, Cheyenne, and North Platte, Nebraska.

At North Platte the night flying was to commence, and Jack Knight was to take the plane on to Omaha. The weather was poor with fairly low ceilings and some snow, but the flight went on just the same. At Omaha there was no plane to carry on for the next leg because the pilot who should have flown to Omaha was weathered in at Chicago. After a brief rest, Knight went on for the next run to Iowa City, and he found the same bad situation existing there. Finally, although dead tired, he got in the plane again and carried on to Chicago, arriving about daybreak. The next stages to Cleveland and New York were carried out by separate pilots during the daylight hours, and the mail went through as scheduled; but the three runs with all the night flying were carried out by Jack Knight alone.

2.

Yackey Aircraft Company

One of the air-mail pilots I got to know, Tony Yackey, left the mail service in 1922 and started his own company, the Yackey Aircraft Company. He started this operation in what had been an old Maywood beer hall. Prohibition was in effect and had been for about four years, so that beer hall was no longer serving its original purpose. It was large enough so that with some large doors cut in the

The shop of Yackey Aircraft Company, part of a former beer hall, in 1923. Tony Yackey is the man with the bow tie, to the far right, and I am to Tony's immediate right. Prince Hamer, a Yackey employee, is standing on the stool to the far left.

We made the Yackey Transport from a war-surplus Breguet 14 airplane. The sign on the hangar reads "Behncke Checkerboard Airplane Service." Dave Behncke, incidentally, was a fixed-base operator and exhibition pilot who later, as a United Airlines pilot, organized the first national airlines pilots union.

side of it you could get airplane fuselages and wings in and out of the structure and assemble them inside fairly well. This beer hall had a former indirect connection with aviation. An elderly woman who had been the wife of the man who ran the place as a beer hall told us that Octave Chanute used to come there quite regularly when it was in operation. Chanute was an engineer interested in aviation and, particularly, in gliding flight. He had been in touch with Lilienthal, and the Wright brothers had been in touch with him while they were involved in their gliding and early aviation activities.

Tony Yackey's first activity was to buy up a fair number of surplus Breguet 14 airplanes (originally two-place observation and light bombers) with Renault engines and convert them to what he called a Yackey Transport. This meant that the front cockpit of the Breguets had to be made over, taking out the controls and squeezing four people into it—two sitting backward and facing the others. Some of these were sold with the original Renault engines, and some of them had Liberty engines installed instead.

This activity interested me, and I spent some evening and weekend hours assisting Tony, just helping wherever I could and working on the airplanes with my hands. I didn't ask for any pay for this, but after a couple of months Tony figured that I had earned something, and he gave me, on condition that I could drive it away, an old car that had been used around the airport. Tony called it the *Grasshopper*. This car was quite a conglomeration of parts thrown together. It was originally a Dort automobile with a Lycoming high-speed engine, but it also had other parts in it. The whole front axle and wheel assembly was from a Metz automobile with full elliptic springs. The radiator and hood were from a Davis automobile. It had a Jenny throttle and a Pierce-Arrow horn. It had no regular body but had bucket seats directly on the frame. Really, it was an old wreck, but I fixed it up and painted it, and it was much better for transportation to and from work in the wintertime than the belt-driven seven-horsepower Harley-Davidson motorcycle. After a while Yackey offered me a job as his superintendant, with one to ten people under me at an increase in salary from the $1,200 a year I was getting at the Air Mail Service to $1,400 a year plus—and this was the clincher—free flying lessons. So in February 1923 I left the Air Mail Service and went with the Yackey Aircraft Company.

To bring in a little extra cash, we often went barnstorming to various fields in the neighborhood of Chicago on weekends. At one of these, at a field west of Evanston, I took Dorothy Church (the future Mrs. Fred Weick) along in the *Grasshopper*. Tony Yackey and E. Hamilton Lee, the senior air-mail pilot, were each taking up passengers in Curtiss Jennies. My job was to help in any way needed, such as gassing up the airplanes with five-gallon cans and selling rides to passengers. Fortunately, there was a lull during which Ham Lee took Dorothy up for her first ride in an airplane. Quite an honor, I thought, to get it from the senior air-mail pilot. On the way home in the *Grasshopper* Dorothy got cold and moved over toward me. "That's right, snuggle up," I said, meaning only for her to get warm, but she took it the wrong way and moved over as far away from me as she could. I guess I learned a little about women at that time, but I have never learned enough.

On another weekend Tony Yackey took a Breguet 14 to Rockford, Illinois, to do a bit of barnstorming. This time I didn't go with him. On the following Monday morning when I reported to work I found Tony all sad-faced. During a take-off with four paying passengers, a full load for the Yackey Transport, he lifted off in a hurry without making use of the greatest length of runway possible—other paying passengers were waiting, and he wanted to get up and back down as quickly as possible. As he pulled up to get over some trees and houses, the plane veered to the left, went down in a left-hand spiral, and crashed. He thought that possibly a rudder cable had broken, but that seemed unlikely since the airplane had two solid wires on each side to actuate the rudder control. I found later that neither wire had broken and figured that the airplane must have stalled in the usual way. One person was seriously hurt, but he recovered later.

The company had a couple of war-surplus Kelly trucks with hard tires, and Tony wanted me to take one of them to Rockford and bring the airplane back. I took one helper along, and when we got there we found that many parts of the plane, including the landing gear and instruments, were missing. People had taken them away for one reason or another. While we were disassembling the plane to put it on the truck, many spectators came around, and I asked them about the missing parts. A few were sympathetic, and a couple told me where I could find some of the parts, referring me to houses where people had taken them. I went to those houses, and in the case of the instruments, for example, the man said he was just saving them for me because he was afraid somebody would take them. In this way I got back the landing gear and most of the instruments. For some perverse reason, many people feel free to take things from an airplane wreck. At any rate, we took the parts back and the plane was later rebuilt.

During this period my flight instruction went along at what I though was a rather slow rate—but I did get it from Tony Yackey himself and from a couple of the other active air-mail pilots. Tony was rather impulsive and "quick on the trigger," and I think I got my best instruction from Rube Wagner, one of the air-mail pilots. He was calm and gentle, which had a good influence on me. Of course, each instructor had his own ideas, and I did not get what would now be considered standard instruction at all. At that time there were no regulations involving either the manufacturing or the flying of airplanes, and a pilot's license was not required. You just soloed when you and the instructor thought you were ready.

One Sunday there was a flying meet at Ashburn Field about 5 miles south of Chicago. Located at Ashburn was Matty Laird, designer of the Laird Swallow in Wichita, who was then working on some new designs. I had a ride down from Checkerboard but was without a way of getting back; however, Johnny Livingston, later a famous racing pilot, was there with a borrowed Jenny, and he offered to drop me off back at Checkerboard. We got in, with me in the front cockpit, and Livingston took off.

Livingston thought he would have a little fun with me by pushing the control stick forward and back and forward and back, getting the plane going like a roller coaster to see whether I could take it. After this didn't seem to bother me, Livingston gained a bit of altitude. We were going along at only about 1,500 feet, I imagine. At about 2,000 feet he put the plane into a dive for extra speed and then pulled back sharply. The plane went into a complete loop!

This would have been bad enough under ordinary conditions but it happened that there was no safety belt in the front cockpit where I was located. Fortunately, during the previous roller-coaster action, I had grabbed on to cross wires on each side of the seat to hold myself in. I was happy to have made that arrangement when this loop occurred because at the top of the loop the speed was a little too slow, and we fell away from our seats and depended on the safety belt, or in my case on holding on to those wires, to keep us in the airplane. This was quite an experience. When I accepted Livingston's offer to be dropped off, I had not meant on my head!

A man by the name of Buck Weaver came to work with us at Yackey's plant for a couple of months. Later in Troy, Ohio, he and two men formed the Weaver Aircraft Company with the trade name Waco. Many famous Waco planes were built. Buck Weaver left the company shortly after it was formed, but one of the other founders, Clayton Brukner, presided over Waco for forty years. Waco was one of the many manufacturers of quality airplanes for the general aviation market until that market collapsed after World War II.

The National Air Races, held in St. Louis on October 4, 5, and 6, 1923, was said later to have been by far the biggest and best aeronautical demonstration in the world up to that time. Both Tony Yackey and his wife, Olive, had been raised in St. Louis, and their folks still lived there; therefore, we all planned to go. I had an opportunity to fly down with Hans Hoyt, a Danish immigrant who worked part-time for Yackey and who had a Curtiss JN-4D, the well-known Jenny of the same type in which I was learning to fly. The Jenny would not go all the way to St. Louis, some 250 miles, with just one tank of gas, and as there were almost no airports downstate at that time, there were very few places where one could stop to refuel on the way. So Hans added another tank above the upper center section of the wing and fixed it so that when the main

Breguet 14 converted to Yackey Transport
Checkerboard Air Mail Field, 1923.

*The National Air Races at St. Louis, October 1923. Top, a Farman Sport
airplane with Hans Hoyt to the far left, me, and a gentleman by the name of
Cruckshank. Bottom, a group photo with the Curtiss Jenny that Hans Hoyt
and I flew down to the races. Note the extra galvanized-iron fuel tank on top
of the center section of the wing.*

tank was partly empty the extra gasoline could be drained down into the main tank. I had taken a fair amount of dual flight instruction, but this was my first long cross-country trip. To me Hans rated as an experienced pilot, though in actual fact he had soloed for the first time only a few months before.

I learned a number of things from that flight to St. Louis, but the main lesson had to do with fuel planning. The flight took a little over four hours, and as we got down into the southern part of Illinois, where the countryside was hilly and bumpy, I got a little edgy—I had learned to fly over the flat, easy country in the north. I am glad we didn't have to force a landing, although at the present time that country looks fairly easy in comparison with the rugged mountainous terrain I crossed over in later flights.

We crossed the wide Mississippi River and a little beyond landed on Lambert Field, which is the same field that is now the main airport of metropolitan St. Louis and the same field from which Charles Lindbergh (who had flown the mail from St. Louis to Chicago) left in May 1927 for New York and his transatlantic flight to Paris. At that time it was just one big, open green field with a couple of hangars in one corner. (Unknown to us, Lindbergh also flew a Jenny into this 1923 event in St. Louis; he was barnstorming at the time.) As soon as we had landed and dragged to a stop, some people at the other side of the field waved to us to come over and park. Hans opened the throttle to taxi over there, but we went only a few feet before the engine stopped: we were totally out of fuel. That taught me a very good lesson, and from that time on I always wanted to plan so that I would end a flight with at least an hour's fuel in my tanks.

In St. Louis we stayed at the home of Tony Yackey's parents and had the opportunity to see his father's factory, among other things. His father made casks and barrels to retain liquids. We also had the great pleasure of driving to the races in a Pierce-Arrow automobile, which was the ultimate in transportation luxury to me at the time. Tony's wife, Olive Koken Yackey, was the daughter of a wealthy man who also had a factory of his own. In his case the factory made equipment for barbers; I believe that Mr. Koken was, in fact, one of the two largest manufacturers of barbers' chairs.

The air meet was a marvelous experience for me. There were races for many different categories of airplanes. In one I saw Casey Jones win a race in a Curtiss Oriole, which had a Curtiss six-cylinder upright in-line engine and a Curtiss-Reed all-metal twisted slab propeller. I believe that was the first twisted slab propeller I had seen. I got to know Casey Jones from that time and ran into him over the years on many occasions.

A number of interesting airplanes were at the meet. One was the sensational Fokker T-2, a huge monoplane with a single Liberty engine which, piloted by Oakley G. Kelly and John A. McCready, had made the first nonstop coast-to-coast flight just a few months before.[1] Another was the Barling Bomber, the largest airplane in existence at that time; it was a large and ungainly triplane with six Liberty engines, two on each side in tandem, one with a tractor propeller ahead of the wings, and the rear with a pusher propeller behind the wings.

The main event of the meet was the 1923 Pulitzer Trophy Race. The fastest racing planes of the day were developed by the military, and they did much to increase our military strength. The year before the army had won the Pulitzer Trophy, and this year the navy went for it full force. The navy had two very sleek Curtiss Racers with Curtiss D-12 engines delivering 500 horsepower and two Wright racers with 700-HP Wright engines. The army entered the same two Curtiss Racers it had entered the year before, one with the same engine in it and the other with a modified, souped-up engine. In addition, the army entered an advanced version of the Verville-Sperry R-2, which had also raced the year before. This was a low-wing monoplane with retractable landing gear. It was not as sleek as the Curtiss Racers, but it was an advanced job as far as the cantilever monoplane construction and the retractable gear were concerned. I did not know Alfred Verville, the designer, at the time, but I did have many years of pleasant association with him afterward.

The race was won by Lt. Alford J. Williams in one of the sleek Curtiss Racers. I did not know Lieutenant Williams then, but I did get to know him later and knew him for many years. In fact, I designed a propeller for the Mercury racer that he was building in the late 1920s but that he never got finished. Williams won the race at the then terrific speed of 245.3 miles per hour, almost 40 miles per hour faster than the speed attained the year before. The speed was great enough so that as we heard the racers coming toward us and looked up as they passed overhead, the planes were well ahead of where we thought they should be, because it took the sound so long to travel from the plane down to us. By the time we heard it, the plane had gotten farther ahead by a substantial amount.

Up to this time, almost all propellers used on airplanes had been made of wood. In this case, William's Curtiss Racer also had one of the Reed aluminum-alloy twisted slab propellers. The metal props were beginning to be used on the fastest airplanes. The man in charge of the design of the Curtiss Racers was William Gillmore, Curtiss's chief engineer. I didn't know him at the time, but I did meet him in St. Louis and had some contact with from time to time later on. All in all, the St. Louis air races were one of my most educational and pleasant experiences in aeronautics up to that time.

A couple of weeks after the air meet in St. Louis, I asked Yackey for a weekend off to go down to Champaign-Urbana to attend the Illinois homecoming game followed by a dance at my fraternity house, Delta Alpha Epsilon. Tony had two younger twin brothers who were then seniors at the university and whom he wanted to visit, and he suggested that we fly down in a Jenny. This suited me fine because I would get some more cross-country experience, and by arriving at the homecoming in an airplane—quite unusual at that time—I'd make quite an impression. There was no regular airport in 1923 at either Champaign or Urbana, so we just looked around for a suitable farm field. Tony finally landed in a pasture about a mile from Champaign. The farmer was happy to have this unusual occurrence and was glad to take us to town in his car. Our flight down was a main topic of conversation at the dance.

The next morning as we prepared to fly back, Yackey decided that the field was too small for the plane to take off satisfactorily with both of us in it, so he took off alone and flew up about 20 miles north to the town of Rantoul where there was an Army Air Service field named after Octave Chanute. I took an electric interurban trolley car of the Kankakee-Urbana Traction Company up to Chanute Field, and both of us flew back to Checkerboard from there. Some of my first bad weather experience was during that flight: for about the first two-thirds of the way we had a nice tail wind, but then right across our path came a squall line with rain and fairly strong headwinds. Fortunately, we made it all right. In those days no formal weather information was available.

My flight training proceeded intermittently, but I still figured that I was more than ready to solo; the occasion just never seemed to come up. In November 1923, though, we attended a sort of barnstormers' air meet at Dixon, Illinois, a town about 100 miles west of Checkerboard Field which, by the way, was the home of the young Ronald Reagan. My guess is that President Reagan would have been twelve years old at the time, and I wonder if he attended that air meet. The second day of the meet was rained out. Even if people had come out to the field that day, a Sunday, we would not have been able to fly because the OX-5 engines most of us were using had a single magneto that was not waterproof and was very likely to short out. While the rain poured down, a number of the pilots and attendants gathered in one of the larger hotel rooms to play cards and shoot craps.

One of those in attendance was Ham Lee, the senior air-mail pilot. He had flown his own Jenny from Checkerboard to Dixon and needed to get back himself to Chicago that night to be ready to take the mail out from Chicago to Iowa City the next morning. His getting to Chicago was no problem, as there was a train going there later in the afternoon, but Lee didn't know how he was going to get his airplane back to Checkerboard. A friend of mine, Prince Hamer, who was working for us at Yackey's and also taking flying lessons for part of his pay, as I was, but not quite for so long, piped up: "Fred will take it back for you, Ham. He's ready to solo." Lee called over to Tony, who was over on the bed, "How about it Tony? Can Fred get the plane back for me all right?" "Oh, sure," Tony said. "He'll get it back for you fine." So it was arranged that my first solo flight would be a 100-mile cross-country ferrying of Ham Lee's plane back to Checkerboard Field.

The rain stopped the next morning and, although the ceiling still hung at only 500 or 600 feet, everyone went out to the field and prepared to fly home. The area was relatively flat, and in those days there were no large radio or television towers to worry about. I had not been able to get hold of a map; in those days we flew by Rand McNally maps, which showed railroads, or by automobile road maps. So I arranged just to follow Hans Hoyt back to Checkerboard since he was also going there. In any case, it was just about straight east, and with the roads and railroads going to Chicago and the section lines being north and south and east and west, and considering how familiar I was with the Chicago area near Checkerboard Field, the lack of a map did not seem too important. Hans Hoyt had just bought himself a brand new OX-5–powered Standard airplane, still in the crates, for $500. He had earned the money by packing a Model T Ford roadster truck full of five-gallon cans of alcohol and delivering them to various small towns in Illinois. Prohibition was on, and we were not supposed to have known anything about this.

Ham Lee's Jenny was not the ideal airplane for my first solo. For one thing, the rocker arms of the valve gear of the OX-5 engine, which were all exposed, were rather loose and could be wiggled from side to side much more than what was desirable. They were obviously pretty well worn. Another problem was that his Jenny was half American Curtiss and half Canadian Curtiss: the wings and tail surfaces were American designs and the fuselage was Canadian. The difficulty for me was that the American Curtisses in which I had had all my instruction had the throttle on the left-hand side, whereas the Canadian Curtisses had the throttle on the right-hand side. When I got into the cockpit that Monday morning I tried operating, just on the ground, the control stick with my left hand and the throttle with my right. But I was afraid to make the change on my first solo hop, so I actually had my right hand on the control stick and crossed over to the right side with my left hand to operate the throttle.

One of the fellows spun the prop for me (we had no electric starters in those days), and after a rather long run because of the soggy field, I got off all right and cleared the wires over a railroad track at the end of the field. Hans Hoyt had taken off a couple of minutes before and was circling the field at an altitude of about 300 feet waiting for me. I flew up following him, and we were on our way.

Before long I got a little worried because the airplane was not flying along smoothly but was bouncing and bumping around somewhat after the manner of the entrance to a stall. The plane did not have an air-speed indicator that might tell me what margin I had from a stall; in fact, the plane did not even have a compass to help in navigation. The only instruments it had were engine instruments: a tachometer to tell how fast the engine was turning and an oil-pressure gauge and a gauge that gave the temperature of the engine's cooling water. The only way to judge my air speed was by the feel of the controls and by the varying tone of the whistle of the wires.

The controls felt solid enough, but I had never been in this particular plane before and was taking no chances on stalling, so I pushed the stick forward and the nose down and picked up a bit of speed and lost possibly 100 feet of alititude. Under those conditions the airplane flew smoothly and everything seemed all right again. I pulled up behind Hans once more, but as soon as I got right behind him, the bouncing started again. And so I learned the hard way a little bit about formation flying. Obviously I needed to pull over to one side to get out of his wing wake and his propeller wash. After doing this, I had no more difficulty on that account.

Shortly thereafter, however, another thing bothered me. With Hans in his brand new airplane and engine and me in Ham Lee's rather old and worn half-breed, I was not able to keep up without having the throttle nearly wide open. With the engine in the condition it was, I did not like to have to do this. So I throttled back to what I considered a satisfactory condition and let him go ahead. He was soon out of sight, but I had no real difficulty navigating because of the section lines and the roads in that part of the country.

When I was about three-fourths of the way home and passing the little town of Geneva at an altitude of 300 to 400 feet above the ground, the high school building stood out prominently. I was particularly interested in this building because one of the English teachers there was Dorothy Church, and I was sorely tempted to circle the building a couple of times, opening and closing the throttle in the hope of attracting her attention, even though it might disrupt the class. I kept reminding myself, however, that Ham Lee was the senior air-mail pilot, and he had been good enough to let me ferry his plane back for him. My first duty was to get his plane back to Checkerboard Field in one piece. And so I bored right along until I got there.

Even in those days of a half-century past, airports were likely to be surrounded by power lines. The approach to Checkerboard was made by flying east over Twelfth Street (now Roosevelt Road), which had a large power line along it, until you came to another power line running north and south. Then, from a relatively low altitude, you merely made a half-right turn for the final approach over the spot where the two power lines crossed. The field was in the shape of a sort of fat *L*, a square with the southwest quarter cut out of it. There was a narrow 15-foot cinder runway along the longest possible diagonal. Satisfied with my approach over the crossing of the power lines and heading southeast onto the narrow cinder runway, I figured my flight was nearly over. But when I was just a few feet off the ground and ready to flare off the flight path for the landing, there in front of me was a whole row of bare trees that *had not been there three days before!*

What to do? The tree line cut the length of the runway in half, meaning that there was not enough runway left for me to get down on the ground and stop before running into the trees. (We had no brakes in those days, so you had to coast using only a tail skid as a slight drag.) So I reached over to the right-hand throttle with my left hand again and opened it full, managing barely to clear the trees. I went around and around the field, wondering what to do. I considered landing crosswind, parallel to the trees, which, I found out later, was what Hans Hoyt had done a little while before. But having had almost no crosswind landing experience, I hesitated to try that. Instead I decided to make another approach like the first one, over the place where the power lines crossed, and come in as slowly as I felt I could and as close to the power lines as seemed reasonable. The plan worked, and I managed to get it down and roll along the runway well before I got to the trees. Then I made a hard turn and ran parallel to the trees until the plane coasted to a stop.

Finally, I had finished my two-hour, cross-country solo flight, managing to get Ham Lee's airplane down in good shape. It was November 1923. It might seem curious to some people now that it would be sixteen years later, in 1939, before I would see any reason to obtain a pilot's license.

After taxiing to the hangar, I found out what had happened. The airport area was part of the Cook County Forest Preserve. The quarter of the field that was not airport was used by a facility that purified the water in the Desplaines River. Since the Air Mail Service had moved to another field about a mile away, the people in charge of the waterworks facility had decided that they did not want flying on that field anymore, and so they planted the row of trees right across the runway, cutting it in two. Within a few days, the trees blocking the runway sort of disappeared, and the runway was actually used for many years after that.

2.

The Gypsy Engineer

(1924–1935)

3.

Navy Bureau of Aeronautics

Earlier in the fall of 1923 I had seen a notice in an aviation magazine that a Federal Civil Service examination was to be given for those who might want to become a junior aeronautical engineer in government service. I was not interested in the job, but because I had not been able to take a full aeronautical engineering course in college, I took the examination simply to find out what a junior aeronautical engineer was expected to know. I was very much disappointed in the exam. It was divided into three parts: one dealing with mathematics, one with physics, and the other with aeronautical engineering. The math and physics parts were satisfactory, but the questions in aeronautical engineering were largely related to mechanical and electrical engineering; they were not really aeronautical questions at all. I did not see the reason for this until later: that there were so very few aeronautical engineering graduates per se to draw from at that time.

I passed the exam and in early January 1924 received a telegram telling me to report immediately to the Bureau of Aeronautics, Navy Department, in Washington, D.C. I did not especially like the military command telling me what to do while I was still a free man, even though that command came directly from the secretary of the navy. But I was now interested in the job. I had started working with Tony Yackey with the understanding that my job would someday soon be to help design a new airplane. But after working in the converted beer hall for several months and talking the matter over several times with Tony, I was sure that it would be a very long time, probably some years, before the infant company progressed to the point where it would be feasible to undertake a complete aircraft production. While several years do not seem so very long to me at the present stage of my life (I turned eighty-eight on July 14, 1987), at that time it seemed an eternity. Chagrined by this dim prospect, I took the navy job. My new salary was $33 a week, or $1,716 a year, enough money, I thought, to marry Dorothy. (In the 1920s, a U.S. senator was paid only $10,000 a year.)

In February 1924 I took the train to Washington and reported to work at the Bureau of Aeronautics. There I was referred to a Mr. Clark, the chief draftsman, who handled the employment of civilian technical men who would be working under naval officers. He was rather dictatorial in his manner, and when he wondered whether to assign me to a job involving drawing up specifications or one designing propellers, I spoke up, upstart that I was, and said I would accept the propeller job but was not interested in the one involving specifications. Fortunately, the propeller job was assigned to me. Fortunately also, the man in charge of the propeller office, Lt. James Shoemaker, a future admiral, was a very understanding and likeable young man with whom I got along fine from the start.

Within a few days I was established in a rooming house at 1815 F Street N.W., only four blocks from the Navy Building and two blocks from the White House. Living and working so close to downtown, I could walk to just about any place I ordinarily needed to go. This situation enabled me to leave my car with my folks in Berwyn, Illinois, where I had lived up to the time of moving to Washington. (The car, incidentally, was a 1921 Model T Ford roadster, purchased after a policeman had seen the *Grasshopper* and asked to buy it; facing the prospect of another cold midwestern winter, I had been rather happy to replace the completely open *Grasshopper* with a closed roadster.) The rooming house was the home of an elderly widow, Mrs. Rose Brown, and her widowed sister, Mrs.

Elizabeth Turner. After some persuasion on my part, I finally got them to give me my breakfast and dinner; lunch I ate at restaurants. After a while the women became "Aunt Rose" and "Aunt Lizzie" to me, and I was substantially part of the family.

The propeller office was responsible for the design and procurement of the propellers used on all of the navy's aircraft. The office was just large enough for two desks and a drafting table and up to the time I came had been occupied by Lieutenant Shoemaker alone. The practice in the Bureau of Aeronautics was to have each section—such as those for propellers, power plants, aerodynamics, structures, and specifications—run by a naval line officer, who would be assigned to the job for only about two years. This was enough time to obtain valuable experience in the ways of Washington headquarters, but not long enough to become really expert in technological matters. I was the first civilian assistant for propellers.

Most of the propellers in use at that time were made of wood, largely birch, but a few metal propellers were just beginning to come into the picture. Many of the metal propellers in the early 1920s were a twisted slab made from a single piece of metal, made famous by Curtiss-Reed. Another type, developed by the army's aircraft engineering division at McCook Field in Dayton, Ohio, under Frank Caldwell, had solid aluminum-alloy blades that were detachable; the Standard Steel Propeller Company had started to manufacture these aluminum blades after its production of steel propellers had not worked out satisfactorily.

Before 1924 the army had done a great deal more to develop propellers than had the navy; in fact, the navy had been using mostly army work and army facilities. For example, the army had built a large electric whirl rig on which propellers could be tested for strength and endurance. Each new wooden propeller design was tested ordinarily for ten hours at 50 percent more power than it was expected to have to absorb in service. A guard was built around the test rig, so that if a blade flew off it would be caught before it flew away and hurt something else. The army had also put out a handbook on propeller design that, together with a textbook published in 1920 by H. C. Watts in England and with reports on wind-tunnel tests on propeller models, provided the basis for our design work at the bureau.

My duties as the first civilian assistant for propellers did not require my full time, and I was able to spend the spare moments delving further into the subject of propellers. In this connection I should mention that while I was working for him, Tony Yackey once bought two freight-car loads of miscellaneous wooden propellers, surplus war material, and it was my job to fit these propellers to whatever airplanes I could. One man who had a Standard airplane fitted with a German Mercedes engine that had a rather large hub came to us for a propeller. I found one that fit his plane's performance requirements but recommended that he not use it because, to fit the hub, it would require too large a hole to be bored out of the center. He took his chances and bought it anyway. He then took off and climbed until suddenly, after reaching about 15,000 feet to take aerial photographs, his engine revved up and he was forced to close the throttle, only to find that he had no propeller! Fortunately, he was able to glide down and make a satisfactory landing.

In my propeller studies I was helped by Lt. Walter S. Diehl, the bureau's leading aerodynamics man and its head liaison officer with the National Advisory Committee for Aeronautics (NACA), who occupied the office right next to mine and Shoemaker's. Diehl was the exception to the rule, because he was a Construction Corps officer who kept the same position at the bureau for many, many years—until he retired from the navy as a captain in the 1960s. (In 1940 the navy abolished the Construction Corps, after which these specialist officers were simply designated "Engineering Duty Only.") I had been in contact with him every now and then, particularly before 1958 while both of us served on NACA committees and subcommittees. I had a good visit with him in October 1976 at an NACA reunion in Asheville, North Carolina; sadly, he died a few months later.) Walter Diehl played a great part in aiding the progress of aerodynamic research in this country; historians should pay his work some attention.

Another big help to my studies, besides Diehl, was the availability of NACA's technical library, only a couple of minutes' walk from our office. NACA had been established by an act of Congress in 1915 for the purpose of guiding and carrying out aeronautical research; the agency's mandate was to aid not only the military air services, which at the time were facing the prospect of entering the war in Europe, but commercial aviation as well.

By 1924 NACA had a Washington office of about twenty-five people and had established, back in 1917, a laboratory at Langley

George W. Lewis, the NACA's director of research.

Field, near Hampton, Virginia; the Langley lab employed about one hundred workers. Fortunately for me, NACA's Washington office was located in an adjacent wing of the Navy Building where I worked. This office was run by Dr. George W. Lewis, director of research, and John F. Victory, chief clerk and secretary. Every now and then Dr. Lewis would visit the various offices in the Bureau of Aeronautics just to find out what NACA could be doing to help solve the technical problems bothering the progress of naval aviation. When he discovered that I was interested in learning all I could about propellers, he invited me to make free and full use of the NACA library. This was a great opportunity for me because this library included significant material from other countries, especially from England. The Europeans had taken a serious interest in the airplane earlier than had the Americans, and as of the 1920s they had done substantially more research work. Becoming familiar with European technical literature in the NACA library improved my knowledge of aeronautical engineering a great deal.

The navy had an air station just across the Potomac River from Washington at Anacostia where a number of airplanes and seaplanes were based and a variety of different flight tests made. Lieutenant Shoemaker, my boss, was a navy pilot, and occasionally he took me on a hop in a DeHavilland DH-4 or a Vought VE-7. The latter plane was a small, neat biplane powered by a 150-horsepower Hisso engine; it had two open cockpits, just like the DH. On one of these flights, in a DH, Shoemaker flew me down to Langley Field, where I had my first opportunity to visit the NACA laboratory and see the two wind tunnels there.

Our reason for going down to Langley was to check on some propeller tests that were being done under contract for the navy. A series of three-foot model air propellers of navy design had been tested in the seven-foot wind tunnel at Stanford University in California by professors William F. Durand—an original member of NACA, an expert on marine propellers, and one of the most eminent authorities on aeronautics—and Everett P. Lesley. (Durand, by the way, lived to be almost one hundred years old; he died in 1958). Lesley had worked with Durand on the model air-propeller tests at Stanford and was now at Langley Field to oversee tests of the full-scale versions of the same design in free flight. Thus, a relationship between the model tests and the full-scale tests would be obtained. I was very happy to meet Professor Leslie and to be in on the conversation regarding the flight test program, but I was just as glad to see Langley's facilities, including the five-foot atmospheric wind tunnel, NACA's so-called No. 1, which had been operating since June 1920, and especially the radically new compressed-air, or variable-density, tunnel, which had been designed by NACA's German import, Dr. Max M. Munk. Until the 1930s NACA's variable-density tunnel was the only one of its type in the world.

When we were ready to start our flight back to Anacostia, Shoemaker noticed that I had a Rand McNally map with a path marked out on it, and he wanted to know what it was. I told him that I had marked down the flight path that we had made while flying down to Langley. The line was not very straight—in fact, it was quite bowed and irregular. Shoemaker explained that he rather liked to follow the rivers and waterways so that he could land in the shallow water near the shore in the event of an emergency. That idea did not appeal to me because I wasn't much of a sailor or swimmer! It was interesting to see later, however, that my line showing the flight back was straight.

In 1924 and 1925 the Bureau of Aeronautics under Adm. William

A. Moffett was intensely interested in airships. From 1921 to 1923 the navy had built the airship *Shenandoah,* manufacturing its parts at the Naval Aircraft Factory in Philadelphia and erecting the airship in the big hangar at Lakehurst, New Jersey. In late 1924 the navy had just received the airship *Los Angeles* from Germany and was preparing specifications for what became the airships *Akron* and *Macon.* However, it was due to the *Shenandoah* that I first became acquainted with Henry Berliner, who later became one of the great influences on my life.

Henry's father, Emil Berliner, was a great inventor who held many patents relating to sound and acoustics. He had invented the microphone used in the telephone and the flat disc phonographic record and was one of the originators of the Victor Company, which later became RCA. Emil Berliner was also interested in the potential of vertical lift aircraft, and in the early 1920s his son Henry was helping him design and build a helicopter. Henry had worked out a very light pair of lifting propellers made essentially of balsawood but covered with a mahogany veneer that was very thin at the tips and worked up to a thickness of about one inch at the root. The navy's *Shenandoah* had a total of six engines, I believe, each with a large and heavy geared wooden propeller that turned slowly. During a visit to the Bureau of Aeronautics, Henry Berliner suggested replacing these mammoth props with the light balsawood propellers that he had developed for his dad's helicopter, arguing that the change would reduce the weight of the airship by several hundred pounds, a weight that could be translated into useful load. The navy liked Henry's idea and gave him an order for a set of these feathery propellers and me the job of optimizing their aerodynamic shape. But just as Berliner got close to finishing them in September 1925, word came from Ohio that the *Shenandoah* had been torn to pieces by a violent thunderstorm. So there was no use for those particular propellers. Henry and I remained good friends until his death in 1970.

When in my college days I had decided to go into the aviation "game"—it could hardly be called an industry then because, with all the war-surplus equipment available, most plants were shut down—it figured that I would just barely be able to make a living, and it would possibly be ten years or more before I could hope to support a wife. After I became established with the Bureau of Aeronautics, however, things began to look a little different. I had paid off my college debts, and with my weekly salary of $33 I was actually saving a little money. I was still in love with Dorothy Church and figured that, if she would have me, it would be practical for us to get married in just a year or two. So just a few days before Easter 1925 I wrote her a letter asking her to marry me. Today I would have phoned, of course, but at that time, because there were not so very many telephones in use, the idea didn't even occur to me. I sent the letter special delivery but, after not hearing from her for a couple of weeks, I expected bad news. As it turned out, the letter had been sent mistakenly to another address. I finally got Dorothy's answer: that "it would be very nice" to marry (which it has been). So we were engaged, and I didn't have to worry any more about her running around Illinois, available.

In 1924 the first round-the-world flight was accomplished. The Douglas Company in Santa Monica, California, which was still a small operation, built the airplanes especially for the purpose. Powered by Liberty engines, the World Cruisers, as they were called, had a wing span of 50 feet and a fuel capacity of 465 gallons. They were two-place open-cockpit biplanes, rather large for being just two-place, with no instruments for blind flying. Considering the weather that they expected and actually encountered, and considering the virgin territories, the wide and desolate areas that they had to fly over, the project was quite a venture. The Army Air Service carried it out, with navy ships helping to service the World Cruisers in some areas at sea. The Liberty engines were not expected to last very long, and it was arranged to put new engines in the planes every fifty hours.

The flight was made from east to west and, in April 1924, four planes, all similar, took off for Alaska from Seattle. In command of one of the planes was Lt. Erik H. Nelson, whom I later got to know when he was a sales manager for Boeing Aircraft in Seattle. Nelson and his colleagues encountered poor weather on the way to Alaska and near the Aleutian Islands, with very low clouds and low visibility. During a snowstorm the flight commander, a Major Martin (who, incidentally, was in command of the army air forces in Hawaii on December 7, 1941), literally flew into the ground, but, fortunately, he and his companion were not injured. The main stops were in Japan, China, India, England, Iceland, Greenland, Canada, and back to the United States, where the first landing was made in Boston.

In early September the flight paused in Washington, D.C., where I, along with a lot of other people, including President Calvin Coolidge, was waiting. It was a raw, uncomfortable day with a rather high wind, and the flight was quite late coming in from New York. A platform about three or four feet high had been erected on one side of Bolling Field for the president and other notables, and the president kept pacing back and forth on the platform trying to keep warm. He waited for well over an hour until finally someone saw four specks in the distance, and the planes came in and landed without incident. After stopping for a few days in Washington, the planes flew on to their starting point in Seattle via seventeen principal cities, each of which held ceremonies honoring those who accomplished the feat. In all, the World Cruisers flew more than 26,000 miles in 177 days. Only two of the planes made the entire trip, one of which was the one piloted by Erik Nelson. And while it may not seem like so very much now, at that time it was a great accomplishment and one that helped to establish the service that airplanes were capable of giving.

Speaking of President Coolidge, he liked to take walks in the neighborhoods nearby the White House, and with all the walking I was doing to and from the Bureau of Aeronautics, our paths often crossed. He would be going along by himself, looking straight ahead but with his head down just a bit, and trailing him by about 50 feet would be two secret service men, watching casually here and there. The country was relatively safe and comfortable in those days. Imagine a president taking that kind of walk now.

A number of aircraft company heads and chief engineers visited the Bureau of Aeronautics, and I got acquainted with some of them. I remember one occasion when Chance Vought, head of Vought Aircraft Company, came to the bureau to visit Lt. Charles McCarthy, head of the structures section. Once I had lunch with them, and I remember, strangely enough, that both of them ordered salads with Roquefort cheese dressing. When it came and I saw it for the first time, I almost got sick; I couldn't imagine anybody eating something so full of decayed material. In time, however, as I saw other people eating it, I got over the revulsion and tried some of the stuff myself; I've now for many years thoroughly enjoyed it. McCarthy left the navy in the late 1920s to become chief engineer for

Chance Vought. I had a fair amount of contact with him in 1929/1930 when all three of us were with the United Aircraft and Transport Corporation.

Two other important men with whom I became acquainted at the bureau were Lt. Theodore P. Wright, navy inspector at the Curtiss plant, and Clare Egtvedt, chief engineer of the Boeing Aircraft Company in Seattle. Over the years I had more contact with Ted Wright, and we became good friends. He later became chief engineer of the Curtiss Company, and during and after World War II got into government aviation activities as a member of NACA and administrator of the Civil Aeronautics Authority (CAA). Egtvedt later became Boeing's president and finally its chairman of the board.

One occasion that I especially remember from my early days in Washington was a demonstration flight of the Berliner helicopter. This happened at College Park Airport in Maryland, the oldest continuously operating flying field in the country and probably in the world; Orville Wright had given flying lessons there to some army personnel in 1908. Up to this time, as I remember it, no helicopter had been flown in free flight, although some had lifted themselves while tethered. On this day Gen. Mason Patrick, head of the Army Air Service, and Admiral Moffett, chief of the Bureau of Aeronautics, were both present, along with a number of their staff. My boss, Lieutenant Shoemaker, was good enough to take me.

The helicopter was equipped like an airplane, with very small biplane wings so that it could glide to a landing in case of motor failure. As stated earlier, two large balsawood propellers were employed, one above each wing tip; they turned in opposite directions so that the torque from the two propellers would be counteracted. A rotary engine drove the props through a differential gear arrangement. Lateral control was obtained by using a brake on one side or the other, making one propeller go slower and the other faster. For pitch control, a small controllable-pitch propeller, also driven by the rotary engine, was fitted at the rear near the tail surfaces.

The flight was made by Army Air Service pilot Lt. Harold R. Harris, a friend of Henry's and already a legendary army test pilot. But before he could lift off, we had to wait for father Emil Berliner to arrive in his chauffeur-driven Pierce-Arrow. As soon as this occurred, Harris started the engine and flew the helicopter straight up to a height of possibly 12 or 15 feet and hovered there for quite some time. The pilot made slight excursions back and forth a few feet in several directions, but never went very far. He landed satisfactorily and then made a few similar flights. The brake for lateral control operated but was a bit sluggish; Henry later improved it by eliminating the differential action and adding flap-like ailerons to the main lifting propeller blades themselves. Limited though it was, this performance by Berliner's machine was better, I believe, than that by any other helicopter up to that time.

After the flight an interesting incident occurred. As Lieutenant Harris came toward our group, various members started congratulating him and shaking his hand. Harris was beaming and reached out his hand to the next man, who happened to be General Patrick. The little, prim general stood there stiffly at attention, waiting to be saluted. Everyone else was somewhat embarrassed.

In October 1924 I took a short vacation from my work at the bureau to visit my folks and my fiancée in Illinois. On the way I stopped in Dayton to take in the National Air Races. These were a disappointment in comparison with the 1923 races at St. Louis, except that for the first time there were more civilian entries than military entries—in fact, about twice as many. Tony Yackey and a couple of his men were there with converted Thomas-Morse Scouts having OX-5 engines in them. The Pulitzer Trophy was won by a plane that had been forced to drop out the year before, the Verville Sperry Racer, which had retractable landing gear and a 500-horsepower D-12 engine. The winning speed, though, was only 215 miles per hour, 30 miles per hour slower than that achieved in 1923 by Al Williams in his Curtiss Racer.

Nonetheless, I enjoyed the three days of aerial activities and got acquainted with a number of designers and pilots with whom I would have contact later. I also visited the Army Air Service's experimental station at McCook Field, where I met Frank Caldwell, engineer-in-charge of the propeller work, and managed to get to see the propeller whirl rig and some other test equipment. Later in my vacation, I drove with Dorothy up to Milwaukee, where I visited the Hamilton Aero Manufacturing Company, a propeller manufacturer, and got acquainted with Tom Hamilton, its president.

In my work at the Bureau of Aeronautics I had developed by this time a system by which one could reduce the time required to design and draw an ordinary aircraft propeller from two or more weeks to about half a day. Dr. George Lewis of NACA had kept up his regular visits to the various offices of the Bureau of Aeronautics and was aware of my new method. One day he told me that NACA was receiving many requests for design information from people who were trying to make propellers for their own home-built airplanes, and he wondered if I could simplify my method still further and write a short technical paper about it that would help these people design their own propellers. I did this, and in January 1925 NACA published my paper, "Simplified Propeller Design for Low-Powered Airplanes," as NACA Technical Note (TN) 212.

Naturally I was pleased to see some of my work in print, but I got a much bigger kick thirty-five years later when the Experimental Aircraft Association (EAA) asked me whether it would be all right to reprint TN 212 in its magazine, *Sport Aviation.* My old paper was reprinted, with a new introduction and a supplement on wooden construction, in the December 1960 issue. So now, over half a century after its original apearance, my work on propeller design is still usable for airplanes of low power and moderate performance.

In response to the requests of Dr. Lewis about how NACA might help the Bureau of Aeronautics, I kept mentioning the need for full-scale propeller tests at high tip speed, where compressibility losses became evident. Compressibility is the physical property by which the volume of matter decreases to some extent as pressure is brought to bear on it. The British had made high-tip-speed tests on two-foot models in a wind tunnel, but the Reynolds number was so low that the results were questionable when applied to full scale. Their compressibility losses were much greater than those indicated by our meager flight tests in this country. At that time, however, I could not see any practical way of making full-scale tests other than in flight.

One day in early 1925 Dr. Lewis called me into his office and asked me how I would like to see a wind tunnel capable of making the full-scale propeller tests. But, I said, in order to make full-scale tests on a 10-foot propeller, the diameter of the tunnel's throat would have to be at least 20 feet, or four times the size of NACA's largest wind tunnel at Langley up to that time. "Yes, you're right," Dr. Lewis said. "But," I said, "in order for it to be practical, the tunnel's airflow would have to reach at least 100 miles an hour, and to achieve that, you'd have to have an immense amount of power—probably a couple of thousand horsepower." "Yes," Dr. Lewis said again. "I've been talking it over with Dr. Munk and we think that such an arrangement might be practical." I was astonished: a 20-foot tunnel would require a structure of 4^3 or sixty four times the volume! Neither the Hampton nor Newport News power plant was large enough to supply electric power, but NACA, Dr. Lewis informed me, had arranged to get two navy surplus diesel engines of 1,000 horsepower each, taken from a T-2 submarine. "If we can get this tunnel built" Dr. Lewis asked me, "would you like to come down to Langley Field and run it for us?" Without hesitation, I said that I would indeed.

When Dr. Lewis made the suggestion that I be transferred from the navy to NACA, the assistant chief of the Bureau of Aeronautics, Capt. Emory S. Land, absolutely refused. The captain could not see losing me to another government organization when I had just become useful in his propeller department. Some time passed without approval for my transfer, until the line officer in charge of the propeller department, Lt. Stanton Wooster, who had replaced my old boss Lieutenant Shoemaker, advised Captain Land that I would probably do the Navy Department at least as much good doing research in NACA's new propeller tunnel at Langley. Moreover, Wooster told him he didn't exactly like standing in the way of a possible improvement for me. So after this polite badgering, Captain Land finally said, "All right, all right," and the transfer was made.

NACA at that time had an annual appropriation of roughly $250,000 with which to pay a staff of one hundred twenty-five, buy buildings and equipment, and take care of operating expenses. As I remember it, the total cost of the bare structure for the propeller research tunnel was about $70,000. In order to get it started as soon as possible, NACA had skimped and saved $35,000 out of its FY appropriation, which ended on June 30, until the early 1970s the end of the government's fiscal year. On June 30 NACA had entered into a contract with the Austin Company to construct the tunnel's outer shell for $35,000. Then on the next day, July 1, it had entered into another contract to construct the internal structure, entrance and exit cones, and return passages. Construction started at once. This all happened before my transfer and was the main reason I was itching to move from Washington down to Langley.

In November 1925 I moved down to Hampton, Virginia, taking Dorothy Church, now Mrs. Fred E. Weick, along with me, of course. We had been married in the Presbyterian church in Berwyn on the sixteenth of May. The wedding had had an aeronautical flavor, for

Tony Yackey and a couple of our friends had flown a formation of three planes over the church and had circled it a few times during the reception. I could not have found a better wife to help me with my aeronautical activities. I have been inclined to make aviation both my vocation and my avocation, and Dorothy has been very tolerant about it, letting me spend most of my spare time, both weekends and evenings, on it. She has listened patiently through many aeronautical discussions, has helped to build an airplane in our own house by sewing the fabric covering, and through all the years has transformed my technical writings into proper English. She has joined me in the fun part, too,

and she will take a fly with me an - y where.

(Adapted from old English song, "My Man John")

National Advisory Committee for Aeronautics, Langley Field

The distance by air from Washington, D.C., to Hampton, Virginia, the town nearest Langley Field, is only about 120 miles, but by road through Richmond it is about 175 miles. In the 1920s these roads were surfaced with gravel and often badly rutted; smooth ribbons of concrete were not to be found in rural Virginia. In our Model T roadster, packed to overflowing, it took us all day to make the trip.

The engineer in charge of the Langley Memorial Aeronautical Laboratory at that time, a Californian by the name of Leigh M. Griffith, appeared unhappy with the idea that I had been placed under him from above; in fact, Griffith must have been generally unhappy with his situation at Langley, for he left within the month. He was replaced by Henry J. E. Reid, an electrical engineer who had been in charge of the laboratory's instrumentation. Reid remained the engineer-in-charge until he retired from the National Aeronautics and Space Administration (NASA) in 1960. The lab had a flight research division headed by test pilot Thomas Carroll, a power plant division headed by Carlton Kemper, and two wind

*Close-up view of one of the propeller research tunnel's diesel submarine
engines. Sitting is my boss, Elton W. Miller.*

tunnel sections, one, the 5-foot or atmospheric wind tunnel (AWT)
section headed by Elliott G. Reid, and, the other, the variable-
density tunnel (VDT) section headed by George J. Higgins. There
was also an instrument shop, model shop, technical service department, and a clerical and property office headed by Edward R.
("Ray") Sharp. The new 20-foot propeller research tunnel (PRT)
was being constructed under the supervision of Elton W. Miller, a
mechanical engineer who had previously been in charge of the construction of the variable-density tunnel. I was placed under Miller
until the tunnel was ready for operation.

By the time I started at Langley, the outer shell of the new tunnel
had been completed but work on the entrance and exit cones and
guide vanes was still going on. The tunnel, which had been laid out
by Dr. Max Munk in Washington, was of the open-throat type then
most suitable for testing propellers. My first job was to design and
get constructed a balance arrangement that measured the aerodynamic forces on the model and the model's reaction to them.
This balance had to support an airplane fuselage, complete with

*Entrance cone of the propeller research tunnel under construction,
November 1925.*

Dr. Max Munk at the variable-density tunnel's observation portals, 1922.

engine and propeller, 25 feet above the floor in the center of the tunnel's 20-foot-in-diameter airstream. All of the pertinent forces, such as drag, thrust, and moments, were to be measured down below by four small and simple beam scales.

Since 1921 Dr. Munk had been holed up in a little office at NACA headquarters in Washington, where he had been turning out excellent theoretical work. Munk had studied under Ludwig Prandtl at the University of Göttingen in Germany and had been brought to this country by the NACA in 1921. His entry into this country required two presidential orders: one to get a former enemy into the country, and another to get him a job in the government. And I guessed this helped him to appreciate his importance.

Without question, Munk was a genius, and, without question, he was a difficult person to work with. In early 1926 he decided on his own that, since Langley laboratory was where all the real action was taking place, that was where he should be. NACA headquarters must have agreed, because it made him the lab's chief of aerodynamics; this put him in charge of the flight research division and the two wind tunnel sections. My boss, Elton Miller, now reported to Munk, and all of my work ultimately had to be aproved by him.

I had known Munk in Washington and had great respect for his abilities. On the other hand, I did not want my balance design turned down at the last minute; so I had taken the pain to take each detail of design, mostly on cross-section paper, up to Munk to get his approval, and I got his initials on every single one of them. This, I thought, would certainly assure his final approval.

The movable parts of the balance supporting the airplane were supported by a structural steel framework about 12-feet high, 12-feet wide, and 16-feet long. In place of adjustable cables, steel angles ¼ by 2½ by 2½ inches provided the diagonal bracing.

A couple of days before we expected to try out the balance using a little Sperry Messenger airplane with its 60-horsepower engine running, Munk made an unannounced visit to the PRT building. Just as he walked into the bare-walled 50-foot cubicle that housed the test section, a loud horn squawked, calling someone to the telephone. This sent Dr. Munk into a tantrum, and I immediately had one of my mechanics disconnect the horn. Before he had entirely calmed down, he walked over toward the balance structure and put his hands on the long diagonal braces. These were fairly flexible, and he found he could move them back and forth a bit. Visualizing the entire structure vibrating to the point of failure and the whole airplane and balance crashing to the ground, the perturbed Munk ordered me to tear down the balance entirely and to design a new foundation and framework for it. He then turned and went back to his office a couple of blocks away.

Naturally I, too, was perturbed. Munk, after all, had approved every detail of my balance design. Not knowing what to do, I waited for some time to give him an opportunity to cool down. Then I went to his office and, as calmly as I could manage, mentioned that I thought the natural frequencies of the long diagonal members would be so low that vibrations would not be incited by the more rapid impulses from the engine and propeller. But mainly I suggested that, inasmuch as all the parts were made and ready to be put up, why not wait a couple of days before tearing it down and make a careful trial using the Sperry Messenger, starting at low speed, gradually increasing it, before dismantling the apparatus. Munk finally agreed, but demanded to be present when the test was made.

I did not like that idea of his presence one iota. To start the engine, the Messenger's propeller had to be cranked by hand from a

*Mechanic George Poe at the top of the balloon ladder
checking the Sperry Messenger's engine installation. It
was on this ladder but in a slightly different position that I
cranked the propeller for Dr. Munk.*

Rear view of the Sperry Messenger mounted on the balance of the propeller research tunnel, 1926. The mouth of the entrance cone is just ahead of the airplane. The picture was taken from within the exit cone, which was larger. I am the man to the right.

balloon ladder that was put up in front of the propeller 25-feet above the floor. (A balloon ladder was like a fireman's ladder but its base was attached to a pair of weighted wheels, which permitted it to be "leaned" out into space. At its base there was a "protractor" that told you how far it could be angled without tipping over.) This sweaty business often took some time. It was not the kind of operation I wanted the excitable Munk to watch. Moreover, since no one else in the PRT section had ever started an airplane engine by turning the propeller, I was the one who was going to have to do it.

I brought my problem to Elton Miller, my boss, and to Henry Reid, the engineer-in-charge. Together, we decided that the only thing to do was to make an end-run around Munk and check out the tunnel balance system in his absence. This was easily done, as Munk worked on theoretical problems in his room at a Hampton boarding house every afternoon. We set up the test run and after a bit got the engine started without any difficulty. We then experimented with it until we could start it easily and felt ready for the final trial.

The problem of convincing Munk remained. We could not simply tell him about the successful test, so we agreed to arrange another "first test" for Munk to witness. Engineer-in-charge Reid escorted Munk to the tunnel the next morning. I casually said, "Good morning," clambered up the ladder, and pulled through the Messenger's prop. Luckily, the engine started on the first try. We then moved the ladder away, ran the engine through its entire range with no vibration difficulty, and then shut it down. Now, I wondered, what sort of explosion will we have? I needn't have worried. Munk walked toward me with his hand outstretched and congratulated me on the success of the operation. Everything had turned out all right. The balance system of the PRT operated satisfactorily with engines of up to 400 horsepower into the late 1930s, when it was replaced by a new and better one.

In 1926 Dr. Munk gave a number of lectures on theoretical aerodynamics to a select group of young Langley engineers. I was very happy to learn these things from him. Ever since graduation from the University of Illinois, I had thought about taking some graduate courses in aeronautical engineering. While working for Tony Yackey, I had read in a magazine article about the graduate courses in aeronautics offered at Massachusetts Institute of Technology. I had written MIT for information and had received a letter back from Professor Edward P. Warner, who had been Langley's first chief physicist in 1919 and would later become assistant secretary of the navy for aeronautics, editor of the magazine *Aviation*, and finally president of the International Civil Aviation Organization (ICAO), which continues to coordinate the rules and regulations for aeronautical activities throughout the nations of the world. I had hoped still to find a way to work in some graduate courses even after reporting to work at the Bureau of Aeronautics. But Dr. Lewis had talked me out of the idea on the basis that formal aeronautical engineering education was inferior to what I could learn if I went to work for the NACA at Langley. I guess he was probably right in regard to the aeronautical courses per se, but on occasion, in later years, I sorely missed the extra mathematics and physics that would have been obtained in school.

As mentioned earlier, the power plant for the new PRT consisted of two 1,000-horsepower, six-cylinder in-line diesel engines taken from a T-2 submarine. These engines were located end-to-end with crankshafts connected to a large sheave or pulley between them.

This sheave carried forty-four Tex-rope V-belts to a similar sheave on the shaft of the propeller fan that drove the air through the tunnel. The shaft of the propeller fan was 25 feet above the ground, and the two sheaves were 55 feet apart center to center. Because we were concerned that some destructive vibrations might occur in the crankshaft-sheave assembly, we decided that a theoretical analysis of the torsional oscillations should be made, with Dr. Munk outlining the problem and a new man, Dr. Paul Hemke, to work out the solution. As a junior engineer, my assignment was to give the measurements and sizes that I would get from the drawings of the engines and sheaves.

I had no difficulty giving them the measurements, but Dr. Hemke was never able to get the gist of the torsional pendulum problem as described by Munk. This went on for some time with no results being obtained. Finally, I looked into my mechanical engineers' handbook and into a couple of textbooks and found that considerable work had been done on the problem and that the solution was not too difficult. I made the computation myself, coming out with a natural frequency of 312 RPMs. Later on, after the tunnel was in operation, some men came down from the navy shipyard in Brooklyn with equipment to measure the torsional oscillations; they found exactly the same natural frequency as I had computed. Hitting it exactly, of course, was a matter of luck, but it helped give me a good reputation, whether I deserved it or not. The success put me in good with Munk, but unfortunately Dr. Hemke was never able to work satisfactorily with him. A short time later he left the NACA. Hemke later joined the faculty of the U.S. Naval Academy, after holding a prestigious Guggenheim Fellowship for research under B. Melville Jones at Cambridge.

Another problem I helped to solve was the design of the 28-foot propeller fan that was to circulate the air in the propeller research tunnel. This fan needed to have eight blades of normal width. The exact energy ratio of the tunnel was not known in advance, so I desired to have blades that could be adjusted so that the pitch could be set exactly right after trial runs. Aluminum-alloy blades therefore seemed the best choice, but the blades we wanted were too large to be forged in the manner of the aluminum-alloy propeller blades then being manufactured. Fortunately, the propeller was to turn at only 375 revolutions per minute, which meant that the stresses would be very low in comparison even with airplane pro-

The PRT propeller fan had a diameter of 28 feet. I am standing at the cast-steel hub. The spinner is below, waiting to be mounted over the hub.

pellers having large diameters. This gave me the idea that a cast aluminum alloy might be used sucessfully, which it was.

I arranged with the Aluminum Company of America to cast the blades in their plant at Cleveland, Ohio. Before the large blades were cast, however, the company made two blades for a small ten-foot model that I then took to McCook Field in Dayton, where they were tested by Army Air Service engineers on their propeller whirl rig. This test showed the blades to be sufficiently strong.

During the period that the blades were being manufactured, I made a number of trips to Cleveland. On one occasion, when I had an afternoon with nothing special to do, I visited the Martin aircraft plant in the city's southern suburbs. I went into the door to the main office and told a young lady at the desk that I was an engineer from the NACA at Langley Field and that I'd like to visit the plant. She ushered me into the office of Glenn L. Martin himself, and he spent a couple of hours showing me around. How different from the stilted, bureaucratized conditions existing today in an aircraft factory! Of course, the Martin plant was small then, with only a few hundred employees. Most of his production went to the Navy Department; in fact, while at the Bureau of Aeronautics, I had designed a couple of the propellers used on his airplanes. Because many of his models were seaplanes and nearby Lake Erie was frozen solid in the winter months, Martin was then looking around to find a place farther south where he could manufacture and fly them away directly from the factory all year round. On this account he asked about the conditions around Hampton and Newport News, a neighborhood that he thought might be quite suitable. I told what I could about the area, and later he made some overtures in this direction. But, as I remember it, the local people at Newport News were not interested. Martin finally moved his factory to Middle River, Maryland, near Baltimore, where local authorities gave him a very good deal.

The NACA held its first annual manufacturers' conference at Langley in May 1926. The meeting was attended by representatives from the military air services, Department of Commerce, and aeronautical manufacturing industry. The morning was spent touring the various laboratories and learning about the research work that was going on in them. The propeller research tunnel was about finished, but Ted Myers, who was in charge of the tunnel's power plant, had not been able to get the diesel engines to run. However, we had the regular starting arrangement by which we turned the engines over by a blast of compressed air until they would start running as diesels. At the demonstration that morning, we ran the tunnel on the compressed air for about one minute; the little Sperry Messenger was up in the test section with its engine running also. In the afternoon, the conference was held at the military officers' club a few blocks away, and suggestions for possible new research were invited. One of the suggestions that was made concerned the cowling of radial air-cooled engines.

When I had started work at the Bureau of Aeronautics, almost all of the army and navy airplanes had had water-cooled engines. The navy, however, was interested in developing radial air-cooled engines. This work had been carried on under the direction of Comdr. Eugene E. Wilson of the bureau's power plant division and had been conducted mostly with the Wright engines designed by Charles Lawrance. The radial engines with their short crankshafts and crankcases and no radiators or water-cooling systems were lighter than the water-cooled engines. But the finned cylinders were cooled simply by projecting them into the airstream, and this caused a high drag. An attempt had been made to reduce the drag by putting propeller spinners over the hubs and cowling the crankcase and lower portions of the cylinders, but the outer ends of the cylinders still extended into the airstream.

During the morning session of the NACA conference, everyone had witnessed the operation of the Sperry Messenger airplane, with its radial air-cooled Lawrance engine running, in the propeller research tunnel. At the afternoon meeting, several people mentioned that tests should be made in the PRT to see how much the cowling could be extended outward without interfering too much with the cooling of the engine. Both the drag and propeller efficiency should be determined, we all agreed, as well as the cooling. During the ensuing months, I laid out a program for these cowling tests.

While studying propellers at the Bureau of Aeronautics, I learned from the propeller work carried out by William F. Durand and Everett P. Lesley at Stanford University the advantages of using a systematic series of independent variables in experimental research. I recognized that the range of variables should extend, if possible, on both sides well beyond the area of greatest interest. One extreme of this series was obviously making use of the bare engine with no cowling at all. The other extreme was to enclose the engine completely. This option had not been anticipated but looked enticing. An engine nacelle would then start with the best airship shape available, and the air could be brought in smoothly at the center of the nose. But how could one get the air out again in a smooth and efficient manner? Elliott G. Reid, who was in charge of the atmospheric wind tunnel at the time, had been making tests on Handley Page wing slots, and he helped me to design an annular exit slot. Together, these forms eventually became the NACA's low-drag cowling.

After I had completed the outline of a tentative cowling test program, the NACA sent it to the military air services and to various manufacturers that had shown interest at the May 1926 conference, and it was approved by all of them. Fortunately, getting their okay took some time, because the propeller research tunnel was at this point in no sense ready to operate.

We had gotten the diesel engines to run satisfactorily in a short time, but the long Tex-rope drive, with its forty-four different V-belts, were always getting so tangled up that they could not stay on the sheaves satisfactorily. It took several months of experimenting with idling sheaves in various locations before the operation became satisfactory. The entire drive, with Tex-ropes and sheaves, had been purchased from the Allis Chalmers Company and had been guaranteed to operate satisfactorily. After spending much money and time on this problem, the NACA sued Allis Chalmers for a sizable rebate. My daily log of operations was used as part of the testimony, and after one futile operation I had put down in disgust, "No soap." Although this was a generally used term in the Midwest, where I came from, indicating failure, no one in the room, all of whom were from the East, knew what I had meant. So I had to explain it in detail, an amusing interlude in an otherwise dull trial.

About three o'clock in the morning of February 24, 1926, my wife, Dorothy, woke up, and it was clear that we were soon going to have an addition to the family. I got her to the hospital in our Model T Ford as smoothly as possible. A nurse seated me in the lobby and took her upstairs to prepare her, saying that I could come up and hold her hand in a little while. The "little while" dragged on for nearly an hour, when I saw the doctor coming down the stairs. Spotting me, he said, "Good morning, Mr. Weick. Let me congratulate you. You have a nice little girl . . . I mean, er, boy." Bouncing all around inside, I had a hard time keeping up with what he said, first, finding out that it was all over, and that we had a girl, then changing it to a boy. After I finally caught up with the events, the doctor took me up to see the new mother and our new little red indian, Donald Victor. Both were doing fine, and after a few minutes they ushered me out and told me not to come back until about two o'clock in the afternoon so my family could rest.

I drove home and got myself some breakfast, and then, having nothing else special to do, I went to work at the usual time. The stores were not open, so I had to get the cigars later in the day. When I relayed the news to my boss, Elton Miller, he couldn't

Standing at the foot of the propeller research tunnel balance are five of us who made up the engineering staff of the PRT in 1928, during the NACA cowling research that won the 1929 Collier Trophy. From left are Donald H. Wood, my assistant; myself; John L. Crigler, William H. Herrnstein, Jr.; and Ray Windler. Melvin N. Gough is missing.

understand why I wasn't out celebrating. But I just didn't know how to celebrate at eight o'clock in the morning all by myself. My justification for including this story in my aeronautical reminiscences is that it shows how, even with the arrival of our first-born, my aeronautical research went right on. Of course, my mind may have wandered a little bit that morning, and in the afternoon I was back at the hospital.

Finally, in 1927, the Tex-rope problem was solved and the PRT was ready for actual testing. The tunnel personnel included Donald H. Wood, a mechanical engineer from Renssalaer Polytechnic Institute who was about my age and who had been with the PRT section from the start; Melvin N. Gough, a young engineer who had come to Langley directly from Johns Hopkins; William H. Herrnstein, Jr., an engineer who had come directly from the University of Michigan; and John L. Crigler and Ray Windler, also engineers. The power plant and shop work under Ted Myers, who was a little older than the rest of us, included George Poe and Marvin Forrest. There were two or three others whose names I have forgotten. At any rate, we had a good team and we all worked together very well.

Just before testing actually started in the PRT, Langley experienced a rather sad affair: a revolt against Dr. Munk, the head of our aerodynamics division. Munk was a wonderful theoretical aerodynamicist, but, as the story of my design of the PRT's balance structure illustrates, he was also an extremely difficult supervisor, not just for me but for all the section heads working directly under him. Eventually all the section heads, including Elton Miller, decided they couldn't work with Munk any longer and handed in their resignations. Munk was then relieved of his job, which I feel was a great loss. If Dr. Lewis could only have kept him holed up in his little office in Washington, Munk could have produced a great deal more of his useful theoretical work.

With Munk's departure, Elton Miller became the chief of the aerodynamics division, and I became head of the PRT section.

In the first months of PRT operation, just to get experience, we merely tested the Sperry Messenger and obtained drag data with various parts of the airplane removed. This was then written up and published as an NACA technical note. Before we could actually make propeller tests, though, we had to design and build a dynamometer that would support the engine and propeller up in the airstream and measure the torque of the engine while it was operating. We mounted the dynamometer in a long structural steel frame of small cross-section. Any engine up to about 500 horsepower could be mounted ahead of it, and any fuselage form could be put on over it. The engine torque we measured directly in foot pounds on a dial-type Toledo scale.

For the first propeller tests, we slipped this dynamometer inside the fuselage of a Vought VE-7 airplane. The engine was a 180-horsepower Wright E-2 liquid-cooled unit, similar to the old Hissos. These tests were made primarily to compare with the propeller data we had gotten from our flight testing and with the small-model data acquired previously from wind-tunnel testing at Stanford University. Three full-size wooden propellers of the same type previously used on the same VE-7 airplane, and models of which had also been investigated in the Stanford tunnel, were tested. The results agreed as well as could have been expected, considering the difference in Reynolds number (the nondimensional coefficient used since Osborne Reynolds's pioneering experiments at the University of Manchester in the 1880s as a measure of the dynamic scale of a flow) between flight and tunnel testing.

An interesting sidelight about the accuracy of aerodynamic testing appeared soon after we began PRT testing. In our final plots, the points of our wind-tunnel data for the full-scale tests had substantial scatter about the curves, whereas the small-model tests had the points right on the curves. I worried about this for a while, until I found the answer. Our results at NACA were plotted with fine points and fine lines at a large scale, and the model tests at Stanford were in printed form with heavy lines and large points. When we plotted our results in the same manner as the model test results, our accuracy was at least as good as Stanford's. I reported these results in NACA Technical Report (TR) 301, "Full-Scale Tests of Wood Propellers on a VE-7 Airplane in the Propeller Research Tunnel," in 1928. TR 300, describing the tunnel and testing equipment, had been prepared just previously by Donald H. Wood and me.

After the technique of making satisfactory propeller tests in the propeller research tunnel had been worked out satisfactorily, one of the first things that I wanted to investigate was the effect of high propeller tip speeds; after all, this had been one of the main reasons for having the tunnel built in the first place. The original propeller-testing setup with a 180-horsepower engine was not powerful enough to cover the range desired in high tip speeds, but we did what we could with it. The tests had to be made with a very low pitch setting that corresponded to angles of attack of the cruising or level range of flight but not of climb or take-off conditions. The range of the tests was from 600 to 1,000 feet per second, about 0.5 to 0.9 times the velocity of sound in air, or in modern terminology, from Mach 0.5 to Mach 0.9. Within the range of these tests, the effect of tip speed on the propulsive efficiency was negligible, and there was no loss due to the higher tip speeds. The results are given in my NACA Technical Report 302 (June 20, 1928). Later on, with a more powerful engine, we were able to test a whole series of propellers at tip speeds of up to 1,300 feet per second, which is well above the speed of sound. The results of these tests are recorded in NACA TR 375 (November 1930) by Donald H. Wood.

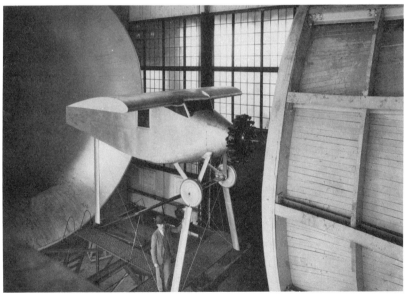

One extreme of the cowling research series: a completely uncowled engine. We made the tests both with and without the stubbed wing to show the results of that structure on the desired results. Donald Wood is standing on the top of the main balance structure. In the adjoining photo, one stage of the completely cowled tests, with mechanic Marvin Forrest standing down below.

After establishing that the tunnel was operating satisfactorily, we carried out several series of propeller tests and cowling tests at the same time. Among other things, this enabled us to obtain the effect of propeller-body interference on each cowling design. The various propeller tests were mostly covered in the following NACA reports: TR 306, "Full-Scale Wind-Tunnel Tests of a Series of Metal Propellers on a VE-7 Airplane" (July 13, 1928); TR 338, "The Effect of Reduction Gearing on Propeller-Body Interference as Shown by Full-Scale Wind-Tunnel Tests" (March 20, 1929); TR 339, "Full-Scale Wind-Tunnel Tests with a Series of Propellers of Different Diameters on a Single Fuselage" (March 12, 1929); TR 340, "Full-Scale Wind-Tunnel Tests on Several Metal Propellers Having Different Blade Forms" (March 18, 1929); and TR 350, "Working Charts for the Selection of Aluminum Alloy Propellers of a Standard Form to Operate with Various Aircraft Engines and Bodies" (March 25, 1929).[1]

The goal that we had set for ourselves in the cowling program was a cowled engine that would be cooled as well as one with no cowling whatsoever. This program proceeded easily enough until the complete cowling, covering the entire engine, was first tried. At this point, some of the cylinder temperatures proved to be much too high. After several modifications to the cooling air inlet and exit forms, and the use of internal guide vanes or baffles, we finally obtained satisfactory cooling with a complete cowling. Don Wood was in charge of the actual operation of the testing, and the first of these modifications was made while I was away on a vacation. When I got back, it was obvious to me that the boys were on to something, and from that time on we all worked very hard on the program.

The results of this first portion of cowling tests were so remarkable that we decided that the NACA should make them known to industry at once. In November 1928 I wrote up Technical Note 301, "Drag and Cooling with Various Forms of Cowling for a 'Whirlwind' Engine in a Cabin Fuselage," which the NACA published immediately. The summary of the report was as follows:

> The National Advisory Committee for Aeronautics has undertaken an investigation in the 20-foot Propeller Research Tunnel at Langley Field on the cowling of radial air-cooled engines. A portion of the investigation has been completed in which several forms and degrees of cowling were tested on a Wright Whirlwind J-5 engine mounted in the nose of a cabin fuselage. The cowlings varied from

the one extreme of an entirely exposed engine to the other in which the engine was entirely enclosed. Cooling tests were made and each cowling modified if necessary until the engine cooled approximately as satisfactorily as when it was entirely exposed. Drag tests were then made with each form of cowling and the effect of the cowling on the propulsive efficiency determined with a metal propeller. The propulsive efficiency was found to be practically the same with all forms of cowling. The drag of the cabin fuselage with uncowled engine was found to be more than three times as great as the drag of the fuselage with the engine removed and nose rounded. The conventional forms of cowling in which at least the tops of the cylinder heads and valve gear are exposed, reduced the drag somewhat, but the cowling entirely covering the engine reduced it 2.6 times as much as the best conventional one. The decrease in drag due to the use of spinners proved to be almost negligible.

I concluded this summary by arguing that use of the form completely covering the engine was "entirely practical" under service conditions, but also by warning that "it must be carefully designed to cool properly."

Having completed the initial round of wind-tunnel tests, we then borrowed a Curtiss Hawk AT-5A airplane from the Army Air Service at Langley Field already fitted with the Wright Whirlwind J-5 engine, and applied the new cowling for flight research. These tests showed that the airplane's speed increased from 118 to 137 miles per hour with the new cowling, an increase of 19 MPH. The results of the instrumented flight tests had a little scatter, and we could have been justified in claiming that the increase in speed was 20 MPH instead of 19, but I wanted to be conservative. I didn't want people to expect too much from this cowling, so we called it 19.

The second part of the cowling program covered tests with several forms of cowling, including individual fairings behind and individual hoods over the cylinders, and a smaller version of the new complete cowling, all mounted in a smaller, open-cockpit fuselage. We also performed drag tests with a conventional engine nacelle and with a nacelle having the new complete design. Though the individual fairings and hoods proved ineffective in reducing drag, we found that the reduction with the complete cowling over that with the conventional cowling was in fact over twice as great with smaller bodies as with the larger cabin fuselage. Data from the AT-5A flight tests confirmed this conclusion.

The first public acclaim of the cowling came in February 1929 when Frank Hawks established a new Los Angeles-to-New York nonstop record (18 hours, 13 minutes) flying a Lockheed Air Express equipped with an NACA low-drag cowling that increased the aircraft's maximum speed from 157 to 177 MPH. The day after the feat, the NACA received the following telegram:

> Cooling carefully checked and OK. Record impossible without new cowling. All credit due NACA for painstaking and accurate research. [Signed] Gerry Vultee, Chief Engineer, Lockheed Aircraft Co.

Some time later, the NACA gave me a photographic copy of this telegram, along with a picture of the cowled airplane.

A few weeks before Hawks's record-breaking flight, I had attended the New York Air Show in Madison Square Garden. At the show Chance Vought told me that Germany's Claude Dornier would like to talk to me about the possibility of putting the NACA cowling on the twelve uncowled radial air-cooled engines of his giant DO-X flying boat—which, at the time, was the largest airplane in the world. These twelve engines (British-made Jupiters rated at 550 horsepower each) were mounted back-to-back in six nacelles, each with one tractor propeller and one pusher propeller. Cowling the pushers would, of course, constitute an entirely new problem.

Before finishing this story, it should be mentioned that a great effort was then being made in a number of countries to develop aircraft suitable for airline use across the oceans, particularly the North Atlantic. The aircraft were of two main types: rigid airships of the Zeppelin type and large flying boats like Dornier's. The wing of the DO-X projected from the top of an ample hull with a span of 157 feet and a chord of 30 feet. Lateral stability on the water was obtained by the use of sponsons, or short and stubby winglike structures that projected from the bottom of the hull on each side. Constructed in the late 1920s at Altenrein, Switzerland, on Lake Constance and near Friederichshafen, Germany, the DO-X could accommodate sixty-six passengers comfortably over a range of 700 to 900 miles, but could not lift any kind of payload over transatlantic distances, the minimum such distance being roughly 2,000 miles. On one flight from adjoining Lake Constance, though, one hundred seventy people were crowded into the airplane (I've heard that nine were stowaways), making quite a record at that time.

The Dornier DO-X in which I was a passenger from Norfolk to New York City in 1931.

Dr. Dornier was staying in a magnificent suite in the Waldorf Astoria Hotel, where we talked for a couple of hours. As it turned out, his problem was not that of reducing the aircraft's drag for improved high-speed performance, but in alleviating the serious engine overheating that was occurring in the long taxiing and take-off runs on the water. As it was, the air-cooled engines were completely uncowled, with the finned cylinders sticking out radially into the airstream. My opinion was that at the low air speeds of the taxi run, it would be extremely difficult to get as good cooling with the NACA cowling completely enclosing the engine. This would be particularly true, I said, for the rear pusher engines with which the NACA had had no experience.

Dornier eventually solved the problem by changing from the air-cooled Bristol to water-cooled Curtiss Conqueror engines, the radiators of which could be made as large as necessary.

Two years later, in 1931, I got a close look at Dornier's DO-X and even got to fly as a passenger in it. During that year the great German seaplane made an epic flight to Africa, across to Brazil, and up to New York City. Then it went back by way of Newfoundland, the Azores, Spain, and Berlin. On the way up our eastern coastline, it stopped overnight at the Norfolk Naval Base on Hampton Roads, Virginia. A few of us from NACA Langley were invited to go along for the 300-mile hop from Norfolk to New York City, and fortunately I was one of them.

Especially after my meeting with Dr. Dornier in the Waldorf Astoria in 1929, I was very interested in checking out the plane's performance. I timed the take-off run and found that we were at full throttle for a seemingly interminable two minutes. The usual take-off run for a land plane at that time was about 10 to 15 seconds, so it was easy to understand why Dornier's flying boat had such a bad cooling problem. Up in the air the cruising speed with the power setting in use was about 100 MPH, but the pilots flew the ship down close to the water—the hull was no more than ten feet above the water's surface—and under those conditions the "ground effect" cut the induced drag down to the point where the cruising speed was about 105 MPH.

Most of the flight was made just outside the Atlantic shoreline at that low height, and when we came to the beaches where people were bathing, such as Ocean City and Atlantic City, the plane was boosted up to a height of about 50 feet until the bathing area was past.

The noise outside the big airplane was deafening. As the plane had passed near Langley Field the day before with all twelve engines running, it sounded like a whole squadron of pursuit planes going by. Inside the cabin, however, with that great wing separating us from the engines and propellers, the noise level was lower than in any airplane that I had ever been in, and conversation was easy. The seating arrangement was like that in a luxurious Pullman car, with two double seats facing each other on each side of an aisle. Each of these sections could be made into sleeping quarters with upper and lower berths. A bar, restaurant, and lounge were provided. A few ladies were included among the passengers, and for a time a dance with music was held in the lounge. It was a very interesting ride with a number of "firsts" for me. On the way to a smooth water landing at Battery Park at the foot of Manhattan Island, and within easy walking distance from Wall Street, I got my first eye-level look at the Statue of Liberty.

Remarkable as the DO-X was for its time, it did not have enough speed or range to operate successfully as a transatlantic airliner. It was not until 1939 that flying boats such as Pan American's Boeing 314-A could cross the ocean satisfactorily on a regular airline basis. Even then, the Boeing Clippers carried no more than two dozen

In 1928 I designed this NACA-style cowling for the Berliner monoplane. The main feature of this cowling was that it could be removed in three separate pieces without taking off the propeller.

passengers, and they had to use intermediate stops for refueling.

Besides Claude Dornier, another airplane designer who had become familiar early on with the NACA's cowling results was my friend Henry Berliner. His aircraft company had started to build a small two-place, open-cockpit, high-wing monoplane for commercial use, and he asked me to design a cowling for its Warner 150-horsepower radial air-cooled engine. I spent a weekend at Berliner's plant in Alexandria, Virginia, a Washington suburb, and designed a cowling that came off in three separate pieces, so that the propeller would not have to be removed to get at the engine. I don't remember, though, what the cowling did to the airplane's performance.

By this time at Langley lab, we had mounted the low-drag cowling on all three engines of a Fokker trimotor airplane. The comparative speed trials proved extremely disappointing. Separate tests on the individual nacelles showed that cowling the Fokker's nose engine gave approximately the improved performance we expected. Cowling the wing nacelles, however, gave no improvement in performance at all. This was strange, because the wind-tunnel tests had already demonstrated convincingly that one could obtain much greater improvement with a cowled nacelle than with a cowled engine in front of a large fuselage.

Some of us started to wonder how the position of the nacelle with respect to the wing might affect drag. In the case of the Fokker (as well as the Ford) trimotor, the wing engines were mounted slightly below the surface of the wing. The upper surface of the fully cowled nacelle then came very close to the under surface of the wing. As the air flowed back between the wing and nacelle, and the distance between them increased toward the rear of the nacelle, the expansion required was too great for the air to follow smoothly. We tried fairing-in this space, but achieved only a small improvement.

As a result of these experiences I laid out a series of model tests in the propeller research tunnel in which an NACA-cowled nacelle with a power-driven propeller was placed in a number of different positions with respect to the wing. Where it appeared pertinent, extra fairing was put between them. These tests were run by Don Wood and his crew after I had left the NACA to work for Hamilton Standard.

The resulting data on the effect of the nacelle on the lift, drag, and propulsive efficiency of the Fokker airplane made it clear that the optimum location of the nacelle was directly in line with the wing, with the propeller well ahead of the wing's leading edge. This position had the least overall projected area, and I suppose the result might have been expected. Without the complete cowling, the radial engine in this position spoiled the maximum-lift coefficient of the wing. With the cowling, and the smooth airflow that resulted from it, the maximum-lift coefficient was actually increased. After this important information was transmitted confidentially to the army, navy, and industry, most all of the transport and bombing airplanes employed radial wing-mounted engines with the NACA-cowled nacelles located approximately in the optimum position.

Eastman N. Jacobs.

This combination, according to some historians, was one of the important advances that enabled airliners to become financially self-supporting, that is, without the need for government subsidy.

Shortly after moving to Hampton, Dorothy and I became acquainted wih Eastman N. Jacobs, a talented researcher in Langley's variable-density tunnel section, and his wife, Ivy. We had much in common and soon became good friends. One day "East" and I saw an ad in *Aviation* magazine placed by Karl Ort, a well-known used airplane and airplane parts dealer in York, Pennsylvania, for a small Macchi airplane with an Anzani engine. The plane was said to be in flying condition, and Ort was asking only $300 for it. East and I decided on the spot that we might like to have that little airplane for our own.

In those days the work week at the NACA laboratory was five and one-half days, including four hours on Saturday mornings. So at noon the following Saturday, we took off for York in my Model T Ford Fayetta to see the Macchi airplane. The trip was a long one, of course, and I proposed that we stay overnight in Washington with my old landladies, Aunt Rose and Aunt Lizzie; then we could drive up to York on Sunday morning.

After we'd done about ten miles, our right rear tire punctured, and we had to change tires and rims. The wheels had demountable rims, and I had one extra rim and tire all ready to go on. After a few more miles, the new tire on the right also blew out. I also carried a couple of spare tubes, but using them meant taking the tire off the rim, putting in the new tube, and pumping it up again. Fortunately, I did have a hand pump, so after doing the work, we were soon on our way again. After a few more miles—yes, another puncture, in the same tire. To make a long story short, we had, believe it or not, thirteen punctures in that right rear tire, with two casings and four inner tubes. After the first tubes had been used, we had to take the tire off the rim, take the inner tube out, find the leak, and put a patch on it with rubber cement. About half of these fixes were made in the dark. We didn't get to Washington until one o'clock in the morning—too late to stop off at the aunts' house. We did find a service station open in Washington where we could buy a new inner tube, and after we put this in, we were able to make it the rest of the way to York and all the way back to Hampton with no more tire trouble.

We arrived in York at about 5:00 A.M., parked right outside Karl Ort's house, and tried to get a little sleep. Being a Sunday morning, we figured that Ort would not be at his shop, but hoped that he would be good enough to show us the airplane. Along about 8:30 a woman who we figured was Ort's mother came out of the front door to get the Sunday paper, and we jumped out and told her our situation. She wouldn't wake him, saying he'd had a hard night. We had to wait for three more hours before he got up, had breakfast, and finally took us out to see the airplane.

When we saw it, we were greatly disappointed. Obviously, the plane had not been flown for years: parts, many of which needed repair, were stacked here and there among many other pieces of junk. To fix, assemble, and put them all in shape for flight would take a great deal of work. Also, the Anzani engine, a three-cylinder radial of about 60 horsepower, as I remember it, had automatic intake valves. East and I knew immediately that the flying machine was not in accordance with Ort's ad and that we didn't want it. We then drove all the way back to Hampton, arriving without incident late that night, tired and sad, but possibly a little wiser.

A few years later Eastman Jacobs designed a small single-place airplane, which he built in his own backyard, and taught himself to fly in it. It was a very light high-wing-braced monoplane with wooden wing structure covered with fabric and a fabric-covered steel tube fuselage. As I remember it, the plane had a little four-cylinder, in-line, air-cooled Ace motorcycle engine. East had never done any welding, but the quality of his work improved with practice. Fortunately, he had thought ahead and made the first welds, which weren't so good, where the stresses were likely to be low. I helped him with the propeller, designing it from my TN 212, "Simplified Propeller Design for Low-Powered Airplanes," and carving it from laminated spruce. He made most all of it himself, though, with his wife's help in sewing the wing covers.

When it was finished he took it out to Pop Morgan's little flying field. Morgan, chief draftsman at the NACA laboratory, had purchased a little farm about halfway between Langley Field and Hampton. It included a grass field about 800 feet wide and 1,200 feet long, bounded by fences. There Jacobs went through a few practice sessions, at first just taxiing to get the feel of the plane. I went with him because I had had a little flying experience and could coach him a bit. After he got the feel of the plane, he taxied faster and then a little faster, until, during a full throttle run, he took it off for just a foot or two and landed, all within the 1,200-foot run. Because the wing loading was very light, the plane, even with its low power, could get into the air in only 300 feet or so. In succeeding days, Jacobs made several short runs like this, each time talking over with me what had happened at the end of each run. Finally, late one afternoon, he went out by himself and made his solo flight. He took off and kept going, flying over to Langley Field, where he made his first real solo landing. After making a number of flights at Langley Field, he flew it back and landed in the little field on Morgan's farm. Thus he had become a pilot.

With the help of his parents, who were well-to-do, Jacobs later bought a Pitcairn Mail Wing–type airplane, a small open-cockpit biplane with a 110-horsepower engine. He kept the plane at Pop Morgan's place in a partially completed hangar that had no door in the front. In the summer of 1933 a severe hurricane passed through the Hampton Roads region, doing great damage to, among other things, the NACA's wind-tunnel equipment, which, because it was on ground floors, was damaged by high water. For some reason

East had his Pitcairn on the south, or Norfolk, side of Hampton Roads when the storm came along. He tied it down as best he could, huddled against a grove of trees. After some hours when the winds died down and things began to look calm and pleasant, he flew the airplane back to Morgan Field and put it in the doorless hangar. After a while the winds picked up again and blew the top clear off the hangar, but fortunately without doing substantial damage to the airplane. We did not understand the structure of hurricanes very well in those days, but now we realize that Jacobs had flown across right in the eye of the hurricane.

Back in 1926, while Dorothy and I were living at a place on the waterfront of Hampton Roads, I did some experimenting with a certain type of propeller that I had thought up; my idea was for it to be light in weight and inexpensive to construct. The blades were formed out of a thin plate aluminum alloy and the root portion shaped into a cylinder so that the pitch could be adjusted. (In 1932 I got a patent—U.S. Patent No. 1,842,466—for the idea.) In my spare time at home I constructed a two-foot model of this propeller. Then I rigged up an arrangement in my basement with which I could load each section of a blade with weights representing both the centrifugal force and the aerodynamic forces; this permitted me to measure the deflection of the blade under operating load conditions. This was a purely private venture, but I decided to write up the method of load measurement nonetheless. My paper was interesting enough that the NACA published it a little later as an NACA technical note.

In order to give my two-foot model a working-strength test similar to the whirl tests made at McCook Field, I rigged up an arrangement to run it from the engine of my Model T Ford. In front of the automobile I made a stand, and with an extension to the car's crankshaft driving a large pulley and a thin belt running up to a small pulley up above it, I was able to turn the propeller several times the speed of the engine. To make sure that no one would be hurt if a blade should break and fly off, I built a large frame around it out of 2-by-12-inch planks. I did not have a tachometer to measure the propeller's revolution speed, but Dorothy helped out in this matter. With the Ford running wide open, the propeller emitted a certain tone that she could detect and carry. She compared this with piano sound and found that it was approximately the tone of middle C—which has a natural frequency of 256 cycles per second. From this, I figured that the revolution speed had to be around 7,680 revolutions per minute. After running under these conditions for about an hour, the propeller broke, a blade flew off, and the barrier served its purpose. Although the propeller was well overloaded under these conditions, the tests indicated that the design needed further refining.

Henry Berliner, who had formed the Berliner Aircraft Company, later became interested in my propeller design, and we entered into an agreement according to which his company would develop it further and possibly put it into commercial production. In 1929, though, Henry and Temple Joyce joined forces to form the Berliner-Joyce Aircraft Corporation. This corporation took over the rights to my design, but it had to have a legal contract drawn up by attorneys. Henry and I, who trusted each other, had had an agreement of less than one page of typing. When the lawyers took over, this became twelve legal-size typewritten sheets. A full-size propeller was constructed, but before it could be tested the Depression hit, and the corporation went broke. Berliner-Joyce was later taken over by North American Aviation, at that time a holding company controlled by General Motors. Nothing more was done about the propeller.

During the spring of 1927 a number of aviators were engaged in a hectic competition to become the first to fly nonstop between New York and Paris. A Frenchman by the name of Raymond Orteig had offered a $25,000 prize for this feat. This may seem a paltry sum in our present state of inflated currency and cost-of-living, but in 1927, $25,000 possessed phenomenal purchasing power. I don't believe that the money was the main incentive, however. Among the contestants were the Frenchmen, René Fonck, flying a Sikorsky, and Charles Eugène Nungesser and François Coli, flying a Levasseur plane whose name in English was *White Bird;* Adm. Richard E. Byrd, flying a Fokker trimotor; Lt. Noel Davis and Lt. Stanton Wooster of the U.S. Navy, flying a modified Keystone Bomber named the *American Legion;* Clarence D. Chamberlain and Lt. Bertram B. Acosta, flying a Bellanca; and an unknown mail pilot by the name of Charles A. Lindbergh, who was flying a Ryan.

Lieutenant Wooster of the Davis-Wooster team had been my boss in the Bureau of Aeronautics and had helped me get my transfer to the NACA, so I felt quite indebted to him. Powering their converted

The modified Keystone Bomber in which navy pilots Noel Davis and Stanton Wooster were killed while preparing to fly to Paris in April 1927.

Keystone Bomber were three Wright J-5 Whirlwind engines of the same type that we were to employ a little later in our cowling tests in the PRT. Before trying to fly it over the ocean, Davis and Wooster flew the plane to Langley Field for a carefully prepared series of tests. The pilots sat right behind the nose engine, and immediately behind them in the fuselage was a huge 1,500-gallon gasoline tank.

The first test was made with only 500 gallons of gasoline in the tank, and the plane performed very well. Thereafter, they increased the fuel load in 100-gallon increments—600 gallons, 700 gallons, and so forth. This was a very sound and conservative procedure that Wooster and Davis endorsed, but then came the news that some of their competitors were about ready to take off for Paris, and they were overcome by haste. They had flown satisfactorily with 1,000 gallons (6,000 pounds), but with this news they decided to jump up to the full load of 1,500 gallons (9,000 pounds).

This was a sad mistake. The plane took off to the north and rose to a height of about 50 feet but could not attain any more altitude. The pilots managed to keep the big bird flying away from Langley Field, toward the far shore of the Back River. Ahead, before the small fishing village of Poquoson, however, was a slight rise and some tall trees, which forced Davis and Wooster to try a right turn. Even though the turn appeared to be a shallow one, the plane could not maintain altitude and sank to the ground. It rolled along the marshy ground for some distance with full power on. It even went through a pond several hundred feet in diameter and possibly three to four feet deep. In climbing up the bank of the pond, though, the wheels stuck. This forced the nose of the plane into the bank, crushing the pilots between the gas tank and the engine.

The cabin was completely crushed, and they must have died instantly, but no other part of the plane appeared to be damaged. Of course, it was a tragedy, and a shame that they did not continue with their carefully planned 100-gallon increments. The flight that would win the contest actually did not take off until a month later. Some time earlier the Sikorsky airplane had cracked up in the attempted take-off for the Paris flight. Byrd's Fokker trimotor had been damaged in a landing accident piloted by Tony Fokker himself. Lindbergh's plane, the famous *Spirit of St. Louis*, was ready for its first test flight but had not yet been flown.

At this point it was April 26. Lindbergh, with the backing of a number of St. Louis businessmen, had made arrangements with the Ryan Company in San Diego to build a plane especially for the transatlantic flight but based on the Ryan M-2. Wisely, Lindbergh had insisted that the cockpit be placed behind the large fuel tank, even though he could not see directly forward without a periscope. The span was increased by ten feet, and the new Wright J-5 Whirlwind engine was used. This was the first radial air-cooled engine to have its valve-operating linkage fully enclosed so that it did not have to be oiled by hand every few hours of operation. The design work on the airplane was done by Donald Hall at Ryan, and a small team of workers under the direction of B. F. Mahoney did a miraculous job to complete the airplane and make it ready for flight in just two months. After a few days of flight testing, Lindbergh gave it a real test by flying it in one hop from San Diego to Lambert Field in St. Louis, where his backers had an opportunity to see it. Lambert was the same field from which Lindbergh had flown the mail for the Robertson Aircraft Corporation, and the same field that I had gone to for the 1923 National Air Races. He then flew it to New York and prepared for the final take-off to Paris.

All of the contestants had been hindered by bad weather reports, and the bad weather was persisting. On May 8 Nungesser and Coli took off from Paris for New York. They apparently got over the ocean but no word has been heard from them since; some think they might have crashed somewhere in the maritime provinces of Canada or in the forests of northern Maine. On the night of May 19 word came that the weather was breaking, and Lindbergh prepared to go. The next morning, at 7:52 A.M., he took off from Roosevelt Field in New York on his history-making flight to Paris, where he landed at Le Bourget airport at about ten o'clock the following night (May 21).

Never had a single flight caused such a stir. Mobs of people were waiting at Le Bourget because he had flown low over Newfoundland, Ireland, and England, and word of his progress had been passed on to the French. After enthusiastic receptions in Paris, Brussels, and London, Lindbergh and his airplane were brought home on a U.S. Navy warship. This ship steamed right up into the Chesapeake Bay and up the Potomac River to Washington, where Lindbergh was received by President Coolidge.

The next morning the National Aeronautic Association gave a breakfast for Lindbergh at the Willard Hotel. I had been a member of the NAA since my days with the air-mail service in Chicago. Dorothy and I had been following Lindbergh's flight from the time he took off from New York, and when we heard about the NAA breakfast we piled into our Model T with our one-year-old son Donald for the trip to Washington. I took in that memorable breakfast and later in the day watched with my family the big parade for Lindbergh that the city put on. After that, Lindbergh flew to New York and got the biggest ticker-tape celebration ever.

Early in 1928 Professor Edward P. Warner of MIT, who had written a textbook on aircraft design for McGraw-Hill, approached me during one of his visits to Langley Field; he suggested that I write a book for the same publisher on aircraft propeller design. I agreed and in due course a contract was prepared and signed. For the next three years I spent nearly all of my spare time preparing this book. It took me only six weeks or so, while my wife and infant son were visiting relatives in Illinois, to complete the book's outline and the first draft of several chapters, but, after that, progress was slow.

About this time the Yackey Aircraft Company finally completed the design and construction of its own airplane. Art Chester, later famous as a designer-builder and pilot of midget racing planes, did the engineering work for it. Yackey's plane was a two-place tandem, open-cockpit, high-wing monoplane with a Wright 220-horsepower Whirlwind engine. The ailerons were operated by Ahrens controls, a type usually employed for throttle operation. When Yackey submitted the airplane for government approval, the inspector for the Department of Commerce thought that the friction in the aileron controls might make the action rather sluggish. Tony, a fighter pilot in World War I, had flown the plane in a race from Chicago to Seattle. He had confidence in the innovative design and wanted to prove the inspector wrong. He took the airplane up himself to demonstrate how maneuverable it was. According to the inspector, Tony put it through every maneuver that could have been expected from a fighter plane, including a high-speed dive to the field to conclude the flight. As he leveled out, however, the wing, which was braced to the fuselage below by struts, failed at the strut attachment points. The airplane crashed and Tony was killed instantly. The plane had not been designed for that sort of high-speed maneuver.

Incidentally, when Dr. Lewis of the NACA read about the crash, he was good enough to get the Department of Commerce inspector's report and sent a copy of it to me. Tony's lovely wife, Olive, went back to live with her folks in St. Louis.

On December 16, 1928, the day before the twenty-fifth anniversary of the first powered flight at Kitty Hawk, Orville Wright visited Langley. He was a member of the NACA and came down to the lab a couple of times a year to see what we were doing and to talk with us about our research work. During this visit John Jay Ide, the NACA's permanent resrepresentative in Paris, France, snapped a picture of Wright examining our new NACA cowling on the Curtiss Hawk AT-5A. Ide gave me a copy of this snapshot, which I still have. The next day there was a pilgrimage of about one hundred people from various parts of the country and the world to Kitty Hawk. Eastman Jacobs and I were fortunate enough to go along to the celebration. East's father, Judge Jacobs, from Greeley, Colorado, was visiting him, and he came along too. East drove us to Norfolk where we got on one of several buses taking the group to a point on Albemarle Sound.

On the bus we had an interesting conversation with an obviously well-informed man whom we took to be English. It turned out that he was Martin Wronsky, head of the German Airlines, or Lufthansa, but he had spent his prep school years in England. In 1928 the bridge across Albemarle Sound had not yet been built, so we took a ferry across to a point near Kill Devil Hill. From there we

The NACA low-drag cowling was first flight tested on this Curtiss Hawk AT-5A trainer in October 1928. The cowling increased the plane's maximum speed from 118 to 137 miles per hour. In the adjoining photo, Orville Wright is looking at that particular cowling during a visit to Langley on December 16, 1928. The picture with Wright was taken by John Jay Ide, the NACA's intelligence officer in Paris, France. Ide was in the United States to attend the ceremony at Kitty Hawk in honor of the twenty-fifth anniversary of the Wright brothers' first flight, which took place the day after this photo was taken.

Orville Wright died on January 30, 1948, at the age of seventy-six. This photograph of him was taken at the time of the twenty-fifth anniversary celebration in 1928 of the Wrights' first flight at Kitty Hawk, and it was autographed by Mr. Wright personally, though his signature is now barely legible. All of the guests at the anniversary celebration received a copy of this photo, and it has been one of my most treasured mementos ever since. During the 1928 celebration, incidentally, Mr. Wright dedicated the large granite boulder at the spot where the first flight left the ground.

Amelia Earhart outside the propeller research tunnel building during the famous aviatrix's visit to Langley in November 1928. I am standing to the far right of the back row. To Miss Earhart's left are Henry Reid, Langley's engineer-in-charge, and Col. Jacob Wuest, Langley base commander. Immediately on her right are test pilot Thomas Carroll and Elton Miller, chief of the aerodynamics division at Langley.

walked to the site of the first flight. There was no real road, just tracks in the sand. During the ceremony a small granite monument, marking the start of the first flight, was dedicated by Orville Wright himself. Also, each one of us who attended received an autographed photo of Orville Wright. I have this picture on my study wall and consider it one of my prize possessions. The picture is still good, nearly sixty years later, but the autograph is fading; I hope to find some means to preserve it. By the way, Kill Devil Hill, which is a large sand dune, had moved several hundred feet during the twenty-five years between the first flight and the anniversary celebration. In about 1925 army engineers had planted certain grasses on the hill, and it has remained fixed since that time. A large monument has been placed on top of the hill, which can be seen for many miles.

One other famous visitor to Langley deserves mention. In November 1928 Amelia Earhart came to Langley, and I had a very pleasant hour-long chat with her outside the propeller research tunnel building. She was a very pleasant, outgoing person, and easy to talk with, about flying at any rate. Incidentally, during her tour of the NACA lab, Miss Earhart had part of her raccoon coat sucked up into our 11-inch high-speed tunnel.

5.

Hamilton of United Aircraft and Transport Corporation

One evening in February 1929, while I was at home in Hampton, I received a telephone call from Thomas Hamilton, president of the Hamilton Aero Manufacturing Company in Milwaukee, Wisconsin. His company had for long made wooden propellers for aircraft and was now also making adjustable aluminum-alloy propellers and steel hubs for both military and commercial aircraft. Hamilton asked me if I would like to become his chief engineer, a job he had offered me a couple of times previously but that I had not accepted because I was very happy with my situation at the NACA.

This time the situation was different. His was no longer just a small propeller company in Milwaukee, but a part of a large organization, the United Aircraft and Transport Corporation. This newly formed organization consisted of four major airplane manufacturers: the Boeing Aircraft Company of Seattle, Washington, which recently had acquired the Stearman Company of Wichita, Kansas, and the Hamilton Metalplane Company in Milwaukee; the Vought Aircraft Company of Long Island, New York; the Sikorsky Aircraft Company of Bridgeport, Connecticut; and the Northrop

Aircraft Company of Burbank, California. It also consisted of a leading engine manufacturer, the Pratt and Whitney Company of Hartford, Connecticut, which had just come out with two excellent new radial air-cooled engines (the Wasp and the Hornet); two airlines, United, which ran from New York through Chicago to San Francisco, following the old air-mail routes, and Pacific Airlines, which ran from San Francisco up to Seattle; as well as Hamilton's propeller company. Two other combinations of companies had been formed at about the same time, but United appeared to me to be the largest and the best. If I was ever to get into commercial work, this was certainly a wonderful opportunity.

I talked the matter over with Dorothy, and she had a strong desire to return reasonably close to our folks in Chicago—only a couple of hours away from Milwaukee by car. In a few weeks the heads of the various United Aircraft companies were going to have a meeting in Washington, D.C., and Tom Hamilton invited me to go up and talk with some of them, which I did. I interviewed with Bill Boeing, chairman of the board, and with Frederick Rentschler, president both of Pratt and Whitney and of United as a whole.

In the end I could not resist the temptation, and in April 1929 we moved to Milwaukee in our 1928 Model A Ford. We went via Buffalo so I could visit the three separate aircraft plants (not belonging to United) run by Consolidated, Curtiss, and Charles Ward Hall. We stayed overnight with Curtiss's Andrew J. Fairbanks, a University of Michigan aeronautical engineer who had worked in the atmospheric wind tunnel section at Langley. At Curtiss, by the way, I met Col. Virginius E. Clark of the Clark Y airfoil fame. From Buffalo we drove through Canada to Detroit, where we took in the 1929 Detroit Air Show. Again, we stayed overnight at the home of an old NACA colleague, Ernest Wilson, formerly of the power plant division at Langley Field. Wilson was then working in the research division of General Motors Corporation under Charles Kettering, who had invented the automobile electric starter.

In Milwaukee we stayed in Tom Hamilton's large house until we found a place of our own. (Hamilton owned another house in Beverly Hills, California, which was where his own family was living at the time.) Carl Schory, Hamilton's sales manager, and his wife were also living in Hamilton's Milwaukee home. Before going into business as a manufacturer of wooden airplane propellers, Tom had been a cabinetmaker. In his dining room there was a beautiful table and set of chairs that he had made.

Our small staff at Hamilton Aero Manufacturing Company in Milwaukee made some large propellers. Left to right, me, draftsman Bob Fox, and engineer Dr. Josef Wegerer.

The propeller plant was a one-story building, about half a block square, located in a partially residential area a few miles north of the center of town. The plant's production manager was a forthright and capable man of Swedish descent named Arvid Nelson. Though I had the fancy title of chief engineer, there was at first only one young draftsman, named Bob Fox, under me. A little later the company added an Austrian engineer by the name of Dr. Josef Wegerer.

In 1930 the Hamilton Aero Manufacturing Company was making both wooden and metal propellers. While wood had been used for almost all propellers of various sizes during the early days of aviation, by 1929 the larger engines were ordinarily fitted with adjustable-pitch metal blades mounted in steel hubs. A wide range of engines was available at that time, but most were air-cooled. The largest of these were the Pratt and Whitney 550-horsepower

Hornet and 450-horsepower Wasp, and the Wright (by then Curtiss-Wright) Whirlwinds, which came with five, seven, or nine cylinders from 150 to 300 HP. The smaller engines included the old water-cooled 90-horsepower Curtiss OX-5 and several different air-cooled radials, including 60- and 90-horsepower models of the LeBlond engine, which had seven and nine cylinders, respectively; 80- and 120-horsepower Anzani engines; English- and American-made four-cylinder in-line Cirius engines; five-, seven-, and nine-cylinder Siemens-Halske engines; and five-, seven-, and nine-cylinder Walter engines. There was also the 80-horsepower Jennott; 110-horsepower Warner; five-cylinder, 40-horsepower Velie (later increased to greater power as the Lambert engine); as well as the in-line Rover and the Dayton Bear.

In order to fit propellers to the various engine-airframe combinations, I used the design methods that I had worked out in the Bureau of Aeronautics and had later refined with the NACA. The results came out satisfactorily with the larger Wright and Pratt and Whitney engines, but with the smaller engines the propellers almost never turned up as fast as they were supposed to on the engine and airplane for which they were designed. I soon found that the large engines delivered their full rating of power as specified at specific RPMs, but that none of the smaller engines did. Moreover, the airplane designer using these small engines usually overestimated the speed that his airplane could actually attain. Together, these factors caused the propeller to hold down the engine to less than its rated revolution speed. At first this discrepancy made it almost impossible to design a satisfactory wooden propeller for smaller engines. I had to make my own guess as to the real engine power and airplane speed.

To get usable data I set up a one-mile speed course at the Milwaukee airport. We arranged to have runs made in each direction with every airplane that came to Milwaukee to get fitted with a propeller. Carl Schory, who had timed various flying records for the National Aeronautic Association, helped me with this part of the program. By knowing the air speed and propeller RPM for any combination of airplane engine and propeller, I could work back from the propeller data to find the actual engine horsepower. After a time I had pretty good information on the real powers of most of the small airplane engines. I still had to make a "guesstimate," though, of the actual air speed likely to be obtained by any new airplane design.

In the design of any wooden propeller, it was necessary to have good sound values for the horsepower and RPM—because if the propeller did not fit, a new one would have to be built. With the adjustable-pitch metal propellers, a slight change in the pitch adjustment could often take care of the situation satisfactorily. Incidentally, making these adjustments in the field had been made easy by a special propeller protractor that I had been instrumental in getting produced a few years earlier while working with the NACA.

In the propeller research tunnel at Langley Field we had needed to make many pitch changes with the propeller on the airplane being tested; this had to be done 25 feet above the floor in the PRT's test section. I had started to design a special protractor for this purpose, when one day a visitor happened to see me and told me that one had already been worked out by a navy mechanic at the naval air base in Norfolk. I went over to see him and found that he had indeed already worked out a very satisfactory protractor. I borrowed it for a time, and we then drew up and built a couple of models for our own use in the PRT and in flight research. I returned the original to the navy mechanic, with thanks. Later, a specialty company in Norfolk produced it for general use from our NACA drawings. By the start of World War II it had become a standard piece of equipment throughout the aeronautical services.

While I was working for Hamilton in late 1929 and 1930, an unusual incident occurred that is worth mentioning in my story as an indication of the difference between the practically trained American engineer and the more theoretically trained European engineer. It happened that in Hamilton's propeller shop a rather large, cylindrical trash can was being jostled out of place now and then, and the shop manager wanted a rope or something to hold it permanently in the place where it belonged. Figuring that a piece of common strap iron (one inch wide and one-eighth inch thick) would be satisfactory, I sent Dr. Joe Wegerer out into the shop to measure the length of strap that would be required to fit against the wall, go around the trash can, and fit against the wall again. Dr. Wegerer did this and gave the required length to a girl in the office who could order the material. Several hours later the girl came to me almost in tears, saying that she had tried all over Milwaukee and could not obtain this material. She said that no one could cut the material to the accuracy required. I asked her what length Dr. Wegerer had given her for the piece of strap iron, and she read off to me "62.2479634913." I laughed and told her to forget the decimal point and get it to the nearest even inch, after which she had no more trouble. Then I asked Joe how he happened to give the girl a figure with ten digits past the decimal point. He said, "Well, I learned pi to ten places and when I multiplied the radius by pi to get half the circumference, I just filled in all ten places as I usually do." How's that for practical engineering?

During this period it occurred to me that narrower propeller blades operating at higher angles of attack would reduce the loss of engine RPM at climbing and take-off speeds and therefore improve the take-off and climbing performances. This appeared to be true as long as the blades were not so narrow that they forced the blade pitch angle to become so high that the blade would stall at the beginning of a take-off run. To test this idea, I had three propellers made with the same diameter and for the same engine power—the Warner 110 HP. One of the propellers had normal blades, one had extremely narrow ones, which we called "the toothpick plan form," and the other was in between the two.

Just when these propellers were ready for testing, James S. McDonnell, future chairman of the board of the McDonnell-Douglas Corporation, was getting well along with the airplane he had designed for the Guggenheim Safe Airplane Contest. McDonnell, one of the designers employed by the Hamilton Metalplane Company, was building his Guggenheim entry, which he called the Doodlebug, in the old Metalplane factory. Since Metalplane had been taken over by Boeing, this factory was no longer in use. Because the safe airplane contest required that the airplane be able to take off and clear a 35-foot obstacle within 500 feet, take-off and climb performance were critical. It happened that McDonnell had fitted his Doodlebug with a 110-horsepower Warner engine, and we tested the three propellers on his plane as soon as it was flying satisfactorily. Though the toothpick design fluttered under certain conditions, the medium-narrow propeller—a Sport Junior type as far as the blade roots and hub were concerned—gave a better performance than did the blade of regular width. McDonnell's plane employed this improved propeller in the Guggenheim competition and thereafter.

In addition to the propeller, I also designed the NACA cowling for the Doodlebug's Warner radial engine.

McDonnell's plane was a very effective design, with Handley Page automatic leading edge slots, slotted flaps, and long-travel shock absorbers. It could fly in and out of very small places. Unfortunately, on his way to the competition in New York there was a malfunction, and Mac had to make a forced landing, damaging the airplane and delaying its arrival in New York to the point where his entry was not quite legal. Among those entered in the contest were Maj. Shorty Schroeder, who had set the world altitude record with an Army Air Service plane, and C. Gilbert Taylor, later of Taylor Cub fame. The contest was won by the Curtiss Tanager, a biplane with leading edge slots, slotted flaps, and floating wing-tip ailerons on the lower wing. Although the performance of some of these airplanes was remarkable, none was put into production. Nor did they influence the design of production airplanes to any significant extent.

One incident occurred during the testing of the Doodlebug that I will never live down so far as my wife is concerned. We had finished testing rather late one afternoon, and I took Mac home with me for a quick supper. Dorothy had just come home from the hospital the day before, after having given birth to our daughter Betsey, and our maid had quit to get married. Dorothy had just prepared some macaroni and cheese and felt chagrined to hand such slim pickings to a stranger. Every now and then I have made it rather tough for her, I'm afraid, but we have had over sixty years of happy married life and are still going at it at this time.

During this period in Milwaukee I continued working on my propeller textbook as much as I could, but because I was so busy with my regular work the book's progress was slow. I do remember thinking quite a bit for the first time about propeller failures due to metal fatigue. As aluminum-alloy propellers became generally used, there were occasional fatigue failures in which after some service a portion of the blade, or even the whole blade, would break off. Little was known, even in 1929, of the characteristic of a propeller blade to vibrate like a tuning fork with various natural frequencies in different modes. Nor were the stress build-ups known that might occur if the natural frequency of the propeller blade happened to coincide with the frequency of impulses imparted by the engine. Because wooden propellers had possessed sufficient internal damping, this problem had not occurred to any noticeable extent. The strengths of wooden propellers had been proved early by operating them for ten hours at 50 percent above the maximum rated horsepower. For metal propellers, we tried increasing this to 100 percent, but even then some failed due to fatigue. With the invention of the DeForest strain gauge, means were worked out to measure the stresses at various points in the propeller blade, as well as their variation with time, while the propeller was actually running. Beginning in the mid-1930s it became possible to tailor the propeller blades so that their natural frequencies did not coincide with the impulse from the power plants, at least throughout the main portion of the working range.

Our flight tests for Hamilton involving propellers sometimes included rate of climb and ceiling, as well as the usual run over the speed course. One such set of tests involved a Ford Trimotor, an experimental airplane that had been flown over from Dearborn.

After an extensive series of flight tests, we attempted to determine the Trimotor's ceiling with the center engine shut off. Climbing on two engines, it was apparent after a bit that it was going to take a very long time to attain the actual ceiling, which was expected to be between 8,000 and 9,000 feet of altitude. We started the middle engine again and climbed up to about 13,000 feet, shut it off, and with the two side engines running full blast, let the airplane settle to the point where it approached the ceiling from the top side. Then we interpolated between the two values for the actual ceiling.

We had made the various climb and ceiling tests in north and south runs, flying back and forth near the Milwaukee airport. The last run had been to the north and had lasted quite a long time. When we were finished with it and started to go home, we discovered that we had no idea where we were. Having expected to make just a local flight over the airport, we had not brought a single chart or map with us, and this particular airplane, being experimental, was not equipped with a compass.

There were three of us in the airplane, including the pilot and a mechanic who had recently come to us from the navy. We knew we had started the run heading somewhat toward the north, but without a compass we were not sure that we had flown a straight course, although we thought we were probably somewhere north or northwest of Milwaukee. I thought we should fly east until we came to Lake Michigan, and the others did not disagree, but we had a hard time telling which was east. It was just about noon and the sun was nearly straight up, but by holding a pencil vertically in the cockpit and gauging by about one-half inch of shadow, I selected a course that I thought would be east, and the pilot followed it.

In a few minutes we came to a lake with which I was not familiar but kept on going right over it, hopefully toward Lake Michigan. Soon we could see the shore of Lake Michigan and well to the north the lower portion of Green Bay—so I thought I knew where we were. We should just turn south and follow the lake, I said, until we came to Milwaukee. The ex-navy mechanic had the opposite idea, however. He was certain that we were somewhere between Chicago and Milwaukee and needed to turn north. I had recognized Green Bay, where I had been as a child, and was just as certain that we should go south. We had quite a spirited and heated discussion, hollering in the bare uninsulated fuselage over the noise of the engines—all three of which were going at that time. Finally I prevailed, and the pilot turned south.

We did not have very much fuel left, and the pilot had maintained an altitude of about 8,000 feet to give him a fair choice of landing fields in case we did run out of fuel. We weren't right at the end of the run, but we did not have enough to play with and go north first and then go back south, and the fields in that part of Wisconsin are rather small. We had visions of having to land in one of them and having to get a truckload of gasoline and feed it to the Trimotor in five-gallon cans with funnels and chamois skins.

After several minutes we came to a small city that had in it a very large building with a number of wings running off from it. The mechanic immediately spoke up, "See there," he said, "that's Kenosha, Wisconsin, where the Nash plant is, and that's the big Nash automobile plant." As we approached the town the pilot went down to an altitude of about 5,000 feet so that we could take a closer look, and fortunately there was a nice big sign on one of the wings of this building that read "Sheboygan." Sheboygan, I knew, was some 50 miles north of Milwaukee, and so we proceeded on our way without further incident and landed with only a little bit of fuel left. Back in Milwaukee we found that there was a very strong south wind which at high altitudes was no doubt much stronger—a matter that we had not considered in planning our flight. The small lake that we had flown over turned out to be Lake Winnebago. It is somewhat ironic for me that the town of Oshkosh is on Lake Winnebago. For the past several years Oshkosh has been the site of the Experimental Aircraft Association's annual fly-in, an event I have attended faithfully since the early 1970s.

Another interesting incident occurred when an airplane dealer from Minnesota who was dissatisfied with the take-off performance of his Lockheed Vega brought it in to Milwaukee to have a new propeller fitted. Actually, the Vega was one of the first of the new commercial airplanes that was clean enough and fast enough to require a very high-pitch propeller—one so high pitch in fact that the blades were stalled partially at the beginning of a take-off run. What the plane really needed was a controllable-pitch propeller, but none was available commercially until a few years later. In this case, aiming to improve the take-off performance, we put on a new propeller. The Lockheed distributor in Detroit, a famous racing pilot named Billy Brock, came to Milwaukee to watch the trials.

After making a few trials with pitch adjustments, the Minnesota airplane dealer went out to try take-offs again. Billy Brock and I watched from the hangar a few hundred feet away. With us was Dan Kaiser, an ex-air-mail pilot whom I had known when I worked for the air mail in Maywood, Illinois, back in 1922 and 1923. This time the pilot started his take-off from the middle of the field instead of using its entire length. He pulled the airplane off and held it at a very steep altitude and very low speed—probably at a speed below the minimum-speed power off, because the airplane flew at a lower speed with power on than with power off. I made the comment that the pilot was certainly relying on his power plant to keep functioning, because he didn't have the flying speed with power off that was necessary to prevent a crash if the engine failed. Both Brock and Kaiser disagreed with me, saying, "Oh, he'd just recover and make a nice landing."

The engine continued to function, however, and he went around the field and landed, stopping at just about the point where he had started his previous take-off. The pilot then opened the throttle again and repeated the take-off. This time, when he was about 200 feet high and with the nose pointed up at a very steep angle, the engine did stop suddenly and there was a reign of very complete silence except for a little swishing of the airplane through the air. The pilot kept the plane in a fairly flat attitude, but it came down steeply and crashed very hard in a severe pancake landing. The landing gear collapsed, and the wing sat flat on the ground. This had happened only 200 or 300 yards from us, and we all started running for it as fast as we could. By the time we got about halfway there, however, the pilot stepped out from the front and turned around to survey the scene with a very sad face.

The Vega's engine had been torn off when it snubbed on the ground and was lying near the plane's tail. This left a gaping hole in the front of the fuselage from which the pilot had merely stepped out. He was unhurt, as was the passenger he had in the cabin. There was a door in the front of the cabin, but the crash had so jimmed up the plane that we had to saw the plywood shell fuselage in half in order to get the passenger out. While neither person was hurt, the airplane was completely ruined.

At this point four or five people from another hangar had driven over. The people from both hangars realized that someone at the field had no doubt called the newspapers and that very shortly reporters would be out to give a great big play to the accident. So we all got together and in about ten minutes put all of the airplane's parts in a hangar and covered them up with a tarpaulin. Sure enough, within a few minutes the reporters and photographers were out there, but there was nothing for them to see.

The United Aircraft and Transport Corporation had a technical advisory committee made up largely of the chief engineers of the various companies. This was an outstanding group that included Boeing's Charles N. Monteith, who had been an officer in the engineering division of the air corps at McCook Field in Dayton and had written a book called *Simple Aerodynamics and the Airplane* (1924). (Monteith was in the process of designing a new airplane for both mail and passenger service. Called the Monomail, it was a very sleek, low-wing monoplane with a retractable landing gear. His plane was never put into production,[1] but a larger twin-engine version called the Boeing 247 not only would be put into production but also would be widely used on some of the first airlines.) The committee also included Pratt and Whitney's George Mead, the main designer of the Wasp and Hornet engines; Chance Vought's Charles McCarthy; Igor Sikorsky of Sikorsky Aircraft; Mac Short of Stearman and later Lockheed; and yours truly, from Hamilton.

The first meeting of this technical advisory committee was held in May 1929, shortly after I started with Hamilton, at the Pratt and Whitney plant in Hartford, Connecticut. In attendance for part of the meeting were Frederick Rentschler and Chance Vought. Each of us told of our recent activities and tried to dovetail them so that we could work together as a whole. The second meeting was held again in Hartford two months later, but I missed it.[2] I remember leaving the office on the last day of June and getting into my car to drive home, but that's the last thing I remember until 9 A.M. six days later when I woke up in bed and asked my wife why I was hurting and why I wasn't at work. Dorothy informed me that six days ago, as I was turning on to our street, a streetcar had come over the hill and run into me. She had heard the crash, and when she arrived at the car I was humped over the wheel, unconscious and moaning. For four days in the hospital and two days afterwards, although I seemed to be normal, I had no real idea of what had happened. It took several weeks before I was able to work even two hours a day.

Feeling better by late August, I went to Dearborn to help the Ford Company in its effort to reduce the vibration in its Trimotor airplane. I took ten different propellers with me in order to see what combination of three might make the plane run more smoothly. I spent several days with a Ford pilot testing out various combinations, making our separate notes and then comparing them later. At the end of one long tiring day of testing in which we had not completed our routine, our notes showed that we both considered the particular trio we had used that day to be the roughest running set run to date. The next day, with smooth air and refreshed minds, we both considered these very same propellers the smoothest we had tested to date. Clearly, our testing by subjective human observation was not producing usable results.

From Detroit I went directly to Cleveland to witness the 1929 National Air Races. Our sales manager, Carl Schory, was in charge of the timing, and I helped him to some extent. Many races for airplanes in different categories were run, and exhibitions of aerobatic flying were put on by Al Williams, Jimmy Doolittle, and Speed Holman. Holman, I remember, looped a Ford Trimotor and flew the big airplane on its back across the airport. But the race that interested me the most was the feature event: a 50-mile free-for-all (with no restrictions on engine power) in which seven planes, including one from each of the military services, were entered.

Military and civilian planes and pilots had not competed against each other for seven years. This made the race special, but what really held my attention was the fact that two of the planes were equipped with NACA cowlings. The navy had entered a Curtiss Hawk but with a liquid-cooled D-12 engine with special side radiators. Its performance would make an interesting direct comparison between the air-cooled and the liquid-cooled installations. The real prize, however, was the new Travelair Mystery Ship, a sleek wire-braced low-wing monoplane; its Wright J-6-9 Whirlwind engine was fitted with a very good NACA cowling.

From the first the two airplanes with NACA cowlings led the field by a good margin. The Travelair Mystery Ship won handily, even though its pilot, Doug Davis, missed a pylon and had to go back and circle it again. This certainly showed what could be done with a radial engine and an NACA cowling, and it made the day for me. (This plane is now in the EAA museum at Oshkosh, Wisconsin.)

The history of the aircraft manufacturing business has been shaped significantly, of course, by patent claims and litigation. By the late 1920s the Curtiss Company had been making Curtiss-Reed aluminum-alloy propellers for several years. The company was in control of Sylvanus Reed's patent, which had far-reaching claims. These claims included very thin aluminum-alloy propellers that would bend too far forward from the air load alone but relied on centrifugal forces to hold the blades out fairly straight. They even included all aircraft propellers made out of aluminum or aluminum alloys. The Hamilton metal propellers were obviously covered by these claims, and litigation was in the offing.

Tom Hamilton figured that the claims were too broad to hold up in court and was willing to fight them. The top officials of United Aircraft, however, took another course. Sometime earlier the Standard Steel Propeller Company had been given an opportunity by the army to bid on and manufacture aluminum-alloy blades and steel hubs for its air service. Though the company's original enterprise—making steel propellers—had not been very successful, its manufacturing of aluminum blades and steel hubs grew, thanks to a license under the Reed patent, into a successful operation. Frank Caldwell, who had been in charge of the army's propeller design at McCook and later at Wright Field and who had designed most of the detachable-blade metal propellers then in use, resigned from the service to become Standard's chief engineer. The United Aircraft executives simply bought out Standard Steel and joined the two companies, forming Hamilton Standard.

Then came a rapid series of major changes. Standard Steel was just finishing a fine new building, so the entire Hamilton plant at Milwaukee was simply abandoned and its activity moved into Standard's new factory in Pittsburgh. United Aircraft and Transport was also developing an airport at Burbank, California, a suburb north of Los Angeles. On this airport, Hamilton was constructing a new factory branch. Frank Caldwell, who was ten years older than I and who had much more propeller experience, was made chief engineer of the production plant in Pittsburgh. Hamilton became chairman of the board of Hamilton Standard and Kraeling, Standard's former president, was made its president. After about a month, though, Kraeling was replaced by Eugene Wilson, the commander who had been in charge of the power plant division at the Bureau of Aeronautics while I had worked there. Tom Hamilton, who was chairman of the board and had also been put in charge of the Burbank airport development, wanted to keep living in Beverly Hills and he decided that I should go to the West Coast branch to carry on development work there directly with him.

Our car had been demolished in the streetcar accident, so we bought a new 1929 Model A Ford sedan. We did not have it provided with a heater, an extra cost, because we would drive to California by the southern route and figured we would not need it. In the middle of November 1929, two months after the stock market crash and the commencement of the Great Depression, we started the drive to Los Angeles with Donald, age three and one-half, and Betsey, three months, riding in a hammock back of the front seat.

It was drizzling when we left Milwaukee, and before we got to Chicago the rain was freezing on the windshield. We stayed overnight with our folks in Berwyn. The next morning we drove to Champaign where I toured the old campus and visited the new Delta Alpha Epsilon fraternity house. From there we drove through St. Louis and Kansas City to Emporia, Kansas, where some of Dorothy's mother's family was located. The next morning we went on to Wichita, where I visited the Stearman plant, which was then part of Boeing. There I met Stearman's chief engineer, Mac Short, for the first time; he showed me not only the plant but also took me to visit Travelair and Cessna, whose factories were also in Wichita.

The farther southwest we went, the colder it got. I had forgotten about mountains and the wintery effects of altitude. About 100 miles west of Wichita we tried to go straight south, but the snow was so deep that the primitive roads—two-lane highways only— were blocked. Some people were even trapped in their cars overnight. We did well to turn around and get back to the main highway to Trinidad, Colorado, where the temperature was minus

The Burbank airport in the 1929/30 period. At this time there were only four major buildings. The Hamilton plant is the small building in the distance, the only one on the far side of the runway. Jack Northrop was working on his Alpha airplane in the largest building on the opposite side of the one runway from Hamilton. The airplane visible in both pictures is Charles A. Lindbergh's Lockheed Sirius. This airport was later the home of the Lockheed plant and looked entirely different.

three degrees F. That was very cold going for a car without a heater. We kept little Betsey warm by bundling her up in the hammock, and the rest of us did what we could with overcoats, gloves, galoshes, and blankets. It stayed very cold all the way to the point where we crossed the Colorado River into Needles, California. When we got to L.A., we stayed with my brother Herb and his wife in their home in Pasadena until we had time to locate a place for ourselves. Finally we rented the upper story of a house in North Hollywood, which was not too far from the Burbank airport.

Hamilton had started his West Coast factory in a rented hangar on Grand Central Airport in Glendale, California. When I arrived the man in charge of it, Fred Denslow, and his helpers were in the process of moving from that site to the new building that had just been finished on the Burbank airport. By the way, a number of movie stars used this airport to do their private flying because it was so close to Hollywood. I remember that Wallace Beery, for example, had an airplane in one of the hangars, and he used to come out and fly quite often.

Before I had the chance to settle in at Burbank, though, I had to go to Seattle to attend another meeting of United's technical advisory committee. The trip up was a real adventure in airline transportation of the time. I left Los Angeles in a Ford Trimotor, which was to take me to Oakland after short stops at Bakersfield and Fresno. Then I was to get on United Airlines, or rather the Pacific Airlines portion of United Airlines, from Oakland to Seattle.

When the Ford was on the ground at Fresno, I noticed that the pilot and mechanic were out in front carefully examining the right-hand engine and propeller. It was a Hamilton propeller, and I got out to see what was wrong. They were examining a black mark, which to me indicated a crack in the portion of the hub supporting one of the blades, and debating whether they should go on to Oakland. I introduced myself, explained the danger, and recommended definitely that they not go any farther. I mentioned that I personally was not going to fly one more mile in the damaged plane. The airliner employees concurred and stopped the flight right there. I took a train to Oakland, arriving there that night.

After spending a night in a hotel, I took off early the next morning for Seattle in a Boeing 40-B single-engine biplane. This plane had really been designed for mail service on the original transcontinental run, but in front of the pilot, who flew from an open cock-

I flew in this Boeing 40-B in 1929 as an airline passenger from Oakland to Portland, trying to get to Seattle. The plane was designed primarily for mail service.

pit, there were two small compartments, each with room for one passenger. I sat in the left-hand compartment and another passenger sat in the right-hand one, with a wall that closed off nearly everything between us. Each of us had a small window to look out of.

We took off from Oakland in the dark, but it soon became daylight as we were flying over the Sacramento Valley. I remember that as we went through a pass between two large mountains the pilot came within 50 feet of the ground. We landed at Medford, Oregon, where the other passenger got off and the plane was refueled. Then we took off for Portland.

As I mentioned previously, I made it a practice in those days to follow the course of my flights on a Rand McNally map. As we approached where I thought Portland should have been, I could not see the city but only the tops of what appeared to be a very low layer of clouds, possibly fog, and I wondered then if we would have to go back to a clear field. The pilot headed a bit to the right, however, and got down very low until we were nearly at ground level. Then he followed a little river, the Willamette, which flows through downtown Portland to the Columbia River. The airport was on

Swan Island in the Willamette, not too far from its confluence with the Columbia. I couldn't see much out of the little window, but every now and then, when the pilot zoomed up, I could catch a view of the mast of a boat under us. Then he would go down again. The next zoom passed us over a bridge. Finally the pilot found the airport and landed, though he couldn't possibly have seen more than a third of the way across the field. I considered this a very unsafe practice, particularly for an airliner, and my thought was verified a week later when one of the pilots failed to miss the same bridge and was killed. Seattle was closed in by bad weather also, so for the second time I had to finish my air run by taking a train. The weather stayed poor for the next several days. We had our meetings at the Boeing plant, but all the time we were there we couldn't see across the field.

One evening we all had dinner at Bill Boeing's beautiful estate. He had a professional entertain us with magic, jokes, and chatter. Before dinner, the Boeings asked each of us what we would like to have for a cocktail. I did not drink much and suggested a glass of wine. Unfortunately, they didn't have any easily available, and the butler had to go down into the wine cellar and dig out a bottle especially for me. The Boeings were very gracious about it, but I still felt a bit embarrassed.

When the meetings were over, Seattle was still socked in by bad weather, and I had to take the train all the way to Los Angeles—a trip of more than thirty hours by rail.

When I got back, work at Hamilton's West Coast factory was really getting going nicely. There were about a dozen workers in all, and although they had nothing to do with the construction of the propeller hubs, they were forming aluminum-alloy blades to their final shape. In reality, it was really more of a West Coast service station than a manufacturing plant. Fred Denslow, the manager, was a fine young man about my age who appeared to me to be very competent. He took me with him to visit all of the airport operations and factories in the L.A. area where our propellers were being used. The driving was pleasant, mostly through groves and other agricultural areas. The entire area is now part of the city, of course, built over solidly.

Three factories I got to know pretty well were Lockheed's, Douglas's, and Northrop's. Lockheed had a small plant in Glendale where one airplane, either a Vega or Sirius, was being turned out every week. The fuselages were molded plywood. Each half, longitudinally, was laid up by hand in a hollow concrete mold. To create the needed strength, thin strips of wood veneer were laid up diagonally, and the next layer was glued to it with its grain at 90 degrees. The Douglas plant in Santa Monica was producing mostly military airplanes. I met Douglas's chief engineer, James H. ("Dutch") Kindelberger, later president of North American Aviation after it became a manufacturing company, as well as the chief designer, Arthur Raymond. I also ran into the man who had been chief draftsman at the air-mail plant at Checkerboard Field, Illinois, when I had been working there in 1922. He was now head checker in the drafting department at Douglas.

Jack Northrop, formerly chief engineer of Lockheed and principal designer of the Lockheed Vega and Lockheed Sirius, had started his own company in 1929 and was now operating under the United Aircraft and Transport Corporation on Burbank Field. It was a small plant, but in a short time had gotten fairly well along in the construction of the company's first model, the Northrop Alpha. This design was similar to the Lockheed Sirius—being a low-wing, single-engine airplane with fixed landing gear. The main difference was that the Sirius had been made entirely out of wood whereas the Alpha was all metal. Besides our Hamilton Standard facility, Northrop's was the only other new building on Burbank Field. Northrop's head structures man was Donovan Berlin, who would later be best known for his design of the Curtiss P-36 and P-40 fighters.[3]

Dr. Clark Millikan, whose father, Robert Millikan, was president of the California Institute of Technology in Pasadena, where Clark taught and did research in the school's new Guggenheim Aeronautical Laboratory, was doing some consulting work for Northrop, and he visited the plant frequently. Dorothy, my wife, had attended the University of Chicago at the same time that Clark had, and she had known him slightly. So we got to be pretty good friends. After Cal Tech hired Theodore von Kármán in 1930, Clark invited me over to see him. I was glad to be able to meet Dr. Ludwig Prandtl, von Kármán's mentor at the University of Göttingen, during his visit to Cal Tech. Prandtl was one of the most eminent early theoretical aerodynamicists; besides being von Kármán's teacher, he had also taught Max Munk. In 1921 the NACA had published some of Prandtl's work in Technical Report 116.

I met Theodore von Kármán (the short man in the middle wearing a double-breasted coat) for the first time during his visit to Langley in December 1926, which was not long after he came to this country from Europe. I am standing in the back row to the far left. Some of the other notables in this picture are George Lewis (far right), Max Munk (front row, third from left), Paul Hemke (just to my left), Henry J. E. Reid (bespectacled, in front of me), Tom Carroll (to Henry Reid's left), and Elliott G. Reid (far right of back row).

Jack Northrop and I often went to lunch together in Glendale, and occasionally Clark Millikan and Arthur Raymond went with us. As one might imagine, interesting aeronautical discussions always took place. During one lunch conversation it came out that I was getting pretty far along with a textbook on aircraft propeller design. Professor Millikan, who was about to teach a course on the subject, asked if he could use my manuscript to teach his class. I was particularly happy to agree to this because it gave me a chance to get the book criticized by one of this country's leading aeronautical scientists and corrected by class use before it was even given to the publisher. And, later, I was even happier to learn that one of Clark's graduate students, W. Bailey Oswald, had used some information from my manuscript to work out for his doctoral thesis a special method for computing the performance of airplanes. His thesis was later published as an NACA technical report, and his method became widely used. Oswald later became an important part of the engineering department at Douglas.

I had in fact been working very hard on the book during this period, because I had hoped to get a lot done before an urgent project came up that would take all of my time and energy. With the young children and unfamiliar surroundings in North Hollywood, my family was not geared for much outside social activity; so after supper I would spend a couple of hours outlining what I wanted to write and then the next morning I would get up at five o'clock and write while fresh for a couple of hours before going to the plant.

Early in 1930 I got a telephone call from Jerry Vultee, Lockheed's chief engineer. Charles Lindbergh had bought a Lockheed Sirius and was pruning it in order to attempt a record nonstop flight from the West to the East Coast. Vultee wondered whether I might arrange to get them a propeller that would give the airplane a little more speed. I found out what propeller the Sirius had and then told them that I had just designed—or selected, really—a new propeller for the Northrop Alpha, which was substantially the same airplane except that it was constructed in metal instead of wood. I informed them that the most they could hope for would be an increase of about one mile per hour, and that to make the tests accurately would probably take a number of flights. I was surprised to find that that did not end the matter, because Lindbergh wanted to try for it anyway.

Lindbergh and I flew the Sirius through a series of runs along the speed course that I had laid out along a railroad track between Burbank and Van Nuys. In those days the country on both sides of the railroad track was farmland almost entirely clear of houses. The railroad had mileposts, which I verified by sending out two men with a 100-foot tape, and with two stopwatches I could check the time for each mile as well as for the total.

I told Lindbergh that in order to get accurate results my practice was first to fly level, and at the right altitude, until the air speed steadied down; I then noted that speed. Then the pilot was to hold that speed while descending and turning on to the course, about two miles ahead of the first course marker. This would give two miles of steady running before the first reading was taken. Lindbergh readily agreed to follow this procedure. First, we made two runs in each direction with the Sirius's original propeller, checking its performance and taking the times for each mile and for the

Flight tests with "Lucky Lindy" and his Lockheed Sirius, 1930. Tom Hamilton is the man in the light-colored suit and hat in two of these photos.

total. Then, if the speed was constant along the course, and if the two downwind runs were nearly the same and the upwind runs were nearly the same, we computed the speed in each case and averaged the results for the final speed.

The results appeared to be quite accurate, but they were a great disappointment to Lindbergh. In earlier speed trials over a one-mile course at the metropolitan airport of Los Angeles, the Sirius had supposedly obtained 177 miles per hour. The speed we obtained in Burbank was 8 miles per hour less, only 169. I told Vultee and Lindbergh that it was easy to pick up a little extra speed in turning and losing altitude down to the beginning of a run, and that with only a one-mile course, a large part of that speed would carry over; that was the reason for my extra care. It was disheartening to see Lindbergh so disappointed, but he really did want to get accurate results. What with having to make several trials with the new propeller and pitch changes to get exactly the RPM as with the original propeller, and waiting for smooth air conditions, it took two or three more days to complete the tests. In the final runs, we did get the speed of the Sirius up to 170, an increase of 1 MPH.

During these days with Lindbergh, I witnessed firsthand how unmercifully the public still hounded the famous aviator. On one occasion following a run we were sitting in my office computing the speeds from the recorded times. My office was on the ground floor (actually we had only one floor), and though large enough for about twelve, the office was occupied at the time only by me and one other man, a draftsman. I sat at my desk with my back toward a row of windows that faced the street. Some distance to my left there was another wall with windows in it also. Lindbergh was sitting on my left, facing an inside wall on my right. He happened to look up and cringed, saying, "Oh, look at that." Every window on both sides of the office was filled with people looking in at what we were doing. I remember one woman raising her arm and waving across to some people on the other side of the street, hollering, "Here he is! Here he is!" We were like monkeys in a cage.

On another occasion a man came into the office, presented a card showing that he represented a publishing company, and said he'd like to see Mr. Lindbergh. I took the card out to Lindbergh, who recognized the company for having something to do with him, and he said, yes, he'd be glad to see the man. I took the fellow out and presented him to Lindbergh, who was very cordial and asked what the business was. It turned out that the man was no longer connected with the company and all he wanted was for Lindbergh to autograph a photograph for him. Well, we were busy and this sort of thing was a continual annoyance. We ate our lunches in a little restaurant in Glendale where Lindbergh had arranged to eat privately in a back room. He was usually stopped once or twice going through the place to the back room, but we had our privacy once we got in there. At lunch we had a number of interesting discussions involving such things as whether you could make airplanes safe enough so that you didn't need to rely on parachutes to get down safely in a pinch.

During my time with Lindbergh I saw how fame also had its little advantages. One day I was driving my car to lunch in Glendale with another man beside me and Lindbergh in the back seat. I was following the general run of traffic and paying no particular attention to speed when a police officer pulled alongside of us, operated his siren, and pulled us over to the curb. He said that I was speeding and pulled out his book and started writing out a ticket. Lindbergh whispered to me not to say anything, opened the rear window on our side, put out his hand, and introduced himself to the officer. After a brief friendly chat, in which Lindy told him that we were pressed for time and that I was trying to get him to a place with dispatch but that he thought I was just rolling right along with the rest of the traffic, the officer put his book in his pocket and went away with a grin on his face.

By early 1930 the West Coast aircraft business was really starting to feel the Depression. In the latter part of February I received a telegram from Gene Wilson, the president of Hamilton Standard, stating that the West Coast branch was being eliminated and that I should wind up my affairs and report for duty at Pittsburgh at once. This was the first inkling that any of us had had of this elimination. Tom Hamilton was miffed that I got notice of it before he did, and I can't say that I blame him.[4] Lockheed moved its plant to the edge of Burbank Field, where it eventually grew to such great proportions that the airport was renamed Lockheed Air Terminal. Jack Northrop stayed at Burbank Field while he produced the Northrop Alpha, but then he left United and formed his own Northrop Aircraft Company.

Dorothy did not like the idea of living in Pittsburgh, which was a rather dirty place in those days because of the steel mills, but we were soon packed up and traveling east in our Model A Ford. We drove first to Chicago, where I left Dorothy and the children with her folks, while I went on to Pittsburgh. I was cordially received there by Gene Wilson and Frank Caldwell—and I'm sure I could have worked well with them—but after my stimulating experience with airplane designers in southern California, I was beginning to question very seriously whether I wanted to spend my whole life working on propellers only. Airplanes and their flying characteristics now held a lot of my attention.

Within a week after reporting at Pittsburgh, the company sent me to visit the Sikorsky plant at Bridgeport, Connecticut, regarding some propellers it was using. On the way back, I stopped off in Washington to get some technical information from the NACA and to say hello to Dr. Lewis and the NACA people. Dr. Lewis said there had been a great deal of difficulty lately with people getting into spins and that much more information was needed on the subject. He invited me to come back with the NACA and help study the spin problem, suggesting that I could be made the assistant chief of the aerodynamics division and could work with any of the wind tunnels and the flight section. I thought a bit and then said that I would consider the invitation if I could work also on nonspinning—or the possibility of making airplanes that would not spin, or could not be spun—and on the problems of stability and control in general. He readily agreed to this, and before I left I had agreed to go back with the NACA at Langley Field.

I resigned from Hamilton Standard and then drove my family from Chicago back to Hampton, from where we had come only a year before. We stayed with our old friends, Eastman and Ivy Jacobs, until we could find a house to rent. After a few months we bought a house at 130 Cherokee Road, and it seems that the name "Cherokee" has been closely associated with my activities ever since.

Back at Langley

During the first few months back in Hampton, I spent most of my spare time trying to complete the propeller design textbook. Dorothy went over it very carefully, unsplitting my infinitives, undangling my participles, and in general polishing my English. She had done this previously for all of my NACA reports. Finally, by September 1930, the manuscript was finished, typed, and with all of its figures completed, sent to McGraw-Hill.

McGraw-Hill used Edward P. Warner as a critic, and after he had read it the company's editor wrote to me saying that Warner's only criticism was that I could have used twice as many words without wasting a single one. Warner had been a professor and I guess he followed the practice of saying everything twice for emphasis. The editor also admitted, however, that Warner's own book on airplane design had been criticized for being too wordy. Since the editor left it up to my own judgment, I left the book as it was. Even with the time we needed for correcting page proofs and mailing them back and forth between Hampton and New York, the book was published before the end of 1930. I imagine that astonishes many present-day authors who sometimes wait for years to see their books come to print.

In those days, before jet airplanes, most technical schools offered a one-semester course on propeller design. I'm happy to say that my book was almost universally used in those courses. I hope the information did the students some good.[1]

Sometime in the early 1930s the Curtiss Company sued the United States government, because the government had never paid royalties on the Reed patent for the Hamilton Standard aluminum-alloy propellers that it had been using for several years. The case, as I remember it, was handled in the Court of Claims and was defended for the government by a couple of civilian U.S. attorneys. I was a government employee again, and they used me as an expert technical witness. I worked with them off and on for the best part of a year and found it both enjoyable and challenging. We—I say we, but the attorneys actually did most of the work—dug up all sorts of prior art, dating way back to about 1880.

As mentioned in the previous chapter, the Reed patent covered two main points. The first one involved blades that were so thin that they relied on centrifugal force to hold them out straight and keep them from bending excessively because of the air load. The second one covered all aircraft propeller blades made of aluminum alloy. Ken Lane, an acquaintance of mine, was the expert witness for Curtiss, and some highly technical arguments resulted.

In the trial I was at a disadvantage because my book on propeller design had just been published, and Ken Lane used a method given in the book to prove a certain point that I would then presumably be forced to concede was correct. Lane made this argument at about eleven o'clock in the morning, and I was given an immediate opportunity to present my thoughts on the subject. I merely said that I could not give a sensible answer without looking over the computations in detail, and that that might take a couple of hours. The judge saw my point and declared recess until 2:00 P.M. This gave me a chance, fortunately, to go over the computations and, as it happened, I lucked out. Ken had used the airfoil characteristics obtained from one method of calculation and had applied them to a different method of calculation—so the results were not exactly in accordance with the methods expressed in my book.

Later in the trial, the effect of centrifugal force on the twisting moments, i.e., those that tended to twist the blades while they were operating, came up. This was a rather difficult technical idea to get across and involved delicate computations. To get the idea across to the judge, I tied one end of a piece of string about two feet long to the middle portion of a pencil. Then, by holding the other end of the string and letting the pencil hang below, the pencil balanced in a horizontal position. After telling the judge that the pencil represented one narrow section of the propeller blade, I whirled it around in a circle, keeping the free end of the string in the center. This demonstrated that the pencil lined up exactly in the plane of rotation and enabled the judge to see that the effect of centrifugal force was to reduce the pitch of any section of the propeller to approximately zero.

As for the use of centrifugal force to keep the blades from bending outward, we had found an extreme example. A German airship designer by the name of Wagner had used a propeller whose blades were made of canvas; with lead weights in the ends of the canvas, centrifugal force alone had held his blades out. We also found a number of cases where aluminum alloy had been used in the blades of propellers of early airplanes.

One difficulty that I had in the Reed patent case was getting our government lawyers to make accurate technical statements. They would ask me to explain a technical point to them, and then in court they would insist on putting it in their own words. It usually came out wrong, and I would have to try to get the matter straightened out.

The government eventually won the case, nonetheless, and the Reed patent was broken.

Back at the NACA's Langley laboratory I had become the assistant chief of the aerodynamics division and had been installed in an office on the second floor of the administration building, right next door to that of Elton Miller, who was chief of the aerodynamics division. Right below us was Henry Reïd, the engineer-in-charge, and Edward R. ("Ray") Sharp, the chief administrative officer. The aerodynamics division included the flight research and the four wind-tunnel sections. Montgomery Knight headed the atmospheric tunnel section, Eastman Jacobs the variable-density tunnel section, Don Wood the propeller research tunnel section, and Smith J. ("Smitty") DeFrance the new 30-by-60-foot full-scale tunnel section. The flight research section, located in the hangar on the field, was under the direction of John W. ("Gus") Crowley. The

The NACA's Committee on Aeronautical Research in Universities, which met at Langley on June 20, 1930, was comprised of some outstanding people from some outstanding research institutions. There are four Langley employees, including me, in this photo, but none of us were members of the NACA committee. Left to right, Richard H. Smith, Massachusetts Institute of Technology; Clark B. Millikan, California Institute of Technology; Theodore von Kármán, California Institute of Technology; myself; Elton W. Miller, Langley; Charles F. Marvin, Weather Bureau, and chairman of the NACA committee; George W. Lewis, NACA, ex officio member of this committee; Everett P. Lesley, Stanford University; F. W. Pawlowski, University of Michigan; Henry J. E. Reid, Langley; and Theodore Theodorsen, Langley. Absent from the meeting was committee member Harry F. Guggenheim.

A picture of Langley test pilot Bill McAvoy. Actually Mel Gough did most of the flying in my oddball arrangements in the 1930s.

pilots were Bill McAvoy and Mel Gough, and the engineering portion of the flight section was under Floyd Thompson.

When I had arrived at the NACA for the first time in 1925, the atmospheric wind-tunnel section, then headed by Elliott G. Reid, consisted of only a five-foot, Eiffel-type open-circuit tunnel. In 1928, after Reid accepted a Guggenheim chair in aeronautical engineering at Stanford University and Monty Knight replaced him as section head, it was decided that the obsolete five-foot AWT would be replaced by two new tunnels. One of these was to be a seven-by-ten-foot open-throat tunnel and the other was to be a vertical tunnel with a five-foot circular test section. The latter was to be provided with a balance with which the forces on an airplane in a spin could be measured.

Shortly after I returned to Langley, Knight accepted the offer of a Guggenheim professorship at the Georgia Institute of Technology. Both of the new tunnels were under construction, and the administration felt that there was no one left in the AWT section with sufficient experience to run it. Therefore, I was given the added duty of running the section, at least until one of the staff could develop to the point where he could run it satisfactorily.

The first year back in Hampton was very busy. One day in the middle of summer in 1931 I came home from work so worn out that we finally decided that I should take a vacation from aeronautics. That evening we hired a local lady for $5 a day to take care of the children (good money for 1931, especially around the Hampton area), and the next morning Dorothy and I were off in our 1929 Model A Ford in a completely free manner, not even knowing where we were going.

We thought we might spend a few days in the Virginia mountains, but that evening found us in Washington, visiting with Henry Berliner and his wife, Josephine. This was the first time Dorothy had met the Berliners, but Henry and I talked aeronautics almost exclusively.

It was natural to go north in the summertime, and so we drifted up that way and found ourselves in the neighborhood of Elmira, New York, where I happened to know there was a glider meet going on. It was the main meet that year, and I couldn't help going over to see what it was like. The gliders were launched off a ridge or bluff with the wind blowing up over it. Some of the gliders were launched with the aid of catapults or big slingshots made of long

Driving Henry Berliner's unique little seaplane of 1932 was an outboard marine engine that was reversed so the air propeller chained to it was above the engine. I saw him make a couple of short flights in this plane.

stretches of rubber shock-absorber cord of the type used in airplane landing gears. Men also ran along at each wing tip, pushing and guiding the gliders. The gliders soared back and forth along the ridge for some time, and then when the lift gave out, they glided down and landed at the Elmira airport in the valley below. (I seem to remember that this place was called "the Meadow," but it was definitely not the area at Harris Hill, which was later developed as a national soaring spot.)

These gliders were in no way competitive with the modern-day sailplanes, but with the proper wind conditions, they were able to stay flying for an hour or two. I found Comdr. Ralph Barnaby at Elmira, practically running the entire meet. Barnaby had been the officer in the Bureau of Aeronautics in charge of specifications under whom I would have worked had I not taken the propeller job. He was active in soaring activities for years.

After a couple of enjoyable days watching this activity, Dorothy and I went up to the Finger Lakes for some canoeing, swimming, and just taking it easy. We then headed for the Virginia mountains, but stopped off at Elmira again to see a little more of the gliding meet, which ran for two weeks. Unfortunately, the weather wasn't good for gliding, so we continued on toward the mountains.[2]

As we were going down through Maryland, it just so happened that our road passed the Fairchild Aircraft Company at Hagerstown. It just happened also that we at the NACA had been using a Fairchild 22 airplane for some time in connection with some of our tests of high-lift and lateral-control devices. This was about 9:00 A.M., and I suggested to Dorothy that I'd like to stop in for a moment and see the plant. I met George Hardmann and Lou Reisner, chief engineer and plant manager, respectively, and they gave me a rather lengthy tour around the plant. All of a sudden someone said, "Won't you go to lunch with us?" I had no idea that the morning was over already and that I had left Dorothy in the car all alone the whole time. I'll have to admit that she was good-natured about it, having been reading and writing letters.

We finally did get down to the Blue Ridge Mountains of Virginia, in an area near Roanoke, and spent several days having a good rest. There were a lot of buzzards flying around, and I spent hours reclining and studying their soaring flight.

So my vacation from aeronautics included the talks on aviation with Henry Berliner, the glider meet at Elmira, the Fairchild plant at Hagerstown, and finally, watching the soaring buzzards in the Virginia mountains!

Many serious airplane accidents in the 1920s had been associated with failure to maintain flying speed and stalling, then entering into a spin. Flight experience had shown that airplanes as they were then built did not have either satisfactory lateral stability or lateral control at angles of attack near the stall, that is, at angles of attack near and above that for the maximum-lift coefficient. Not only would the ailerons not give satisfactory roll control, but the wing itself was unstable laterally; given an opportunity, the wing would tend to autorotate or spin. In order to study this condition further, I laid out an extensive series of tests in the seven-by-ten-foot tunnel, which was still being constructed, with the idea of investigating autorotation characteristics on a series of wings having various items that might give control at angles of attack above the stall: such as floating wing-tip ailerons where the ailerons themselves were not stalled even when the wing was, and spoilers that might give desirable yawing and rolling moments. The tests were to be run not only at the ordinary angles of attack used in flight, but also through and well past the stalled area.

Because I wanted to be able to make a large number of tests with various lateral control and high-lift devices, and naturally wanted to spend as little time as possible on the reduction of data, we needed to lay out a special balance system for the new tunnel. Today, in the 1980s, computers can of course reduce hundreds of measurements of forces and moments in pounds or grams to coefficient form in a matter of seconds, but in those days the computing was done by hand and always took a large amount of our time.

My idea was to run all of the tests at the same value of dynamic pressure—in this particular case, it turned out to be the value of q for 80 miles per hour in standard air. My next thought was to use a standard-size model wing, which was 10 inches in chord and 60 inches in span, giving an aspect ratio of six. Tapered wings would have the same span and area. We then constructed the balance system with individual dial heads so that all of the lift could be directly and instantly read on the head of one scale, all of the drag directly on another scale, all of the rolling moment on another, the yawing moment on another, the pitching moment on another, and the side force on the sixth one. With the wing span and area constant in all cases, and all tests at a constant value of the dynamic pressure, the results could then be put directly on the scales in terms of the coefficient form desired. In other words, when the test run was completed, so was the data reduction. This system worked very well and was used by the NACA for hundreds of tests over a period of many years.

In order to investigate more about the behavior of airplanes in stalls, and in particular the dangerous flight path that followed them, I also set up a certain series of flight tests.

In about 1930 the NACA had just obtained a new, very sensitive Kolsman altimeter. The marks on this altimeter were spaced 10 feet apart, and interpolations could be made in between. Along with this altimeter, I used a bank of stopwatches that was arranged so that all of them could be started at the same time and then also stopped one at a time. I would have the pilot go through a series of stalls, starting from different air speeds, and using no power in some cases and full power in others. Acting as the in-flight observer, I would start all of the watches while we were at a steady speed, definitely above that for the stall, and then for every 20-foot change of altitude, as the stall occurred, I would stop one of the watches. At the same time we recorded air-speed readings, and from these we could later plot the plane's approximate path.

In the beginning we made these tests on two or three airplanes that were available to the NACA at Langley Field. Then, at the 1930 National Air Races in Chicago, I managed to get the tests run on a number of airplanes of various kinds. The smallest was a two-place Monocoupe with a Velie engine, and the largest was a twin-engined Curtiss Condor transport plane that could carry about twenty passengers. In between there were several, including a four-place, high-wing Verville and a single-engine, all metal, low-wing Northrop Gamma (which was larger than the original Northrop Alpha). The aviation community was fairly free and easy-going in those days, and I got the various airplanes tested merely by going around to the operators or pilots, telling them my story, and getting them to go up and make the test with me. In practically every case they cooperated readily. The results of my ad hoc stalling tests were published by the NACA in February 1931 as Technical Note 363, "The Behavior of Conventional Airplanes in Situations Thought to Lead to Most Crashes."

During the nine days of the races, there were seven derbies flown from various cities to Chicago and thirty-four closed-course races. Every day army and navy squadrons displayed beautiful formation flying, with Jimmy Doolittle in his Travelair Mystery Ship and Al Williams in his Gulf Hawk (which was rigged for inverted flight) putting on sensational aerobatic displays. James McDonnell had his Doodlebug there and put on an exhibition every day. Right in front of the grandstand he staked out a circle 150 feet in diameter with little flags. He would take off from within the circle, fly around, and land with his entire landing run within the circle, also. A couple of Pitcairn autogiros performed too, but they were clearly outstaged by the superior performance of McDonnell's plane.

The last and fastest event was the first run of the later world-famous Thompson Trophy Race. This turned out to be a free-for-all. The only service contestant was a Curtiss Hawk, flown by Marine Capt. Arthur Page, which had been made by the navy into a monoplane by removing the lower wing. It was powered by a 700-horsepower Curtiss Conqueror engine cooled by means of wing surface radiators, and its short individual exhaust stacks had been cut off flush with the cowling surface. The pilot was in an open cockpit directly behind the engine but some distance back.

When I saw this arrangement, I was alarmed. A couple of years before we had had just such an arrangement in a set-up in the 20-foot propeller research tunnel. In our installation we had a Curtiss D-12 engine similar to the Conqueror but slightly smaller. We were running a series of propeller tests at an air speed of 100 miles per hour, and the "static pilot," as we called him, NACA engineer Bill Herrnstein in this case, sat in the cockpit and operated the engine and ran the tests at various revolution speeds up to the maximum. The entire run took between thirty and forty minutes. We had made many similar tests with other engine arangements, but not with this particular engine and body combination. When the run was completed, a ladder was put up so that the static pilot could climb down to the floor of the test chamber, some 25 feet below.

But Herrnstein was so groggy and weak that he could not hoist himself over the side of the fuselage. We had to practically carry him down. After reviving him a little, we found that all of his last recordings had been wavy irregular lines with no meaning. Immediately we took him to a doctor, who found that he was suffering from carbon monoxide poisoning. It took about three days before Bill recovered to the point where he could work again.

When I saw the arrangement on the modified Curtiss Hawk a couple of days before the race, I looked up the pilot, Captain Page, and told him about our experience at Langley Field; I recommended very strongly that he not fly the airplane in the race. Page said he had flown the plane and had noticed nothing troublesome. He admitted, though, that his flight experience in the plane amounted to only ten or fifteen minutes. He did not take me seriously and adamantly insisted on racing the plane. I then looked up Ted Wright, who was chief engineer of the Curtiss Company, and told him about the danger. We both talked to Captain Page, but he remained fixed in his idea to carry on with the race. Although Ted Wright was Curtiss's chief engineer, the airplane now belonged to the navy, and he had no real control over it.

Captain Page had the fastest plane in the race, and he immediately took the lead and held it as long as he flew. The race, incidentally, was a hard one, consisting of twenty laps around a 5-mile course, for a total distance of 100 miles, and including nearly sixty tight turns with accelerations for the pilot up to possibly four or five g each time. On his seventeenth lap Page flew wide around the pylon in front of the grandstand and, continuing his wide turn, flew right into the ground. He had been overcome by the carbon monoxide fumes and he died the next day. I was miserable, but I didn't know of anything further that I could have done, under the circumstances.

The race was won by Speed Holman in a Laird Solution biplane with a Pratt and Whitney Wasp Junior engine equipped with a complete and well-done NACA cowling. The plane had been finished in Laird's factory at Ashburn Field, just south of Chicago, on the very day of the race. It was called the Solution because it was designed to "solve" the problem of beating the Travelair Mystery Ship—which it did by just two miles per hour in this same race. Incidentally, I had visited Matty Laird several times during visits to my folks in the Chicago area and particularly while I had been located with Hamilton in Milwaukee. I had fitted some propellers to his airplanes—a couple of times after Speed Holman had flown them to Milwaukee. In addition, I had given Laird some pointers on the detailed design of the NACA cowlings. In this year's Thompson Trophy Race, both Laird's winner and the runner-up, the Travelair Mystery Ship flown by Jimmy Haizlip, were fitted with the NACA cowlings. Third place was taken by Ben Howard in his little 90-horsepower Pete. Incidentally, I had helped Carl Schory with some of the timing at this meet, also.

Our flight investigation of the stalling problem at NACA Langley continued through the fall of 1930 and most of 1931. We used eight airplanes, including the Doyle O2, Fleet XN2Y-1, Consolidated PT-1, Verville AT Trainer, Boeing PW-9 pursuit plane, Curtiss Falcon A-3, and Fairchild FC2W-2. Initially the upper deflection of the elevator in each of these airplanes was limited to the point where the airplane could not be made to spin without the aid of power. As a result of this experiment, we found that the minimum speed with the stick pulled back was surprisingly close, within a couple of miles per hour, to that corresponding to the maximum-lift coefficient. Thus, if the airplanes had only this amount of longitudinal control or up-elevator travel in each case, we were sure that they would have good lateral stability and control and be free from losing control and possibly spinning in a stall, throughout the entire usable speed range.

This was true only for power off, however. All of these planes trimmed at a higher angle of attack with power on than with power off, and to obtain the spin-free condition with full power engaged was going to require an additional limitation of the elevator

In 1934 Jimmy Doolittle's nephew flew a strange little airplane called the Arup from South Bend, Indiana, to Langley for testing. The airplane, which was powered by a 37-HP Continental A-40 engine, was a very unusual all-wing design with a very thick and very low aspect-ratio wing, whose leading edge was straight. The wing was so thick, in fact, that the pilot was entirely enclosed within it, except for his head, in a supine attitude. This meant that the pilot had no view at all either downward or to the sides. At the center in the rear of the plane there were small flaps that worked as elevators, and farther out toward the tip there were other small flaps that worked as ailerons. The Arup's lift coefficient was quite high, because of the low-aspect-ratio wings, but the high lift occurred at such a high angle of attack that it could not be used in take-off. In landing, the plane squatted down at a steep angle and rolled only 50 to 70 feet before stopping. The Arup was an interesting design, but it could not compete with the conventional configurations.

angle, for the various airplanes, of from 6 to 25 degrees. But with this limitation, power-off flight was not ordinarily feasible. Therefore, we determined that it would be desirable to have an airplane that trimmed at the same angle of attack with power on *and* with power off, particularly near the stall. When held in a glide with the stick pulled back to the limited position, these airplanes all had moderate rates of descent—in the neighborhood of 15 feet per second.

It then occurred to me that a pilot could make a satisfactory emergency landing merely by holding the stick all the way back and gliding right to the ground, if only he had a landing gear strong enough to absorb the shock. In fact, the McDonnell Doodlebug, with its slots and flaps and long-travel landing gear (some 18 inches of shock-absorber travel) had been landed without difficulty or damage a number of times at rates of descent in the neighborhood of 20 feet per second. Moreover, the Doodlebug was now in the possession of the NACA at Langley Field. A little while after the completion of the Guggenheim Safe Airplane Contest, James McDonnell had approached me with the thought that the NACA might be willing to purchase his plane, because it would make an interesting subject for a number of difficult experiments. I took this up with my superiors, including Dr. Lewis, with the result that we did purchase the Doodlebug. We made many tests both in the full-scale wind tunnel and in flight on this very interesting airplane. Incidentally, McDonnell's total venture had cost about $30,000, financed largely by Philip Wrigley of chewing gum fame. The NACA got the plane for $5,000.

After a while we put the Doodlebug's shock-absorber struts on the Verville AT Trainer, one of the airplanes that had been subjected earlier to our stall test program in flight. Because of the configuration of the Verville's landing gear, however, only 13 of the Doodlebug's 18 inches of shock-absorber travel could be used. (Later we bought special landing-gear struts for the Verville so the Doodlebug could have its own struts back again.) The purpose of this equipment on the Verville was to make actual landing tests with straight-in glide landings, some with the control stick held full back to a limited position. With repeated straight-in landings of this type, I became locally famous, or rather infamous, for the so-called "socko" landing, some even with a certain amount of flare-off in the flight path.

Finally, on a gusty day with a wind speed estimated as varying between 5 and 25 MPH, one of our test pilots, William H. McAvoy, attempted a straight-in unflared glide with the control not limited but held in a certain position. McAvoy saw that he was coming down unusually fast and tried to get engine power by opening the throttle, but the engine just coughed and he hit the ground hard. The average vertical velocity between 50 feet and the ground was calculated to be about 30 feet per second. This was too much for the Verville to take, and one side of the landing gear and the wing tip on that side were badly damaged. McAvoy was okay, though.

This difficult experience prompted us to study the gustiness of the air in the vicinity of the ground by putting anemometers and wind vanes at various heights up to the top of a 50-foot-high pole. After taking records under various gusty air conditions and making some computations, we finally realized that under certain gusty conditions an extra 15 feet per second or so would have to be added to the vertical velocity.

Now it happens that the shock-absorber length, assuming equal efficiency, varies as the square of the velocity, which means, for a 30-foot-per-second vertical velocity, we needed a shock absorber four times longer than that which we had been using. A shock absorber over 50, perhaps even up to 72, inches long would be quite awkward and impractical, of course, so there went the unflared, or "socko," landings. But we reported our test results anyway, in NACA Technical Report 418, "Preliminary Investigation of Modifications to Conventional Airplanes to Give Non-Stalling and Short-Landing Characteristics" (January 25, 1932). Also I did get a patent on the limited-elevator control feature (U.S. Patent No. 1,848,037), dated March 1, 1932.

3.

Reworking the Airplane for the Private Flyer (1931–1948)

7.

The W-1 Experiment

By late 1930 we had the seven-by-ten-foot atmospheric wind tunnel operating and were beginning to turn out test results. There were some capable men in this wind-tunnel group, but I was dissatisfied with the lackadaisical manner in which most of them approached their work. In order to add some interest and zest to the atmosphere, I started a series of informal seminars—held at the end of the working day—on light plane flying and the personal use of airplanes. The subjects pretty well covered the fields and included such items as desirable landing and handling characteristics, the field of view that the pilot needed or desired, and so forth.

Each man in the seminar picked a subject and then studied it for a week or two. Each week a man would give an illustrated talk on his particular subject, followed by a period for questions and answers and group discussion that lasted until we were ready to go home. We had some very interesting discussions, and the interest in the seminars increased noticeably as the fellows began to see that some real good could come out of our studies.

As we got some usable results and firm ideas from the wind-tunnel tests and flight research, I couldn't help getting the thought of putting some of these ideas into an actual experimental airplane aimed at being especially suitable to the private flyer. Ultimately, I decided to go ahead with the design and construction of the airplane as a private hobby venture.

I wanted to have two or three of the fellows help me, but did not want to play favorites by picking particular ones. Therefore, I let all of the men in the atmospheric tunnel section know of my intention and invited any one who might be interested in helping to come to my house on the evening of November 4, 1931. To my great surprise, twelve showed up.

I opened the meeting by reviewing the proposed program of activity. First, I said, a relatively detailed design of several types of airplanes that we thought might be capable of developing into the ideal machine would have to be made. Second, the performance of each type would be calculated in detail to form a preliminary estimate of its desirability. Third, a five-foot-span flying model of each type would be constructed and test glided in the return passage of the full-scale tunnel for general flying characteristics. Fourth, on the basis of the above calculations and tests a type would be chosen for full-scale construction. Fifth, upon completion, one or more of the experimental aircraft would be test flown.

In some regards my preliminary specifications were rather extreme: the minimum speed was to be 30 miles per hour; the take-off and landing runs were to be kept under 100 feet and 50 feet, respectively; and the rate of climb was to be 400 feet per minute (which we later decided was too low for a safe airplane). The plane needed to have good lateral stability and control at all angles of attack that could be maintained both with power on and off. Its pilot should have an excellent range of vision in the air and on the ground, and he should have better protection in a crash than what current designs were offering. Vibrations should be small and unobjectionable and noise so minimal that conversation between the two passengers while cruising would be as easy as in an automobile (we didn't accomplish that!). And, perhaps most importantly, control and operation of the airplane were to be simple and easy, not complex. This would be accomplished by eliminating either the directional control or the lateral control and combining its function with the other.

Initially we had many more desirable flying characteristics in mind, but obviously we were in a preliminary phase of thinking about the design and would change many of our notions as the project evolved and we gained new knowledge.

One thing that helped us refine our own concept was my getting to know something about Bill Stout's little Skycar, a small all-metal monoplane whose design, flying characteristics, and purposes were similar to the ones we had in mind. William B. Stout had become famous for designing the all-metal mail and transport plane that ran on the Stout-Ford airlines between Chicago, Detroit, and Cleveland, and for initiating the design of the Ford Trimotor. I knew that he had just built the Skycar, so, in January 1932, on the way home to visit our folks in Chicago, I managed to visit Stout at his small engineering laboratory in Dearborn, Michigan, close to the Ford airport and airplane factory.[1]

Stout told me that the Skycar had been designed with the idea of meeting the requirements of the average private owner. This meant giving the pilot maximum visibility and comfort and providing him, more importantly, with landing gear that would ensure safe and easy landings, without the danger of nosing over.

In his Skycar two people were housed in tandem in a nicely furnished cabin. Behind the rear passenger was an inverted in-line air-cooled Rover engine with a pusher propeller. A triangular trussed structure from the bottom of the fuselage and points on the wing outside the propeller tapered back to carry the tail. The Skycar had a high-aspect-ratio tapered wing with a span of 43 feet—which was very large for a two-place airplane. Stout believed that the airplane could glide safely into a landing at a very steep angle, above 30 degrees. With its relatively clean configuration and the high-aspect-ratio wing, however, I felt that the steepest gliding angle was probably no greater than 12 to 15 degrees.

The Skycar's landing gear consisted of two main wheels with low-pressure tires and oleo shock-absorber travel of 12 inches, located directly in line with the airplane's center of gravity. In addition, the airplane had a small tail wheel located only a few feet in back of the main wheels. In the front there was a reinforced portion of fuselage that the nose portion of the airplane could skid on. When empty, the airplane rested on the main wheels and the rear wheel, but when loaded it rested on the main wheels and the reinforced portion of the fuselage.

By the time of my second visit in January 1932, Stout had put a

Carl Wenzinger with his flying test model of the W-1 in 1932. Notice the fixed auxiliary airfoil.

fixed-axis nose wheel up in front in place of the reinforced fuselage. Turns were made on the ground by hoisting the nose up with the elevator and using brakes on the main wheels; these brakes were controlled together or individually by means of a special handle. When the airplane was on the ground in the full-load condition or at the conclusion of a landing, the main wing was very nearly horizontal and had a very low lift coefficient.

All in all, it was a rather neatly arranged design—certainly the most advanced step in the direction that we in my group at Langley were heading; many of the Skycar's features were in line with the ideas that had surfaced and developed in our seminars.

After two or three meetings of my group at Langley, and before my visit with Stout, we had decided to go ahead with three different five-foot models: a tractor, a pusher, and a tail-less design. Each member of the group had decided for himself which model he wanted to work with. I had explained that the project would take a lot of time and effort and that it would not really be helped by anyone who did not put in his full share. A couple of the fellows had dropped out immediately because they saw that the work involved more than they had expected, but nine remained: Jack Bamber, Tom Harris, Johnny Lockstampfer, Dick Noyes, Bob Platt, Bob Sanders, Joe Shortal, Carl Wenzinger, and Charles Zimmerman. All of these men were engineers, with the exception of Lockstampfer, who was a mechanic. I had known that nine men were too many and that we wouldn't get much effort from a few of them, but I didn't know what to do about it.

Of the three models, only the pusher turned out to be worth testing. Aerodynamically, the most novel feature of the pusher model was a narrow auxiliary airfoil placed ahead of the leading edge of the main wing (which, by the way, employed the popular Clark Y airfoil). This was a fixed airfoil with no moving parts, which had been developed in our seven-by-ten-foot tunnel.

Using the auxiliary airfoil, we obtained a 30 percent increase in the overall maximum-lift coefficient, which meant that we could use a smaller wing to achieve the same minimum speed. This increase was due to the fact that the stalled wake of the auxiliary airfoil flowing over the upper surface of the main wing caused a turbulence that kept the lift of the main wing increasing up to an angle of attack of 24 degrees instead of merely 15, which was the maximum lift angle of attack of the original main wing. At the same time, the minimum drag was increased only 9 percent, and with the auxiliary airfoil, the speed range was also increased. With this arrangement, then, a much wider range of glide path angles would be available for approaches to landings.

We tried to prove that this wide range of angles was in fact available with our pusher model by making glide tests in the return passages of the full-scale tunnel where the ordinary currents of outside air would not be a problem. These passages were 70 feet high at the deep end and several hundred feet long. We made the tests on weekends, when the tunnel was not operating and the air inside was still and smooth. I made a catapult to launch the model from the very top of one of the passages and used a balloon ladder to get up there. The ladder was not perfectly steady and it took me quite a while to get used to the situation, and get so that I could change the focus of my eyes from the things up close to the concrete floor 70 feet below without being somewhat uncomfortable. I had to use both hands to hold the catapult and mount it on the wind tunnel's guide vanes, so I finally took a stout piece of rope and made a harness around myself and tied it to the ladder. Then, if I slipped and fell, at least I would be caught by the rope.

We made a satisfactory set of glide tests showing a wide range of angles; however, we also found that there were sizable air currents even within the supposedly still chamber. Even though we had a spirally stable model that would continue to fly straight if properly trimmed, these currents made it difficult for us to glide it straight all the way to the floor without flying into a wall. Still we were reasonably satisfied with the tests and decided to go ahead with the full-size airplane.

For the airplane's engine we selected an English Pobjoy rated at 75 HP for continuous operation and 85 HP for short periods. This air-cooled radial engine had seven cylinders, weighed only 135 pounds, and was geared so that when the engine turned 3,300 RPM at maximum power, the propeller turned only 1,500 RPM. This allowed a large (7½-foot-in-diameter) propeller that could give good thrust for take-off and climb. We bought a Pobjoy engine that had been used only a short time in a racing plane from the Nicholas Beazley Company of Marshall, Missouri. It cost us $550.

We also decided to use a high-wing arrangement with a span of 30 feet, with the propeller located just back of the wing. The tail would be supported on two beams going back from the wing just outside the propeller, and vertical fins would be formed right on the booms. The pilot and passenger were to sit in a tandem arrangement, with the pilot ahead and the passenger under the wing. The lower part of the fuselage would be only about a foot off the ground.

I laid out the plane's general arrangement and distributed the various parts of the detailed design to other members of the group. We called ourselves the Chesapeake Aircraft Company and had stationery printed so that we could buy our spruce, steel tubing, aircraft nuts and bolts, and the rest of the material we needed at wholesale prices. The wing and tail surfaces we constructed completely out of wood. The wing spars and the booms were box beams made of spruce cap strips with diagonal plywood for the sides. The surfaces were covered with grade A cotton fabric, and the fuselage structure consisted of a frame of welded steel tubing, with curved spruce formers and longitudinal stringers to give cross-sectional curvature, and the whole thing covered in fabric.

A great deal of special effort was put into the design of the landing gear, for we wanted the contact with the ground to require very little skill. Even if the plane were to be landed with its wings off level laterally or at a speed up at least to twice the minimum, we felt that the landing should still be safe, even in a crosswind. Also, on a reasonably smooth grass field, it should be almost impossible

My children's bicycle (with my older son, Donald, and my daughter, Betsey) helped me to determine the most suitable angle for the steering post of the W-1's castering nose wheel. The outside diameter of the bicycle wheel was approximately the same as that on our W-1. The airplane had a large air tire, however.

to nose the plane over, even if a landing were made with the brakes fully applied and held during the entire run. And the landing gear should have stable taxiing and easy steering characteristics, being entirely free from ground-looping tendencies.

Ground looping was a serious problem in the early 1930s. All landplanes that had been manufactured for production since World War I had been equipped with tail skids, or when paved runways came into use, with tail wheels. These gears had their main fixed-axis wheels located ahead of the center of gravity, were naturally unstable directionally, and thus tended to ground loop. Automobiles, bicycles, and motorcycles were stable in this regard because their main fixed-axis wheels were in back of the center of gravity. The conventional tail-wheel-type gears also nosed over easily, because the main wheels were just a little ahead of the center of gravity. Some of the early pushers popular around 1910 had had a single wheel well ahead of the center of gravity and two wheels in back of the center of gravity, which took care of the nosing-over difficulty reasonably well. But all wheels were on fixed axes and could not be steered very well on the ground.

The landing gear of Bill Stout's Skycar met a couple of our specifications, but not all of them. To meet all of our specs, we finally devised an arrangement that I later named the "tricycle gear," and this name appears to have stuck. The gear's two main wheels were placed a short distance behind the center of gravity. With the pusher arrangement it was possible to put the nose wheel well forward, which of course decreased the likelihood of the plane nosing over. The airplane had a very stable wheel base of eight feet. The gross weight of the plane was 1,150 pounds.

Because we wanted it to be steerable, the front wheel was supported so that it castered. All three wheels were large low-pressure Goodyear air wheels; the rear ones had shock-absorber travel of 18 inches, the front one (which was of the same size) only of 12. The structure around the front wheel, however, was stressed to about 10 g so that it could take extra shock loads. The nose wheel was steered along with the rudders by the rudder bar. (In those days, most airplanes had rudder bars instead of pedals). Mechanical brakes were applied by means of a hand lever that was connected to the rudder bar in such a way that if the rudder bar were moved for a right turn, the right-hand wheel would get more braking than the left. This reaction of the wheels would in fact help the airplane to turn.

We did all of the actual construction in my one-car garage. I built a full-length bench along one side and jigs or fixtures for building the spars and tail booms on the other side. As one might guess, our family car was parked outside for a number of years. When the wings with ailerons and auxiliary airfoil and the tail surfaces were finished, they were hung up on the garage ceiling or alongside the wall, leaving just enough room for the fuselage.

About the time we got nicely into the design activity, Bob Sanders (who, by the way, was Henry Berliner's nephew) left to go with Pan American Airways in Lima, Peru. He and Bob Platt had come directly to the NACA after graduating in aeronautical engineering from MIT. The only bachelors in the group, they spent a fair amount of time visiting with us at our house, and we got to be good friends. Sanders's leaving was a real loss because he was one of the two or three fellows who put a substantial amount of effort into the project.

Another thing that we put into our airplane was an innovative windshield design. Anyone who did much flying, of course, knew

The W-1 structure assembled for a weekend of work outside of my one-car garage. The picture was taken from the roof of our house. After checking the airplane's control system, we would then disassemble the W-1 and store its parts in my garage until the following Saturday.

how hard it was to see out of an airplane windshield when it was raining hard. I studied this matter some and came up with the idea that the airflow going around a windshield in front of an open window tended to move the air outward. This seemed to mean that, if the cabin width at the rear of the open window was an inch or two wider than it was at the rear of the windshield, and if a gutter could be arranged to drain off the windshield water so that it would not spray or even dribble back into the cabin itself, much of the problem would be solved. We set up a spray system in the seven-by-ten-foot tunnel that simulated rain and then ran a series of tests until a satisfactory solution was achieved. The arrangement was then used on the airplane, which by then we were calling the W-1, although I don't remember ever flying it in the rain.

I should not proceed with my story of our design of the W-1 without saying that we did *not* aim for high speed and low drag. We knew how that could be done, but it meant extra work, so we aimed directly at the results mentioned previously. I should say also that we *did* intend to modify the plane later to include a special glide-control slotted flap, which we had worked out in the

Langley wind tunnel, in place of the auxiliary airfoil. In addition, we aimed to try out the W-1 with two instead of three controls, eliminating either the rudder or the aileron control. We had made studies along this line, both in theory and in flight, and had included a five-degree angle of dihedral in the wing, so that reasonable rolling moments could be achieved by using the rudder alone.

By the spring of 1933 we had made some progress, but the progress seemed to be very slow. Carl Wenzinger, who came from Philadelphia and had gone to nearby Swarthmore College, had happened to run into two young men who had just graduated from high school in Swarthmore but could find no jobs. The Depression was still on, and by that time it was hitting very hard. Carl told the young men about our W-1 project, and they said that they would come and work for us if we would house and feed them. Dorothy cooperated, even though it meant a lot of extra work for her, and we set them up in the front bedroom. Our agreement was for them to work only six hours a day and have the rest of the time for recreation.

One of them, Gordon Hill, was a fair mechanic and started to help right away. The other, Bob Johnson, although a good-natured fellow, was less adept and could operate at first only as a helper. Later on, though, he could do simple repetitive jobs like assembling and glueing ribs in a jig. With this arrangement the work progressed more rapidly.

One morning in late August 1933 Gordon stayed in bed with a severe stomachache, and when I returned from work late that afternoon he was still in bed and in some pain. I thought he should go to the doctor right away, but he insisted it was just a stomachache and didn't want to go. Both of the boys had just turned twenty-one (they had taken a bit of extra time to get out of high school), and so I didn't have to feel that they were not adults, but on the other hand, I did feel a certain amount of responsibility for them, and I insisted that I take Gordon to the hospital.

I waited in the lobby for a few minutes until our doctor came to me in some alarm with the bad news that the boy had an acute case of appendicitis and needed to be operated upon immediately. The boy refused to let him operate, however, and would not even tell him how he could get in touch with his parents. The doctor asked me to talk to Gordon because he considered it a matter of life and death, which of course I did. The boy was worried among other things about the cost, but we told him to forget that for the moment, that this was more important than money. After a bit he agreed to the operation. Within half an hour the surgery was completed and the doctor showed me the removed appendix in a glass tube, saying that it was in terrible shape and that it would have burst very soon.

As time went on, Bob Johnson seemed to pay less and less attention to his work and to spend more and more time just having fun. Once I came home in the middle of the day and found Bob sitting across the street on the neighbor's porch talking to the daughters of the woman who lived there. This wasn't the first time, and when he came back over I told him he was through. He took it good naturedly enough and even said that he knew he deserved it. But his pal Gordon became very angry, and he quit. They left our house, but remained in the neighborhood for a while, finally getting jobs at the Newport News shipyards.

A month or two later the NACA headquarters in Washington received a letter signed by President Franklin D. Roosevelt in the White House, wanting an explanation of the mistreatment of two young men by a government employee, Fred E. Weick. Gordon Hill's father had written to President Roosevelt, complaining about my mistreatment of the boys and demanding suitable action. The letter was forwarded to me at Langley for reply. Fortunately, Bob Johnson and I were still on friendly terms, and when I called him over that evening and showed him the letter, he was incensed. He sat down, then and there, and wrote a letter, stating that he objected to the complaint to the president, that I had always treated him and Gordon well and justly, and that in addition they had had a very good experience working here. And Bob was the one I had fired.

We included his letter with our answer to the president's office, and nothing further was ever heard of that.

By the end of 1933 the W-1 was completed except for the covering of the main wing panels and the fuselage. The tail surfaces and ailerons had been covered with fabric sewn up by Dorothy, and because of bad weather outside, they had been doped in our own bedroom. In order to adjust the control linkages, we had to take the various parts of the airplane out of the garage, assemble them, make the adjustments, disassemble them, and put them back in the garage. All of this had to be done between early Saturday afternoon, after getting off work at Langley, and sunset Sunday.

In 1933, with FDR's initiation of the New Deal, the Bureau of Air Commerce (under the Department of Commerce) had worked hard to promote and help develop private flying. In particular, the bureau chief, Eugene L. Vidal, had started to look for a simple, easy-to-fly airplane which, with quantity production, could be put out to the public at the average price of an automobile, $700. I applauded Vidal's idea, but his $700 figure made me wonder about the soundness of the whole thing.

In early January 1934 three men from the Bureau of Air Commerce visited the NACA laboratory at Langley Field looking for possible aid in their newly established project to develop private flying. They were John Geisse, a specialist in private flying who reported directly to Eugene Vidal; Luke Harris, an air-mail pioneer; and Dick Gazely, who was in charge of aeronautical structures for the bureau. Because I was the one who handled research in this field at Langley, they were referred to me, and I told them what the NACA had done and was doing. I told them also about the tricycle gear, even though it really was not yet an NACA project.

John Geisse then said, "This is all fine; it's just what we want. But where can we see an airplane with these characteristics in it?" I said nothing, because I was still wary of getting connected with what I thought to be the dubious $700 project. A friend of mine next to me, however, piped up with "Fred's got it all built in his garage." They all demanded to see it, and so I took them out to the house and showed them the parts stacked up in my one-car garage. Geisse then asked me to write him a letter telling him all about our private project, which I did, fifteen pages of it.

A short time later the Department of Commerce requested officially that the NACA test the W-1 for them and that it be put in shape for testing in the shortest possible time. I was not in a very good position to refuse this and felt, furthermore, that we would get some very good test information from the full-scale wind tunnel and flight tests, so I went along.

John F. Victory, the executive secretary and legal authority for the NACA, recommended that in loaning the airplane to the government for these tests we had better form a corporation, because as it was, we would be considered partners, and each of us would

The W-1 in the full-scale tunnel at Langley, March 1934.

The W-1 with its experimental auxiliary airfoil out in front of the main wing. Notice also the enlarged fins. The other aircraft in the photo is a Pitcairn autogiro.

be liable for it in case of an accident and a suit. We did this, calling our corporation Fred E. Weick and Associates, and from that time on did all our business under that organization.

In just a few weeks the W-1 was completed and tested in the full-scale tunnel. These tests determined the plane's lift and drag, as well as pitching and yawing moment characteristics, measured the cylinder head temperatures of the engine, and checked the pilot's control operations. Though its directional or weathercock stability was found to be marginal, the plane was considered on the whole suitable for immediate testing in flight.

The NACA made the flight tests in April 1934. Langley Field was just a big grass field with no runways at the time. Though it did not have hard runways, the field did have a wide concrete ramp about one-half mile long running in front of a row of hangars. NACA test pilots Bill McAvoy and Mel Gough took turns taxiing the W-1 up and down this ramp and even made screeching sharp turns at relatively high speed without difficulty. They then took it straight off to a height of 20 or 30 feet and landed again, trying out the controls. When all this seemed satisfactory (they were especially impressed with the unusually satisfactory performance of the new landing gear), McAvoy took it off the grass and flew up to an altitude of about 3,000 feet. When at an altitude of about 300 feet he made the last turn to his final approach, however, the ailerons would not bring the wing up out of the bank. He had a scary moment, but finally, by using full rudder with the ailerons, the wings leveled out, and a satisfactory landing was made. The directional stability, which had been found to be low in the tunnel tests, was not sufficient to overcome the adverse yawing moment of the ailerons. To remedy the problem we doubled the size of the fin area. This took care of the situation satisfactorily.

As each set of tests was completed and its data worked up, I phoned the results up to John Geisse at the Bureau of Air Commerce in Washington. Geisse used these results as a good part of the basis for a set of specifications that he was preparing for the Department of Commerce's forthcoming simple-to-fly airplane design contest. This contest would ultimately be won by the Hammond airplane (later Stearman-Hammond); the airplane's price, as I remember it, turned out to be in the neighborhood of $3,500. A few of the Hammond airplanes were made (in anticipation of buying Douglas DC-4s, the Dutch airline KLM bought one, circa 1938, and used it as a trainer to accustom its pilots to tricycle landing gear), but I don't believe the contract with the government for 25 airplanes was ever completed because it cost the company more to make the airplanes than they were getting for them.

After the official NACA tests on the W-1 were completed, the plane was returned to us. Except for getting a little flight time in Eastman Jacobs's Pitcairn Mail Wing, I had not done any flying for a long time. NACA test pilot Mel Gough was good enough to check me out in the W-1 and then watch from the ground while I made a number of take-offs and landings. It was all right that I did not have a pilot's license, so long as I did not cross state lines or engage in interstate commerce. (When I had flown Jennies in the early 1920s, there had been no government licenses for either pilots or airplanes. One could get a license from the Aero Club of America, and later the National Aeronautic Association, to fly in air meets, however.) The W-1 did not require a license, either, but it did require a registration number, NS67.

We kept the airplane in a rented hangar at Pop Morgan's little field, but, with the permission of the Army Air Corps, still continued to do most of our testing at Langley. On one of my familiarization flights, just after taking off and turning left—so that I was facing directly away from the field, a little bit off of it, and possibly 50 to 60 feet high—the engine stopped suddenly and completely.[2] There was a small field to my left, bounded by 20-to-25-foot trees, and I managed to make a partial turn over the trees and land. I used only a little over half of the available space, but the field happened to have been sown a few years before in a crop that had rows crosswise to my path, meaning that my path was still very rough. The W-1 had vinyl windows on each side of its fuselage, and the front portion would slide back to open. The tracks were only about one-quarter of an inch deep, however, and the front window on the left-hand side had been thrown out by the jolting.

Mel Gough, who was watching from a couple of hundred yards away, came right over, and soon a number of other people from Langley Field were there, also. We thought of taking the plane apart and trucking it back, but Mel looked the situation over carefully and thought he could take off by going along with the grooves in the ground. He took off satisfactorily but, just as he was clearing the trees by a good margin, there was a thud.

The rear panel of the side window, which was not reinforced at its leading edge because it was normally inside the now missing

front panel, had blown out and hit the pusher propeller. The propeller had thrown it into one of the booms, right where an elevator
control cable was located. I had protected this cable at that point
by a piece of copper tubing, but the flying window had bent the
soft tubing and kinked it so firmly that Mel could not move the elevator. So he throttled back and made a glide "socko" landing in the
next field, about 25 feet in front of another row of 25-foot trees.

We all ran toward the plane and saw Mel get out, his hands
covering an important part of his anatomy; during the "socko"
landing, his forward motion had been stopped by the control stick
between his legs.

After that, we did disassemble the W-1 and truck it over to Pop
Morgan's field, where we rented hangar space. It took about six
weeks to get it flying again since a portion of the auxiliary airfoil
and the front of the fuselage had also been damaged.

While repairing the plane, I began to wonder how small a field
the airplane could be operated from on a regular basis. Obviously
the Morgan field, with its 1,200-foot long runway and its 800-foot
short one, surrounded by ordinary fences, was comfortably adequate. In fact, a number of contemporary light airplanes, including
Jacobs's Pitcairn and a Doyle owned by NACA engineer Nathan
Scudder, were using the field without difficulty. And the W-1 could
take off and land in a much shorter distance than those airplanes.

For the trials we laid out a little strip, at first 50 feet wide and
300 feet long, and marked it by means of small white flags at each
corner. The strip was laid out parallel to the wind for the first
trials, but later we tried it at all angles with respect to the wind,
including direct crosswinds. After my experience of engine stoppage, we still kept the strips near the edge of Langley Field but flew
in such a way that we went around the edge of the field and could
always land back in Langley if something happened.

From the very first neither I nor Bob Platt, the only other one of
our group who also flew the W-1, had any difficulty taking off and
landing within the 300-foot strip, and we were both inexperienced
pilots. We pretended that the front edge of the strip was a cliff and
that we *had* to put the wheels down beyond it. After we got a little
sharper, we cut the length of the strip down to 200 feet and found
that we could ordinarily stay within that limit, but not always. We
would glide in toward a landing at an air speed of possibly five or
six miles per hour above the minimum and then, when approach-

ing the ground, pull the stick clear back in such a manner that the flight path would level off at 4 or 5 feet above the ground. Then, with the stick still held full back, the airplane would sink to the ground at somewhat less than its minimum gliding speed and with a fairly large but acceptable sink rate. By holding the brake on during the entire maneuver, the plane, as contact was made, would press down toward the ground with two to four times its regular weight. Using this method, the total ground run with ordinary winds of five to ten MPH would be only about 60 feet.

That's not to say that all of our landings were smooth. But with our very effective shock-absorber arrangement, even our shortest landing runs, with vertical velocities of up to about 20 feet per second, were not too bad.

In the summer of 1934 President Roosevelt created the Federal Aviation Commission, generally known as the Howell Board, to investigate the state of aeronautics in the United States. The board was chaired by newspaper publisher Clark Howell and included among other people Edward Warner, the editor of *Aviation*, and Professor Jerome Hunsaker of MIT, both of whom I knew because they were members of the NACA. At any rate, the Howell Board visited Langley laboratory and asked me to give a flight demonstration of the W-1.

I decided that the short field performance would be demonstrated more effectively from Morgan's field, so we took them out there. I remember making a short field landing and then a normal landing, using only about half of the 800-foot runway, and then going around and making a fast landing, putting the plane down at 60 MPH, applying the brakes, and still using only about 600 feet.

We had limited the elevator control by that time so that unstalled flight could be maintained with the control full back, either with power on or off. I demonstrated this at an altitude of a few hundred feet, making climbs and glides with the control full back and, in both cases, turns in both directions. The members of the Howell Board appeared to be well impressed by the performance. They asked me to prepare a summary of my thoughts on the light airplane, as well as on the civil aviation picture in general, and about a month later I gave this at a hearing in Washington.

By the end of the summer of 1934 I figured that we had pretty well proven the capability of the tricycle landing gear and that the airplane had demonstrated reasonably good stability and control at all angles of attack that could be maintained in flight (or, in other words, that the limited elevator control was effective). We then initiated the next part of our test program, in which we tried out our two-control operations and a flap with spoilers for lateral control near the stall. In the NACA wind-tunnel tests we had worked out a spoiler system with a slot carrying air past underneath it, which we called a "slot-lip" aileron, and the results looked promising. Before a flight test I made about a month after the Howell Board demonstration, I asked Bob Platt, who was staying on the ground, to check my height as I crossed the northern fence of the 800-foot runway. I took off and climbed steeply, and his report afterward was that he thought I had reached about "three span lengths high," or 90 feet, when crossing the north fence. I kept on climbing and, at an altitude of about 150 feet, the engine suddenly jerked to a stop, and everything was quiet. I was told later that Henry Reid, Langley's engineer-in-charge, who was shooting at a nearby range at the time, looked up into the sudden silence and said, "Now we'll see what it can do."

From one standpoint it didn't do very well, but from another it did. Just north of the flying field there was a half-mile oval racetrack for practicing with horses. This was an area about 1,000 feet long, and I was nearly over the middle of it. The natural place to land might have been the tennis courts, which were just north of the racetrack, but people were playing tennis, and anyway they were surrounded by a high wire fence with steel poles. To the left was the Morgan farmhouse, and to the right was a large area where the earth had been excavated and taken away to fill in at Langley Field, leaving a plot about 8 to 10 feet below the natural surface of the rest of the earth, filled with little 3-foot mountain ranges left by the earth-moving machinery. I pulled all the way back on the stick and turned about 45 degrees to the right, coming down and landing right in the turn of the racetrack.

I came down at a very high rate of descent, but the nose was just a little bit below the horizon and the airplane struck the ground in a relatively flat attitude. The nose gear didn't fail but it pushed the front end of the fuselage up, and the right landing gear did fail. The right auxiliary airfoil and the right wing tip were also damaged where they hit the ground, and there were a number of other portions somewhat deformed. But all in all the damage was not so very bad.

I was not hurt except for a little scratch on my forehead. I really believe that the characteristics of the airplane saved me, because if I had been in an ordinary airplane and had pulled the stick all the way back that way, and had started to turn, it would have surely stalled and started into a spin. I would have hit the ground pretty well nose down and that, very likely, would have resulted in a fatal, or at least very serious, accident. I don't suppose, however, that the spectators saw it that way. The tennis players and the range shooters came rushing over, took a quick look, and went back to their activities. Bob Platt went to hire a truck to get the plane back to the hangar, which was only about half a mile away, and I got out my tools and started disassembling the plane on the spot. Another NACA engineer, Dave Biermann, who was at the airport with his own airplane, got his tools and came over with hardly a word and helped me disassemble it. Dave was also the only one who helped out afterward, and I sure appreciated it.

Biermann and his brother Arnold, who was a power plants expert, later disassembled the engine for me, and together we found what had caused the difficulty. The master connecting rod of the seven-cylinder radial engine had pulled right in two. This rod was constructed of two pieces held together by means of two large rivets, and one piece had merely pulled through past the rivets. It had simply been made too light. We remedied this defect by changing to the one-piece master rods used in later Pobjoy engines.

This effectively completed the W-1 portion of the story, and we were ready to go ahead with the next stage involving the flaps, slot-lip ailerons, and two-control operation.

It occurred to me that since our efforts and money had helped to initiate the Bureau of Air Commerce's private airplane program with no financial return to us, and since that bureau was now starting to purchase airplanes that would be designed to specifications based largely on the characteristics of our W-1, that we might possibly get some financial aid for the next part of our test program. So in October 1934, I prepared two proposals and sent them to John Geisse, chief of the aeronautics development section of the Bureau of Air Commerce. One proposal, for which I suggested a price of $2,200, covered the installation and testing of a flap that could be used both as a high-lift device and as an air brake that could control the glide angle to a landing without changing the air speed. The other proposal, for $2,500, involved the elimination of the regular ailerons as a primary means for control. (The elevator, rudder, and ailerons were typically the three primary controls.) In place of the regular ailerons, we wanted to install a slot-lip aileron, a form of spoiler involving a slot that we had developed in our NACA lateral controls tests. These devices, which were substantially free from the usual adverse yawing moments of the ordinary ailerons, gave good rolling moments, especially near the stall.

Geisse appeared favorably inclined, but Dr. Lewis, the NACA's director for research, called me up and said, "Fred, we can't let you sell reports on research work to the Department of Commerce, because you'd be competing directly with the product of the NACA. Why don't you just sell them the modified airplane?"

Well, we didn't exactly like the idea of letting go of our airplane before we had a lot more fun with it, but ultimately we agreed. On November 15, 1934, Geisse wrote me a letter in which he made a definite Department of Commerce proposal to purchase the airplane. The bureau did not consider it proper procedure, however, to purchase a home-built airplane from a group of government employees. It was suggested that we have the repairs and modifications made by a recognized aircraft manufacturer, and that they, the bureau, would then purchase the airplane directly from the manufacturer. We did make such an arrangement with the Kreider-Reisner Division of the Fairchild Company in Hagerstown, Maryland, the very plant that I had visited in 1931, during my "vacation from aeronautics."

The W-1 was immediately trucked up to Hagerstown, where the rebuilding and modifications commenced according to our plans (but with the detailed drawings of the new parts made by Fairchild). This work went on during the winter of 1934/35 and well into the spring. Every two or three weeks during that period, I would drive up to Hagerstown to meet with the Fairchild engineers, taking along either Carl Wenzinger or Bob Platt. We would start at five o'clock on a Sunday morning, stop off for breakfast somewhere between Richmond and Washington, and arrive in Hagerstown at about 10:30 A.M. About 4:30 we would start back, arriving home late at night. A few times the hills had ice and snow on them, and we did not always make them on the first attempt, even though at that time we always had chains along. At Fairchild we spent most of our time with George Hardmann, the chief engineer, and another engineer by the name of Lew Fahnestock, who led the work on our project. Both of these men cooperated very well with us, and the work made good progress.

In the late fall of 1934 a young man, Robert T. Jones, twenty-three years old, started a temporary, nine-month job at Langley as a scientific aide. Previously Jones had been an employee of the Nicholas Beazley Company in Marshall, Missouri, for which he had designed, among other things, an airplane with a Pobjoy engine that had entered the 1930 Chicago Air Races. In fact, the engine that we purchased from Nicholas Beazley for the W-1 may have been one that had been in Jones's racer. (The airplane had not actually flown in the 1930 race because of engine trouble.)

Jones was unusual in that he read the Greek philosophers and studied mathematics and physics for his own pleasure and satisfaction. When the Depression hit hard, he had been lucky enough to get a job in Washington, I believe, running an elevator in one of the federal buildings. During this period, and even though he had only one year of college at the University of Missouri, Jones took a graduate course in theoretical aerodynamics at Catholic University under Dr. Max M. Munk.

When he came to Langley with the lowly rating of a scientific aide, Jones was given the job of making simple routine calculations, reducing data to coefficients in my atmospheric wind-tunnel section. One day not long after he began doing this for us, I mentioned to the fellows that we needed a new correction factor for a particular setup in the tunnel, and then I went back to my office in the afternoon and worked one out. The next morning "Jonesy," as we soon called him, sidled up to me and said, "You know, you mentioned you needed a new wind-tunnel correction factor. I worked one up last night, and maybe you'd like to see it." I did, and we had both arrived at the same correction.

It wasn't long before I found that Bob Jones had greater mathematical ability than any of the rest of us, and I soon got to using him in various theoretical analyses. Two of these joint efforts resulted in published NACA reports by Jonesy and me: TR 570, "The Effect of Lateral Controls in Producing Motion of an Airplane as Computed from Wind-Tunnel Data" (April 20, 1936); and TR 605, "Resume and Analysis of N.A.C.A. Lateral Control Research" (April 20, 1937).

Jones was obviously competent, and we tried to get him a permanent professional rating, but the Civil Service Commission would not let him take the junior aeronautical engineering examination because he did not have a college degree. By this time, I was writing the questions for some of these exams, and with the help of engineer-in-charge Henry Reid, I asked the CSC people if we could give Jones a special examination right at Langley. We prepared a set of questions for this purpose and we sent them in through channels. The CSC soon gave an examination using these questions. However, because the commission's experts considered the questions so difficult, they wouldn't let anyone take the exam who did not have a *doctor's* degree. Eventually we got one employee who passed the exam, but to retain Jonesy we had to keep giving him additional temporary employment and always at a low salary. Finally, in 1936, after he had two years of experience with us, Jones was allowed to take an unassembled oral exam, based largely on his own experiences. With success on this test, and the talent he demonstrated in the NACA reports he had written, Jones finally received the rating of an assistant engineer. And we were able to get him the next grade (P-2) above the lowest professional grade (P-1)—for which the academic requirement, though presumed, was not specifically mentioned.

The reason for bringing him into the W-1 story at this point is that Jones, who is now famous as one of the world's leading aerodynamicists, made an important theoretical analysis of the optimum conditions for two-control flight (using either the rudder or the ailerons alone). This analysis indicated that a pure rolling control, without either adverse or favorable yawing moments, would be close to the ideal. Thus we knew that the slot-lip ailerons that we were planning to install should therefore do quite well.

As soon as the master connecting rod of our Pobjoy engine had pulled apart, we put in a strong complaint to both Nicholas Beazley and the Pobjoy Company in England. It turned out that about a year before Pobjoy had issued an advisory saying that the connecting rods should be changed, but Nicholas Beazley had not forwarded this information on to us. After some haggling, it was finally arranged that we would send the engine back to Pobjoy in England, and its people would rebuild it with improved parts. This was done, and we got the engine back in time for Fairchild to install it in the W-1A.

Upon completion in the spring of 1935, the W-1A, now belonging to the Bureau of Air Commerce, was trucked down to Langley Field

*The W-1A, with me in the cockpit, in front of the NACA
hangar at Langley Field, circa 1935. The adjoining photo
shows me in front of the airplane.*

and mounted for testing in the full-scale tunnel. As I remember
them, the tests were just standard ones, measuring the lift, drag,
and moments.

The airplane was in the test section for the NACA's tenth annual
aircraft engineering research conference on May 22, 1935; in fact,
the conference group photograph, which was always taken inside
the FST because that was the only place big enough to hold all the
conference attendees, highlights the testing of the W-1A. The caption for this photograph reads: "VIEW SHOWS DEPARTMENT OF
COMMERCE LIGHT AIRPLANE MOUNTED FOR AERODY-
NAMIC TESTS." This photo, by the way, was the frontispiece for
the NACA's *Annual Report* to Congress for 1935.

For that conference, incidentally, I made a small model of a tricycle gear, possibly 18 inches long, and another model of a similar-
sized tail-wheel-type gear. These models were just of the gears
alone, without the rest of the airplane, but they had the centers of
gravity in approximately the right place. I ran these models down
a sloping track that flared off and allowed the gears to ease onto a
concrete floor, as in a landing. Of course, the tail-wheel gear turned
ever more sharply into a turn and ground looped just about every
time; it was obviously unstable in taxiing. The tricycle gear, however, with its two main wheels behind the center of gravity and its

castering nose wheel, went straight down the runway every time, even when set at a good angle of yaw. As it contacted the ground, the tricycle gear turned immediately with its nose pointing in the direction it was traveling—not in the direction in which it was originally pointed.

Most of the people in the audience had not been aware of this difference in taxiing stability, and it made quite an impression on them. Some had found, however, that if they took a model of an airplane having a tail skid or wheel and rolled it along a flat surface like a floor, the model would turn to one side and ground loop, but if they turned it around and rolled it backward, or tail first, it would go straight.

At the next NACA conference a year later, Orville Wright made it a point to tell me that, although people were saying that my tricycle gear was just a reversion to the three-wheeled gears that had been used on pusher airplanes before World War I, he wanted me to know that he realized that this was not the case. He realized that the airplanes in those days had *fixed* nose wheels and that the operations took place in open grass fields with lots of manpower available for the handling of the airplane, meaning that people in those days had not cared whether the gear was stable in taxiing or not. Wright wanted me to know that he thought my gear was a new line of thought and a worthwhile improvement, all of which gave me quite a lift.

The first interest in applying the tricycle gear to large airplanes was shown by the Douglas people in about 1935. Arthur Raymond, Douglas's chief engineer, sent F. R. Collbohm and W. Bailey Oswald to Langley to find out about the tricycle gear on the W-1 and to ask questions about what it might do for larger airplanes. Oswald, as you may remember, was the graduate student in Clark Millikan's class at Cal Tech who had used my then yet-to-be published textbook's method for obtaining propeller efficiencies in his doctoral thesis on the analysis of airplane performance. I had some contact with Mr. Collbohm and Dr. Oswald, but they were more interested in what the pilots who had flown the W-1 had to say about the new type of gear.

After the visit by Collbohm and Oswald, the Douglas Company in cooperation with the army tried the tricycle gear on one of its Dolphin airplanes, which originally had possessed a tail-wheel-type gear. The Dolphin was an amphibian flying boat, and the

Douglas engineers simply moved the wheels of the main gear back a bit and put a castering, steerable nose wheel under the front of the hull. These tests confirmed the advantages of the gear.

On October 21, 1935, I wrote a six-page memorandum in response to a request from D. W. Tomlinson of TransContinental and Western Air (as TWA was known before 1950) for information about the possible use of the tricycle gear on a transport airplane. My memo pointed out the various advantages that I have already outlined, plus the fact that with a twin-engine transport airplane one could extend the forward part of the fuselage sufficiently to support the nose gear well forward and also provide a satisfactorily long wheel base.

Soon thereafter three or four airlines got together with the Douglas Company in the hope of getting a transport airplane that was larger than the DC-3. Edward P. Warner was a consultant to this group, and he visited me at Langley Field to go over the possibilities of applying the tricycle gear to such a large transport. Warner had of course been familiar with my activities since the mid-1920s, and he had seen the W-1 demonstrated at Morgan's little field. The result of this activity was the one-and-only Douglas DC-4E, the first large transport plane to use the tricycle gear. Even then, the Douglas engineers made provisions for returning to a tail-wheel-type gear in case they were not entirely happy with the tricycle gear. During World War II, a wholly different version of the DC-4 was used widely in military activities as the C-54, and after the war it was used on airlines, as well as in the Berlin airlift. The tricycle gear was also used on most of the war's later military airplanes, such as the Lockheed P-38, the Bell P-39, the Convair B-24, and the PB4Y-2. Today, of course, it is the conventional gear for most all military, airline, and general aviation airplanes, which gives me a touch of satisfaction even though people in general are not aware of my association with the establishment of its use in the 1930s.

After the NACA's tests of the W-1A were completed, Bob Platt and I were given the opportunity by the Bureau of Air Commerce to make our own trials. According to the FST test results, the plane's glide control flap had attained its maximum lift with a deflection of only about 20 degrees and with a relatively low drag coefficient. It could be deflected farther up to 80 degrees with no substantial change in the lift coefficient but with an enormous increase in the drag coefficient. The flap was operated by a separate hand lever that had a notch for the 20-degree flap angle.

After making preliminary practice flights to get used to the new controls, Platt and I investigated the flap control operation further. When coming in for landings, we deflected the flap first to the 20-degree angle, which gave a relatively low drag and flat glide. (The airplane was trimmed to fly hands off at a suitable approach speed, about 55 MPH.) Then, if a steeper glide path was desired, we merely pulled back the flap handle farther, to whatever extent desired. This resulted in an instantaneous steepening of the glide path, because there was no change in the angle of attack or the lift coefficient.

Incidentally, the first NACA trials had shown that with a flap angle of 80 degrees, the angle of descent and the corresponding vertical velocity were so great as to be alarming. Thus to be safe, the flare-off for a landing had to be started at least 50 or 60 feet above the ground—unless power was applied to help flare out the flight path. We then reduced the maximum flap angle to 60 degrees.

At first Platt and I found the simultaneous operation of the flap lever and the control stick to be rather awkward, but after a few landings, the operation became easy and apparently natural. After landing the plane consistently a number of times within a few feet of a particular point, we concluded that it was definitely easier, more direct and satisfactory to land on a short field with the W-1A's glide control flap than it had been with the W-1's fixed auxiliary airfoil.

To make the approach to landing at a given spot even easier, I devised a simple sighting instrument. This consisted of a little pendulum hanging just inside the windshield in front of my eyes, with a cross arrow on it showing the desired glide-path angle in reference to the ground, rather than to the airplane. Then, to make a pinpoint landing, all the pilot had to do was change the flap angle so that the arrow would keep pointing at the spot on the field where contact was desired. After some practice, this system worked fairly well.

I think that Wolfgang Langewiesche's later system was better than mine, however. With it, the pilot just kept the spot on the runway that he hoped to touch down on lined up with a certain portion of the windshield. If the touchdown spot went up with respect to the windshield, it meant that the pilot was undershooting; if it went down, he was overshooting. This was simpler than my instrument method.

I made my first attempts at two-control flight simply by taking my feet off the rudder bar and using the slot-lip ailerons as the sole means of lateral control. After some turns in the air, I tried making straight upwind landings in the 50-by-300-foot strip, controlling the glide angle with the flap. These landings seemed satisfactory, so I tried jogging in by making an approach to one side and an *S* turn just before contact. This also seemed satisfactory, so I tried landing by throttling the engine at an altitude of 400 feet and making 180-degree turns to the landing strip. These also gave me no particular difficulty.

I then tried using rudder and elevators only, holding the ailerons in neutral. I found it easy to make reasonably satisfactory turns in the air, but it was difficult near the ground; the airplane skidded noticeably in entering a turn and slipped downward noticeably when starting to recover. In the turns to a landing at a particular spot, it thus seemed to wallow around considerably, and I could not prevent myself from using the ailerons occasionally to pick up a wing rather than wait for the effect of the rudder.

With the idea that I could not give the rudder a fair test because I had become so accustomed to flying the W-1 with the ailerons, I had Bob Platt try the rudder-alone operation first. After he had made a few flights with all three controls to familiarize himself with the W-1A, the ailerons were locked in neutral and Bob spent a full two hours landing the plane in the 50-by-300-foot strip. He had the same difficulty I had experienced in skewing around considerably when making landings from turns. I then tried it again, this time with the ailerons locked, but the results were no better. We both found that straight landings could be made satisfactorily either upwind or crosswind, but that when we attempted curved approaches to the strip, we wallowed around to an alarming extent and gave the landing gear an opportunity to prove its worth.

We then locked the rudders and tried the ailerons as the sole lateral and directional control. The cables were removed from the rudder bar so that it was used to steer the front wheel only. We found that turns could be made with less slipping with the rudder locked than with the rudder free, and that the entrance to turns could be made with substantially no slipping or skidding. The steady portion of the turn was always accompanied by a slight inward slip, but the recovery was quite satisfactory. Both of us agreed that the control was decidedly better with the ailerons alone than with the rudder alone.

To verify it we made turns and recoveries, S and 180-degree-turn approaches, and upwind, crosswind, and downwind landings, all with ease and as well as with all three controls. The flight trials were thus in complete agreement with the theoretical results found by Bob Jones. We then tried a wheel control in place of the stick (the front landing gear still being steered by means of the rudder bar), and decided that we liked the wheel at least as well as the stick, if not better. The wheel control would make a very satisfactory arrangement, we thought, if it were connected to steer the front wheel also for two-control operation.

In January 1936 I presented a paper on the W-1 and W-1A projects to a meeting of the Society of Automotive Engineers (SAE) in Detroit. In its conclusion I stated that the projects had demonstrated to our satisfaction that each of the main features of our little experimental airplane would indeed help to make flying both simpler and safer.

This paper received fairly wide public notice; it was published in other countries and was translated into different languages. Originally, I had entitled it simply "A Development Toward Simpler Flying," but the SAE people suggested changing this to "Everyman's Airplane: A Development Toward Simpler Flying." I thought this title was rather corny but finally agreed to it, and I suppose that the new title accounts for a fair amount of the public attention the paper received. In many cases the aeronautical press started referring to the W-1 as "a foolproof airplane." This I objected to strenuously because I knew that there was no such thing as a foolproof plane, and I didn't want our work associated with one.

I have since learned definitely that you can make an airplane that is easy to fly safely, but the ultimate safety depends on the operation of the pilot.

That almost ends the story of the W-1 and W-1A, but not quite. When the Hammond airplane was completed for the Bureau of Air Commerce's competition, the nose wheel of its tricycle gear was on occasion exhibiting a shimmy so severe that it threatened to shake the nose of the airplane apart. The bureau asked the NACA to study the problem and see what we could do about it.

We approached the problem from both theoretical and experi-

Stearman-Hammond Model Y. This aircraft was the winner of the safe aircraft competition that was sponsored by the aviation section of the Department of Commerce, forerunner of the FAA. Only a few of these aircraft were produced and at a cost far in excess of the low cost desired (which was $700 per airplane). The Model Y was designed on the basis of specifications obtained following the tests on our W-1.

mental standpoints. I handed the theoretical problem to Arthur Kantrowitz, a young mathematical physicist from Columbia University, who had recently started working in the variable-density tunnel section under Eastman Jacobs. Besides making calculations, Kantrowitz (we called him "Arky") also made some model experiments from which he found that a castering wheel with an air-filled rubber tire would oscillate or shimmy in a purely kinematic way due to a characteristic mode of distortion affecting the tire. Arky also found that shimmy could be prevented by giving the wheel some lateral freedom—that is, allowing it to slide laterally on a somewhat curved axle that was lower in the center. Although this solution looked simple, it has never been used by airplane designers.

We decided to make some shimmy experiments with the W-1A. During its flight trials, the little plane had shown no such difficulty. We knew, though, that this was probably due to the fact that, because the nose wheel was connected to the plane's control systems, and because of the particular castering conditions and tire pressures that we used, there was sufficient friction to overcome any tendency to shimmy. We decided, therefore, to disconnect the nose wheel from the air controls, lubricate the shaft generously, and then taxi the plane until the shimmy occurred. The shimmy tests were continued with various modifications until eventually the airplane—which now belonged, of course, to the Department of Commerce—was no longer considered airworthy. Some time after I left the NACA permanently, the airplane was surveyed, meaning that a few useful parts were taken off of it and the plane was then destroyed.

Between 1931 and 1935 I applied for two patents covering the innovations of the W-1 and W-1A. My patent attorney was Allen E. Peck of Washington, D.C., who had been a pilot during World War I and thus knew something about aeronautics. In February 1931 we applied for a patent on the limited elevator control arrangement; this patent was granted to me thirteen months later as U.S. Patent No. 1,848,037. In 1934 we applied for a patent covering some of the airplane's other features, including combinations of the tricycle gear with two-control operations. In addition we made claims involving the use of a flap to aid take-off when a tricycle gear was used. This application remained in limbo for several years, however, because our claims interfered with an application by Joseph M. Gwinn, Jr., of Buffalo, New York. He had been working on a little airplane called the Gwinn Aircar, which had aims somewhat similar to those of the W-1 and W-1A.

Trying to stay out of court, I drove up to Buffalo, taking my NACA colleague Carl Wenzinger along, to meet Mr. Gwinn and see if we could work out a reasonable agreement. I had met Gwinn at the Consolidated plant in Buffalo in 1934, when Joe was chief engineer for the Fleet and Consolidated trainers. At that time the W-1 was flying, and I had told him about it.

Wenzinger and I made this visit to Gwinn in early 1936, and as I remember it, his first Aircar was not yet finished. It was a small compact biplane but with rather ungraceful, homely lines. The Aircar had a rather closely spaced tricycle gear and was fitted with a two-control operation using ailerons alone and a rather large fixed fin area at the rear. In addition, in order to avoid stalling and to maintain lateral control through all the angles of attack, it used my limited elevator control.

Obviously, Gwinn had been thinking along the same lines that I had, but he was going even further with regard to making it like an

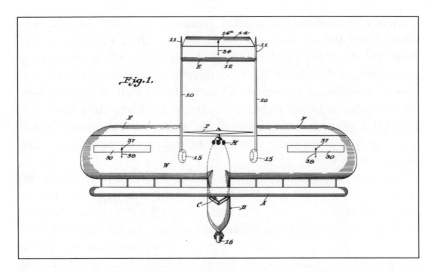

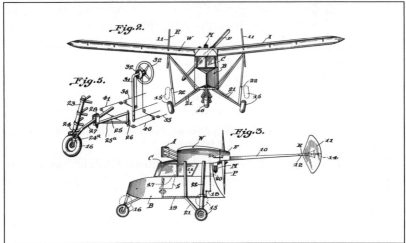

Two drawings from my 1938 airplane patent.

automobile. The cabin was made to look like the inside of a car, with an Oldsmobile steering wheel and Oldsmobile instruments. He even had a brake and clutch pedals—to put the plane's flaps down to a take-off position, one simply pressed down on the clutch pedal. Later in fact, when the Aircar was finished, take-offs could be made merely by taxiing up to a high speed and then pushing down on the so-called clutch pedal to put the flaps down. Gwinn even put a two-tone automobile horn into the Aircar, which he later honked at people as he passed over a hangar or grandstand.

Although Gwinn obviously leaned much further toward the automobile than I did, our ideas were somewhat alike, and we agreed to put our cards on the table through our attorneys to determine who had really come up with the competing ideas first. We agreed, however, that neither one of us would be frozen out—because our airplanes had certain key differences, such as that his used ailerons and a fixed vertical tail to overcome adverse yawing moments whereas mine used ailerons and rudder—and that some rights would be given to the loser.

It turned out that my date of conception for the W-1 was about a year earlier than his, so in March 1938 I got the patent, and he got certain rights.[3]

The first public showing of the Gwinn Aircar was in September 1937 at the National Air Races in Cleveland. There, between the racing events, it was demonstrated every day by pilot Frank Hawks, who apparently made quite a hit with the audience when he tooted his horn in front of the grandstand. The climb performance of the first Aircar was poor, and the second one was fitted with a more

Beware the optical illusion! This is in fact a small model, made by Carl Wenzinger and me, with folding wings that we thought could be developed into a "roadable" airplane. After playing with the idea, I finally determined that a combination automobile and airplane would have certain disadvantages that would not make it worthwhile for me to go after the idea any further.

powerful, 90-horsepower Pobjoy engine. One unfortunate feature of Gwinn's plane was, in my opinion, that its pilot had a poor field of view both forward and downward, because the Pobjoy engine was rather high in the front of the fuselage.

This problem with pilot view might have had something to do with the Aircar's final demise, which occurred when Frank Hawks was giving a demonstration ride to a prospective investor. Hawks took off and was apparently not climbing well enough to clear a row of trees. He turned to an open spot between the trees but hit a power line. The airplane crashed, and both were killed. After this unfortunate experience, the Aircar project died. It was a real shame that this accident put an end to Joe Gwinn's Aircar development, because some of his more promising ideas could have been improved to the point where people could be taking advantage of them in actual use.

In the following years, there would be a small number of other attempts to produce a "roadable" airplane or flying automobile. In the 1940s one of them was made by Robert Fulton, a descendant of the steamboat pioneer, in which the wings and tail surfaces could be removed in case a person wanted to drive the vehicle on the ground. Another was by Moulton B. Taylor of Longview, Washington.

In early 1950 Wismer Holland of Valdosta, Georgia, modified an Ercoupe (see following chapter) so that the outer wing panels from the landing gear to the tip could be removed quickly and easily and supported over the top of the airplane longitudinally without changing the center of gravity location. Then, with a protecting wire cage installed around the propeller, the plane could be taxied along the roads like an automobile.

The "roadable" airplane is still an enticing possibility to me, but only as a fun experiment.

ERCO and the Ercoupe

In October 1936 Henry Berliner invited me to join his company, the Engineering and Research Corporation (ERCO) of Washington, D.C., as chief engineer. At ERCO my main project would be to put the ideas we had developed in the W-1 and W-1A into an airplane to be put into commercial production for private use; the goal was an airplane that would be unusually simple and easy to fly and free from the difficulties associated with stalling and spinning. Although I would have been glad to stay with the NACA and carry on research work for the rest of my life, I could not resist the opportunity. In November I moved my family to a house in Bethesda, Maryland, and, on December 1, reported to work at ERCO.

Before relating the story of my years with ERCO and the design of the Ercoupe airplane, however, I want to mention two episodes from my last years with NACA Langley. The first episode involves my participation on the contest board of the National Aeronautic Association (NAA) in 1935. The second involves a supposedly top-secret test in Langley's full-scale wind tunnel of the Boeing B-15 four-engine bomber in 1936.

The NAA contest board decided that something should be added to the National Air Races of 1935 to stimulate interest in private flying, and I was assigned the job of working out such an event. Being an engineer, I naturally came up with a sort of performance contest. This contest consisted of taking off over a barrier (a light, harmless string with a few flags on it), racing in both directions over a 3-mile course, making a 150-mile cruising run with credits being given for speed and for load carried and debits for fuel consumed, landing over the barrier, and stopping in the shortest possible distance.

The National Air Races of 1935 were to be held from August 30 through September 2 in Cleveland, Ohio. The contest board did not want to clutter up the very active Cleveland agenda with the many tests that would be required for my contest, so we arranged to run all of the contests except the cruising contest on a little-used field about 150 miles from Cleveland and then to run the cruising part of the contest from that place to Cleveland. We selected Wayne County Airport, west of Detroit, which at that time was about a mile-square grass field with only a couple of hangars on it and no hard runways. It was in open farm country and an ideal place to run the tests (today it is part of the Detroit Metropolitan Airport). The *Detroit News* chose to sponsor the contest and offered a fine trophy to become the permanent possession of anyone who won it three times.

Five airplanes arrived at Wayne County airport to engage in the contest, and they covered a wide range. The largest was a Beech Staggerwing biplane with a 300-horsepower Wright Whirlwind engine. The next largest was a Cessna Airmaster, a cantilever monoplane with a 145-HP Warner engine. Then came a two-place Monocoupe with a 110-HP Warner engine, a low-wing wire-braced Ryan ST with a Menasco engine, and a Piper Cub with a three-cylinder 40-HP Lenape engine. With those airplanes I met a number of fine people, some of whom I have had contact with now and then ever since. Wichita's Dwane Wallace, Cessna's chief engineer, was there with the Airmaster, along with the plane's pilot, George Hart. Pittsburgh's Helen McCloskey, the attractive daughter of Gen. Manus McCloskey, was there with the Monocoupe, along with her pilot Jack Morrison. Also Howard Rough, an inspector for the Bureau of Air Commerce, was there to make sure for us that the airplanes conformed to all of the regulations. (Incidentally, Rough eventually married Helen McCloskey; I'm not certain, but I believe that this was the first time the two had met.)

The pilot of the Ryan ST was Tex Rankin, who was, about that time, the country's aerobatic champion. Ironically, he was so conservative in his take-offs and landings over the obstacle that he did not make a competitive score.

Originally we had intended for all of the planes to start out for Cleveland on the cruising contest at about the same time and for all of them to land directly at the Cleveland racing field. While still at Wayne County, however, we received word that there was no suitable spot open for us. We therefore ran the cruising contest to the Akron airport, where we could take time to measure the fuel consumption accurately.

Early the next morning we all hopped over to the Cleveland airport at about the same time. Later in the day we staged a combined event to show the Cleveland audience what our competition had been all about. In this event all five of the planes lined up and made a race-horse start over a ten-foot obstacle, then headed for a scattering pylon and, all within sight of the grandstand, made two laps around a five-mile course. The event concluded with each plane landing over the same ten-foot obstacle and coming to a stop in as short a distance as possible. Dwane Wallace, a determined but always considerate sportsman, won the competitition in his Cessna Airmaster.

The following year, 1936, I was involved in the second running of the Detroit News Trophy Contest, held at the NAA races in Miami, Florida. This time the main schedule was not so tight, so we were able to run all of our events, except for the cruising contest, right on the main field, the Miami airport (which is now the location of the present Opalaka airport, north of the city).

I knew almost nothing about Florida so, for the cruising contest, I asked the local people where there was a good landmark about 75 miles away that could be used as a pylon, so that we could make our 150-mile run by going there and back again. The Red Lighthouse at Jupiter Inlet about 75 miles up the coast to the north was suggested, and it looked good to me, so I drew a straight line on the map from the Miami airport to the Jupiter Lighthouse. When the Bureau of Air Commerce inspectors saw this course, however, they objected strongly. They said that if anyone went down along it, all that there was to land onto was soft swamp; the pilot and plane might never be found. (Today, that entire area is drained and built up with business buildings, factories, and residences.) So they made us fly instead east to the coast and up the beach to the lighthouse and then dogleg back the same way.

Dwane Wallace once again won our competition in his Airmaster. Later he got permanent possession of the Detroit News Trophy; for many years, this trophy has been on display in the entryway to the main office of the Cessna plant in Kansas.

In 1936, an interesting incident occurred that bears on military security in American aeronautics. I was visiting Wright Field in Ohio with Don Wood, a fellow NACA engineer, regarding some propeller research that we might be doing for the army. During this visit, a couple of officers asked to talk with me about some possible research in our 30-by-60-foot full-scale tunnel. They said that the air corps was interested in a very large four-engine bomber that might be built by Boeing. They wondered how large a model could be tested in the FST and whether the model could be tested with operational power plants, each driving a propeller, so they could get test results for both power on and power off. I told them that the model could have a span up to about 35 feet, and that it would be entirely practical to run it with four operational propellers. They said that the project was top secret but that I should inform our NACA officials, particularly Dr. Lewis, when I got back to Langley that the army soon would be making an official request for such tests to be made.

From that time on, only a few people at Langley were to know anything about the project; this group included Dr. Lewis, engineer-in-charge Henry Reid, chief of the aerodynamics division Elton Miller, and FST head Smith J. ("Smitty") DeFrance. Being only the assistant chief of the aerodynamics division, I did not need to know about the project and, after delivering the army's message to George Lewis, was not supposed to know anything more about it. In fact, all Langley employees, including myself, were to consider the FST temporarily off limits while the top-secret testing of the new bomber was being done. This seemed a little odd to those of us who knew that I had had the first contact with the army on the project—but those were the army's orders, and we carried them out as far as possible.

One day thereafter Edward P. Warner, who was by that time the assistant secretary of the navy for aeronautics, came down to

Langley from Washington to show the NACA laboratory to a distinguished visitor from Nazi Germany, a Mrs. Sturtevant, who was in this country ostensibly to sell German planes to American airlines. The scuttlebutt that went around indicated that she was really a spy; so great care was to be taken to show her only things that did not matter.

For a portion of their visit, I showed Mr. Warner and Mrs. Sturtevant around the lab. Then Henry Reid and I had lunch with them at the officers' club, where as it turned out many of the officers seemed to know Mrs. Sturtevant socially, calling her by her first name (which I have forgotten). Some of the men asked her if she was going down next month to the air maneuvers in Miami, and she replied that she probably would.

When we left the officers' club in a car to go to another part of the lab, there were two flatcars on a railroad siding, about an eighth of a mile away (too far to read any signs), each car with a large box on top of it. Mrs. Sturtevant piped right up, "Oh, there is the model of the four-engine Boeing bomber that you people are going to test shortly in the full-scale tunnel." Security is a marvelous thing.

In the railcars was, indeed, the model of the Boeing XB-15, the service's first large four-engine bomber. Only one version of the XB-15 was built; it was not put into production. However, the smaller B-17, which drew on the experience of the XB-15, had a great amount of service later on, in World War II.

From this point on, the rest of this chapter will deal with my early work at ERCO, including the development of the Ercoupe airplane.

All of the shares of the Engineering and Research Corporation were owned by its president and chairman of the board, Henry Berliner himself, except for a few shares held by members of his family; so Henry virtually had complete control. Henry's brother-in-law, Milton King, was ERCO's secretary and legal advisor. In December 1936, at the time I started with his company, which was located in a rented factory building at 6100 Sligo Mill Road, just inside the District of Columbia's northeast boundary, there were eighty-five employees, but only three men in engineering. One of them was Lee Marchant, who had invented the automatic punching and riveting machines ERCO was then producing. The other two were Frank Lane (at that time, Frank Levy), who did most of the general engineering work, and a Spaniard by the name of Alfero.

Henry Berliner, about 1940.

Both Lane and Alfero had done some previous aircraft design work.

Up to 1936 ERCO had never been involved per se in building airplanes; but its products had consisted entirely of machines for making airplanes. These machines included propeller-profiling machines, sheet-metal flanging machines and stretch presses, and the automatic punching and riveting machines invented by Lee Marchant. Upon my arrival, however, I started immediately on the design of an ERCO airplane. Since all of the work on the plane was being done under ERCO job order no. 310, at first we simply called the plane Model 310.

My original idea was that a private airplane should take a person from one small field to another small field in a short time, at good cruising speed (100 MPH), and with economy, ease, and comfort. Henry Berliner's idea, however, was different. He had had a couple of airplanes of his own and had used them for his private transportation. Henry had a cottage on Rehoboth Beach, Delaware, and flew back and forth from Washington to Rehoboth during the summer months. Sometimes he landed right on the beach, close to his cottage, but he did not make a practice of it because he could not get the airplane serviced anywhere near there. He thought that, in general, the owners of private airplanes would want to land where their planes would be well taken care of when they were left. He therefore argued that we should design the ERCO plane so that it could get in and out of the smallest ordinary airports, but not for extremely small places that would be used very seldom. A smaller wing could then be used, he said, and extra speed obtained for cruising flight. After some deliberation, I went along with his idea, and I have been glad ever since that I did.

Berliner also thought that it would be much easier to sell a tractor airplane than a pusher, which had the disadvantage of having the engine behind the people in a crash. Though knowing that it would be much more difficult to get satisfactory limited elevator control, both power on and power off, or to design tricycle gear anywhere as effective as that we had achieved for the W-1, with a tractor, I agreed to try the design, with the understanding that if it did not work, we could go back to a pusher.[1]

The general arrangement of the new airplane was more or less obvious to me from the start. In order to have effective limited elevator control with both power on and off, with the tractor it was desirable to have the propeller thrust line as high as possible and the wing drag in as low a position as possible. At low speeds, with power on, the tractor arrangement would give, I knew, an extra tail-depressing reaction. This would be the case for two reasons: one, extra slipstream velocity produced extra downwash over the center part of the wing; and two, extra velocity over the up elevator tended to depress the tail down farther. Thus, a low-wing arrangement was dictated, with the propeller axis located as high as possible, but still giving the pilot a good field of view over the nose. The pilot's field of view could also be enhanced by using a flat or inverted engine, rather than a radial, because with the inverted engine very little of the engine structure would have to protrude above the propeller axis. I could, in effect, raise the thrust line still higher by inclining the engine down at the nose so that the line of thrust would have a larger moment arm about the airplane's center of gravity.

I wanted an engine of about 60 or 65 horsepower, but none was available at that time, so we started designing the prototype to use a Continental A-40 engine, which was available. This engine delivered only about 37 HP, but we were planning to use it only until a more powerful engine could be obtained.

In selecting the airfoil section for the wing, I went over all of the latest work done by Eastman Jacobs and his cohorts in Langley's variable-density tunnel section, and by cross-plotting, determined that the NACA 43013 airfoil would be the optimum shape for our needs. Knowing the NACA's test data for this airfoil enabled us to calculate the approximate wing area of our proposed airplane and to make a reliable series of performance computations. Climb performance computations with different wing spans led us to select 30 feet as the span. By now, former NACA engineer Bob Sanders, who had helped quite a bit with the W-1 project before leaving for work with Pan American Grace in South America, had returned to the States and was also working for ERCO.

Not long after work on the ERCO airplane was under way in 1937, Henry Berliner asked me to visit Europe to learn as much as possible about the design of a new type of wooden propeller that was being manufactured by the Schwarz company in Germany and by Airscrews Ltd. in England.

ERCO had sold many of its machine tools for the construction of aircraft to most of the major European countries, but in Russia and Germany the company could not receive payment that could be transferred into American dollars; instead, it had to make some sort of barter arrangement. From Germany, it got the right to make Schwarz propellers, which were being manufactured in large quantities not only by Schwarz but also by Airscrews Ltd. in England. The Schwarz blade consisted essentially of a main core of laminated spruce or other light wood, which merged into a root of impregnated and compressed hardwood known to us as "compreg." The compreg root was threaded and screwed into a steel ferule that supported the blade in the hub. The remainder of the blade was covered completely with a heavy coating of reinforced cellulose acetate sheet, whose leading edge was armored with a flush strip of metal. Thus, the wooden core was well protected against climatic conditions and warping, as well as against injury due to contact with pebbles, cinders, sand, rain, hail, seawater, and so on. (These propellers are described in detail in a paper entitled "Composite Wood and Plastic Propeller Blades," that I gave at the annual meeting of the SAE in 1939, and that was printed in the SAE journal in June 1939.) The main advantage of the Schwarz propellers lay in their light weight, as compared with the large aluminum-alloy propellers which at that time were being used with the most powerful reciprocating engines.

In England I spent two or three days visiting Airscrews and was very happy to meet the company's technical director, Dr. Henry C.

Watts, who was England's foremost propeller authority. In the early 1920s Watts had written a book, *The Design of Screw Propellers for Aircraft*, which I had used before writing my book on propeller design. One evening he took me to his home, a large three-story building with some fifteen rooms, for dinner. His house was on a good-sized lot with nicely arranged landscaping, and he and Mrs. Watts took me on a tour of their lovely outside surroundings. Although it was wintertime, the grass was fairly green and there was green shrubbery all around the edges. As we rounded the house to the rear, I ventured, "Your backyard is very attractive." Mrs. Watts came back instantly with, "Our *rear garden* is made up of . . ." and so forth. I was obviously just a bumpkin from the American Middle West.

Up to that time, most of the houses in England were still heated by fireplaces. Of course, the English winters were not very severe and the people dressed warmly with wool underwear and wool suits. Dr. Watts was proud of the fact that his house had a central heating system, which he wanted to show me. While going through the first floor of the house, we went from the kitchen into a little pantry, where there was a small coal stove about four feet high and next to it a little coal scuttle with a small hand shovel in it. I noticed a couple of pipes leading from it and was just about to say, "Oh, I see this is your hot water heater," when I suddenly thought, and stopped, just in time, for this was the central heating plant for the fifteen-room house that Dr. Watts was so proud of.

I flew from London to Berlin on a KLM Dutch airplane with a stop at Amsterdam. The good old Douglas DC-3s had just come out, and this was my first ride on one. The stop at Amsterdam was long enough for me to get a quick look at the Fokker factory, which was at the airport.

In Berlin, on Henry Berliner's recommendation, I stayed at the Adlon Hotel on Unter den Linden, the city's main boulevard. The Adlon was a quaint old place with good service. It had an open elevator that went up from the lobby, the passengers being protected by fancy iron grillwork. The hotel was destroyed by our bombing during World War II. Now, I believe, the Russians control that part of the city.

The Schwarz propeller plant was in Oranienberg, a northern suburb of Berlin. I spent the working days of about two weeks in the plant. It was easy enough getting along with the German engineers because they could speak English, but I had a rougher time with the shop technicians because most of them could not. However, with the two years of German lessons I had had in high school, a week's practice with a young German on the ship coming over, a small English-German dictionary, and a lot of handwaving and sketches, I got along fairly well with them, too. I never could manage to use the guttural German pronunciation, though.

One of the first things I did after arriving in Berlin was to look up our United States Air Corps attaché—ironically, a man by the name of Captain Kaiser. He arranged for me to see a couple of the nearby aircraft plants. I wanted in particular to see the Deutsche Versuchsanstalt für Luftfahrt, or DVL, which was the equivalent of the NACA's Langley laboratory, though it was more closely connected to the military. Captain Kaiser said almost immediately, "Oh, I'm sorry, but that's impossible. That's out of the question because it takes at least six weeks of preparatory paperwork." I asked him to give the DVL a ring and try it anyway, even if he got turned down, but he didn't want to do this. When I didn't give in, Kaiser reluctantly made the call, and he got the answer he expected.

Two or three days later, while I was at the hotel, I got a telephone call from Dr. Friedrich Seewald, the head of the DVL. He invited me to visit him the next morning in his office. I appreciated that, but mentioned that I would also like to take a look around the laboratory if possible and see his wind tunnels and other equipment. He ignored that part of what I said and merely repeated a warm invitation to come and visit, saying that he would send a car to pick me up and take me back home again. I accepted but said that I would have to get back by noon so I could spend the afternoon at the Schwarz plant, because I was getting behind there. Early the next morning there was a Mercedes limousine with a chauffeur waiting for me in front of the Adlon, which took me the 10 or 12 miles to the Berlin suburb where the DVL was located.

After greeting me, Dr. Seewald called his chief of flight research into his office, and, together, they plied me with questions for about an hour. They asked about the tricycle gear, which I was happy to explain because all of the information about it was published, and about the stability and control work that we had been doing at the NACA. Since the results of this research were also published, I could also answer these questions without too much worry.

Finally, Dr. Seewald asked, "All right, and now what would you like to see in the laboratory?" Fortunately, I knew what I wanted to see, and they took me around and showed me everything that I asked for. Their largest wind tunnel had a highly classified model in it, but they put a cloth over the model and showed the tunnel to me, anyway. They also had a vertical free-spinning tunnel, which at the time they were trying to get to operate satisfactorily. They knew, of course, that Langley had a similar tunnel, and therefore asked me how to keep the models from hitting the walls, but this I did not tell them. My friend Charles Zimmerman, the designer of Langley's spin tunnel, had had to learn the answer to this question the hard way—although he might have gotten part of the answer from the British.

The answer was very simple. One merely screened the tunnel so that the air velocity over the center portion was uniform but so that, at the edges, the up velocity of the air was greater than it was at the center. Thus, when spinning models got near the edge, they were turned back toward the center.

Going back to London, I took a Lufthansa Junkers trimotor to Brussels and then was to transfer to the Belgian Sabena airline using an Italian Savoia-Marchetti airplane. I made the transfer fine and was sitting in the Macci airplane when the station attendant came out running and said, "No, you can't go; there is fog in London," or words to that effect, in French. We all got out and went back to the little terminal building to wait to see what would happen. I could not converse with the ticket agent because he spoke only French and Flemish; however, I noticed an attractive young lady, who was obviously also going to London, speaking fluently in French to the agent. I thought that she must in fact be French, and when she had finished, I asked her if she spoke English, and she spoke English, English-English, that is, so well that I thought she must be a native of the island. At any rate, she straightened out my affairs and, as it turned out, we were the only ones going all the way to London.

The Belgian airline arranged for the two of us to take a bus to the railroad station in Brussels, where we caught a train for Antwerp. From there we took a night boat to Dover, and then a morning train to London, getting there about noon. I found out during the trip that the woman who had helped me was married to an Englishman and lived in London, but that she had been born and reared in Germany near the French border and could speak French and German equally well. Her English sounded like English-English to me, but when I told her that she laughed and said that her husband's folks were often amused by her accent.

I had expected to arrive in London early enough the previous afternoon to make some arrangements for the weekend. I got to my hotel just after noon a day late, however, and because it was Saturday all the aeronautical offices were deserted. I remembered, however, that C. G. Grey, editor of *The Aeroplane* magazine, had written that foreign visitors sometimes came to his office to find out what was going on. I immediately took a cab to Grey's office, which was not far away, and found one writer still working. I forget his name now (it might have been Leonard Bridgeman), but I had read some of his articles. He welcomed me and informed me that there was to be a demonstration that afternoon of a new type of autogiro—a Haffner, with feathering blades instead of the hinged ones like those on the Cierva autogiros. He said that the flying field was about 25 miles east of London and that I could take an electric train out to it. He also mentioned that at the field there were a clubhouse and two small factories, one in which the Pobjoy engine was made and one in which the Monospar airplane was made. This all sounded very good to me, and I immediately took the train out to the field.

I walked half a mile or so from the train station and upon entering the field, having not gone more than 100 feet, a man came toward me and said, "Hi, Fred, what are you doing here?" It was Capt. Frank Courtney, a noted English test pilot of large seaplanes and autogiros, whom I had met at Langley only a year or two before. He had come to the NACA lab because he had wanted to get pertinent information about our tricycle gear for a small amphibian he was designing for Curtiss-Wright. During this visit to Hampton, he had eaten lunch at my house.

Courtney took me by the arm and started showing me around. After about ten minutes we ran into Dr. Gustav Lachmann, the only other man from England who had ever had a meal in our house in Hampton. With Lachmann was Sir Frederick Handley Page, who, after talking with me for a few minutes, invited me to his residence in London for tea the next afternoon.

We saw the Haffner autogiro fly, and though it appeared to perform about as well as other contemporary autogiros, I never heard afterward of any further development of it. The Pobjoy engine and

I met Dr. Gustav Lachmann, middle, for the first time when he visited Langley in June 1930. John W. ("Gus") Crowley, head of flight research at Langley at the time, is to Lachmann's left. Lachmann invented the wing slot in Germany at about the same time that Handley Page invented it in England. Dr. Lachmann had a meal at our house, and one interesting little incident occurred. Dorothy told him that I had mentioned his name to her from time to time, and Dr. Lachmann immediately stood up straight and bowed to her from the hips, keeping his back straight. It's odd, isn't it, the little things that make a lasting impression on us.

Monospar airplane factories were closed on Saturday afternoons, but we could see much of what was going on inside through the windows. Both were small plants. Frank Courtney took me to the field's clubhouse for tea, and I spent that evening with the Lachmanns. The next afternoon Dr. Lachmann took me in his American Buick out to Handley Page's residence.

The Handley Page estate was situated right in the middle of London; it involved about ten acres, I guess, with trees, gardens, and riding horses—all in all, quite a mansion. After tea, Handley Page asked if I might be interested in serving as a technical witness for his company in a court case against the United States. I would like to have helped him out, but under the pressure of my new job at ERCO, I simply did not have the time, and declined. Our conversation (which included Dr. Lachmann) was interesting, and it went on to the point that we were invited to dinner; after some lengthy conversation after dinner, we returned to my hotel about 11:00 P.M. By the time we started home heavy fog had rolled in, and I had to open the door of the Buick and watch the side of the driveway carefully so that Lachmann could drive safely off the estate and into the lighted main streets.

I spent the next few days at Dr. Watts's Airscrew Ltd. plant at Weybridge, rounding out the information that I needed for the design and manufacture of the Schwarz-type propellers. During my sessions at the plant, I took notes of everything in a little three-by-five-inch book that I kept in my breast pocket. And I took them as I went along without regard to subject. Altogether, I filled twelve of these notebooks. My intention was to sort out all the data according to subject while making the ocean voyage home and then dictate a report on the whole thing to a stenographer. The ship did not have a public stenographer, however, and afterward I was glad of it. The weather was stormy all the way across, and the ship pitched and rolled so badly that papers would not stay on a desk. In the dining room, the crew had to put little fences around the edges of the tables to keep the dishes from sliding off onto the deck. I did manage to get the items sorted according to subject, but that was all.

It had taken the United States Lines *S. S. Washington* only six days to take me across to England, but because of the stormy weather the *Washington*'s sister ship *Manhattan* took eight days to return me to New York. During those same eight days, the fast English ship *Queen Mary* was trying to maintain its rapid schedule coming from America on the way to England and, according to the information relayed to us on the *Manhattan*, some one hundred people were injured—one fatally—on the *Queen Mary*, forcing it to slow its pace.

Soon after getting back to ERCO and finishing my report, we got the Schwarz-type propeller activity under way. As time went on, we made quite a fair number of large propellers of this type, mostly for experimental airplanes, because the props were light and could be designed and manufactured quickly, requiring no special tooling. Hollow steel propellers soon dominated this market, though. Our only real quantity production of propeller blades at ERCO occurred during World War II, when we manufactured quite a number of all-compreg blades for adjustable-pitch propellers used on planes like the Stinson L-5 Grasshopper reconnaissance plane.

Construction of the parts of the first ERCO Model 310 airplane started in the spring of 1937. The plane's overall design, which was still going on, was being accomplished—as was the case with most light airplanes—without wind-tunnel tests of the exact configuration, though the results of many previous NACA wind-tunnel tests provided a general basis of technological knowledge from which to work. We were planning to obtain the final characteristics of the airplane by making a series of flight tests involving desirable modifications.

Our idea was to make the structure of Model 310 entirely out of aluminum alloy, except for a small amount of fabric that was to cover a portion of the wing. So far as feasible, we used ERCO's own production machines, particularly the stretch presses and the automatic punching and riveting machines. One of our aims was structural simplicity. The fuselage aft of the cockpit, for example, consisted of four sheets of aluminum that were riveted together in the flat on the automatic punching and riveting machines, wrapped around four bulkheads, and then fastened in place with a small number of hand-driven rivets. Our machine riveting was many times faster than hand riveting.

The center wing section carried the landing gear, and when the outer panels were removed, the rest of the plane was complete and resting on all three wheels. The wing had a single main spar at 25 percent of its chord back of the leading edge, and it had a small false spar where the ailerons attached. Diagonally between these spars there were a small number of pressed aluminum alloy ribs, which gave a torsionally rigid structure with very few parts.

We completed the experimental Model 310 in late September and flew it for the first time on October 1, 1937. As first flown, it had all three controls set separately and had a vertical tail consisting of a fin and rudder in the center. The plane also had a tricycle landing gear with a full-size nose wheel. Unfortunately, though, the gear had a much shorter wheel base than that of the W-1.

During the next few months, we alternated test flying and modifying the airplane until a configuration was arrived at that we thought was suitable for production. Most of the test flying was done by former NACA engineer Bob Sanders, and some of the test flying was also done by another company pilot, Charlie Snyder.

First experimental Ercoupe Model 310 as first flown with single vertical tail.

The biggest change in the configuration involved the tail surfaces and resulted from two-control flight trials. With the W-1A, the slot-lip ailerons had given good lateral control with negligible yawing moments but, because of the continuously open slot, had also demonstrated an excessive amount of drag. For Model 310, I decided to try ordinary ailerons with some adverse yawing moments, but to link them together with the rudders in such a way as to overcome the problem. This linkage enabled us to get the optimum relation between rolling and yawing moment at a given flight condition. In our case we wanted that relation to occur at a low speed, because that regime involved the most difficult conditions in which to obtain satisfactory control. At high speed, the linked system would provide slightly larger yawing moments than what was ideal, but this disadvantage would be noticed in flight only if one made an extremely sharp turn; moreover, the system would help to make slight heading adjustments in cruising flight.

In power-off glides and power-on cruising, all of this worked out nicely. In a low-speed climb with full power, however, the airplane tended very definitely to turn to the left. Ordinarily, with three-control operation, this tendency required extra right rudder deflec-

Experimental ERCO 310 with twin fins and rudders.

tion; this was because the single vertical tail surface was substantially above the center of the slipstream, and a twisting slipstream tends to move the tail to the right and the airplane to the left. In order to fly the plane straight in a slow full-throttle climb with two-control operation, however, it was necessary to put in some right rudder. Since the ailerons and rudder were in this case connected, this entailed giving it some right aileron and balancing the plane with its right wing somewhat down instead of with its wings level.

To reduce this tendency to turn left, we first tried adding vertical fin area on each side of the horizontal stabilizer near the tip, both above and below, and outside of the propeller slipstream. (Our arrangement was something like the one used later in some of the Bellancas.) This resulted in some improvement, but not enough to be satisfactory. Next, we went to two separate fins and rudders at the tips of the stabilizer, which would make them entirely free of the slipstream, as was the case for the W-1. This resulted in a large improvement, but did not cure the problem entirely.

Except for the very small reaction to the engine torque, the only other thing that could be making the airplane turn left slightly with full power on was, as far as I could see, the shape of the body immediately behind the propeller. Since the engine cowling was just about all below the propeller axis, and since the airflow in the twisting airstream in that area was from right to left, I could imagine how local pressure might be moving the airplane's nose to the left. To overcome this possibility, we decided to cant or angle the engine somewhat to the right. With the engine sloped three degrees to the right, we found that the plane, with wings level, would trim as desired in a full throttle climb. The trim conditions with both power on and power off were then considered acceptable.

Our selection of a low-wing arrangement and our decision to tilt the engine downward five degrees gave the ERCO plane reasonably satisfactory longitudinal trim performance throughout the whole speed range, and enabled a single elevator limitation to serve for both the power-on and power-off conditions. Of course, at this time we had an engine delivering less than 40 HP. At any rate, we did get satisfactory lateral stability and control at all angles of attack that could be maintained in flight, and we also got the condition where the airplane could not be spun. The fin area of the new tail system, by the way, was an additional assurance: if the plane did start to spin, the effect of the fin area was to make sure that the plane immediately came out of it.

After we were pretty well satisfied with the flight characteristics, I invited NACA test pilot Mel Gough, with whom I had done so much work at Langley Field, to come up and fly our airplane critically, both with three and two controls. He did this, and his comments were favorable. On one occasion when the wind was gusting, Gough flew the plane alternately with three, two, and three controls, and was considerably surprised to find less bumpiness with the nonconventional two-control arrangement. With only two controls the pilot realized that he had less than complete control over the attitude of the plane in all of the three directions, so he did not try so hard to overcome the effects of gustiness. When he let the airplane's inherent stability do the work for him, there was thus a smoother ride.

After Gough's positive evaluation, we decided it was time to start the design of our prototype for production. The only major change we planned, aside from the more powerful engine that we hoped to get, was to lengthen the fuselage and put the tail back one foot, to give us a little more longitudinal damping.

During the period of redesigning Model 310 for production I figured that if I was going to do much flying with the new ERCO plane, I had better get a pilot's license; after all, it had been about fifteen years since I had first soloed. So I looked up what was required, took the written examination, and then, after practicing a bit at the College Park, Maryland, airport with a rented Cub, applied for a flight check. My inspector was Len Povey, who later was one of the founders of an airline between Florida and the Bahamas.

The flight check proceeded all right, with Povey no doubt allowing for my lack of formal training. Finally, he said, "Okay, take her back home." I sat back and relaxed, not sure that I had passed, but happy that the test was just about over. Over a wooded area, at about one thousand feet, however, Povey suddenly closed the throttle and said, "Engine failure, forced landing." To me, there was no acceptable place to put the plane down, and I hesitated longer than he thought I should, but I flew it toward a narrow slot in the trees cut through for a power line with steel towers. The opening was probably just big enough for a skilled pilot to slip through under the wires and land between the towers.

At an altitude of about 100 feet, though, Povey opened the throttle again—which made me, and no doubt him, too, very happy. Then we really did go back home. And I got my private pilot's license— which I still have, incidentally. I never went further and obtained a commercial license, because I did not do any flying for which I was paid directly. As an engineer, I've tested various experimental aircraft, but I've never been paid for doing so, like a pilot.

In the late spring of 1938, I began to look seriously for a suitable 65-HP engine for ERCO's production airplane. At that time the Continental A-40 was still the only reasonable engine that was commercially available. After writing some letters and making some telephone calls, I took a trip to the Continental plant in Detroit to see what its officials might be able to do to meet our special needs.

At Continental I saw a demonstration of the advantages of mass production. At that time Continental had a contract with the Ford Motor Company to furnish replacement pistons for the Model A engines, which had gone out of production. These pistons had to be made to rigid specifications, both as regard to the quality of the material and to the closeness of the dimensional tolerances. The machining of these pistons for Ford was being accomplished, automatically, in an area about 8 feet wide and 60 feet long filled with machines of one kind or another designed especially for this purpose. At the end of the line there was an automatic inspection system that discarded all of the pistons that were not within the proper tolerances. On the same floor of the building, in a machine shop, the pistons for Continental's A-40 engine were being made more or less by hand on turret lathes and other such equipment. Though the A-40 pistons weighed only about half what the automotive pistons did, the aircraft pistons cost more than twice as much.

Continental's engineer in charge of small engine design was Harold Morehouse who had previously designed a fine little two-cylinder engine that had been used on some versions of the Aeronca airplane. As it turned out, Morehouse had already designed, about a year before, a suitable small engine that could be used anywhere from 50 to 75 HP; it was a flat four-cylinder air-cooled design of the same general arrangement as the Continental A-40 that we already had in the ERCO plane, but a much more advanced and powerful type. I tried hard to get Continental's business officers to say that their company would produce Morehouse's new engine soon enough that we could use it for our airplane, but they hemmed and hawed. The best I could get from these officials was an agreement to produce the engine if the demand ever really came. I was very discouraged by this attitude, as was Morehouse. As he drove me to the train station, Morehouse related that Continental had been talking that way for the past year and he didn't think the company would ever produce his engine. He had run out of patience.

Morehouse then startled me by asking if we really needed an engine of 60 or 65 horsepower, why didn't we make it ourselves? I responded that I thought it was quite a big project for a little company of eighty-five people making machine tools for the construction of airplanes just to take on a new airplane, but to take on a new engine also seemed more than we should attempt. Morehouse said it was not really such a big project: the little Aeronca company had done both successfully, and other small airplane engines had been made without much equipment. For example, the well-known Warner engine had been made by having the castings and forgings all made outside and by having the machine work done by the Eclipse Company. Warner had only a few mechanics assembling the parts and running a test on each one for about an hour before delivering them—at a rate of possibly one a week. If ERCO was willing to build its own engine, Morehouse volunteered to leave Continental and design the engine for us.

The next day back at ERCO I went over the matter with Henry Berliner, and he agreed to go ahead and make our own engines. I hired Harold Morehouse immediately—incidentally, at the rate of $65 per week. Because he wanted to do the designing near foundries, forging shops, and the sources of engine accessories, Harold chose to stay in Detroit rather than move to the Washington area. He set himself up in a room adjacent to a dentist's office.

Morehouse agreed with my desire to have an inverted in-line engine because of the extra field of view it gave the pilot. Because the engine was to have no experimental features, we settled on all the specifications in a short time. Harold hired a single draftsman to work with him, and in three months they were ready to order the manufacturing of some of the parts. Within six months they had completed the design, and companies in the Detroit area had filled our order for enough parts to build the first six engines. At this point Morehouse moved to our ERCO plant, where he directed our assembly of the first engine.

After a few satisfactory preliminary trials, we made the 50-hour full-throttle run necessary for government approval. We then installed our new engine in Model 310 in place of the Continental A-40 and began service trials. From this time on, we called our Model 310 the Jeep, the name of a strange little creature in the "Popeye" comic strip. (This was a couple of years before the army jeep appeared.)

While we were making the service trials of the Jeep, three men from New York flew down for a visit in a Fairchild 24 airplane. These men were Leighton Collins, who had just gotten his *Air Facts* magazine started; Jack Nelson, a financial expert who dealt in securities; and Doug Robinson, a nephew of President Franklin Roosevelt. All three became good friends of mine, and each became quite interested in the ERCO airplane. Leighton Collins wrote an article about it for his magazine, and the other two became Ercoupe dealers for a time.

In the fall of 1938 ERCO moved from the District of Columbia to a 50-acre parcel of land in Riverdale, Maryland, just south of the College Park airport. The new plant was much more spacious and attractive, with limestone facing and a couple of acres of lawn in

Finished prototype Ercoupe with ERCO engine as first approved in January 1940. Bob Sanders is standing.

Ercoupe as produced in 1940/41 with flat Continental A-65 engine, in front of the new ERCO plant in Riverdale, Maryland, with its nice limestone front. I am at the controls. Notice that we gave the Ercoupe a translucent sliding sunscreen so as to permit comfortable flight even with the windows open.

front. At first the company did not have a paved airport but flew from a 1,000-foot stretch of grass. Eventually, though, it built two runways each about half a mile long, most of which was paved.

Construction of the production prototype began as soon as the first drawings were ready, and it was completed in late 1939. Tests for certification by the Civil Aeronautics Authority (CAA), which in the meantime had replaced the Bureau of Air Commerce,[2] went on into January 1940. Because of our airplane's spin-proof and two-control features, government testing was exceedingly thorough. To give a reasonable margin of error for the spin test, for example, we had to put the center of gravity at 27 percent of the mean aerodynamic chord, even though in the approved version a rearward limit of 24 percent was required.

In late January 1940 the CAA finally certified the plane and even required that we put a placard on the instrument panel saying that the airplane was "characteristically incapable of spinning." This was true for both the two-control and the three-control arrangements. This first production plane had a hand brake only so that it could be used with either the two-control or three-control arrangement, and the CAA also insisted that when the two-control arrangement was in use the rudder pedals be removed so that pilots wouldn't be confused into thinking that they might have separate rudder control, when actually it was connected to the ailerons. Personally, I liked the idea of having the rudder pedals left in, because then in cruising the pilot could take his hands off the wheel and hold course by the pedals alone.

Just before the airplane, which incorporated our ERCO engine, was certified, Continental suddenly made up its mind and came out with a version of Harold Morehouse's engine rated at 50, 65, or 75 HP depending on the RPM used. We could buy this engine from Continental for $425, or only half as much as it was costing us to build our own ERCO engine since we were making none of our own engine parts. Since this would make about a $600 difference in the airplane's list price, we could not ignore the saving. Immediately we moved our little darling from the nose of the prototype airplane and installed one of the new 65-HP Continental engines. Fortunately, by sweeping the rear edges of the engine cowling back as it went up, we could fit the wider nose cowling to our original fuselage form in a reasonably satisfactory way. At the same time we were able to provide a good exit slot for the cooling air to come out smoothly on each side. To me, the airplane lost some of its sleekness because of this change, but the people who liked the idea of greater power felt that the new airplane looked better than the original one.

We got our approved type certificate (ATC) with the Continental A-65 engine in the spring of 1940 and immediately went into production for a batch of ten airplanes. Many of ERCO's sheet metal workers came to us from the Luscombe Company in New Jersey, which not only made sheet-metal airplanes but also ran a school for teaching young men how to work in sheet metal. At that time the Depression was still hanging on, and these workers, depending upon experience, were paid between 35 and 55 cents an hour. The federal minimum wage, established in 1938, was 25 cents an hour.

With the first production batch of ten, one of the bright fellows in the company's advertising firm named the airplane the "Ercoupe" by simply adding "upe" to the trade name. From that time we have always pronounced the plane's name "Ur-coupe," though many people out in the field have called it "Air-coupe" or even "Aerocoupe."

The first four airplanes were purchased by the CAA, which showed significant consideration for our new development. The CAA was training two groups of people to fly; one group would use two of these Ercoupes, and the other group would use Piper Cubs. These trainees, none of whom had previous piloting experience, included college students, tradesmen, businessmen, and housewives, ranging in age from eighteen to forty-six years. One of the Ercoupe students soloed after only two hours and fifteen minutes of dual instruction, and the average time required before soloing with one of the Ercoupes was only four hours and eighteen minutes. Some of the students continued their training to the point where they obtained private pilot certificates with Ercoupes. To achieve this certification required on the average a total of only twenty-one hours and fifty-five minutes. After running these trials, the CAA reduced the time required before soloing with the Ercoupe from the usual eight to five hours. Moreover, for all airplanes having the Ercoupe's main unconventional features (i.e., the tricycle gear, two-control operation without rudder pedals, and antispin features), the CAA cut the time required for certification as a private pilot from the usual thirty-five to twenty-five hours.

We were, of course, highly pleased by the CAA's wonderful recog-

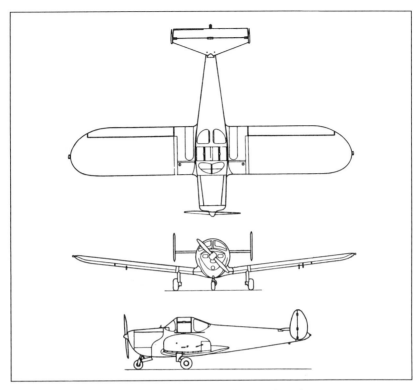

Outline drawing of the Ercoupe as it was first produced.

nition of the flight and handling characteristics of the Ercoupe, and this recognition no doubt helped not only to get more people flying but also to sell more Ercoupes.[3] Orders poured in rapidly, and by midsummer we started a batch of 100 airplanes; these airplanes sold for $2,590 with only one control wheel and no rudder pedals, and for $2,665 with two control wheels and rudder pedals. Mind you, this was in a day when a *new* Ford, Chevy, or Plymouth cost less than $900. All of these planes were suitable for either two- or three-control operation and were available either with or without rudder pedals. All of them had to be cranked by hand, having no batteries, starters, or generators. Those that had radios were equipped with wind-driven generators.

Looking back with today's perspective, however, I believe the CAA's recognition of the Ercoupe as an extraordinarily safe airplane did more harm than good. Although one can design and build an airplane that is very easy to fly safely, safe operation always depends in the end on the pilot's understanding the capabilities of both the airplane and himself. It's the old story of the most important "nut" in the airplane being the "nut" at the controls! The pilot must have the skill, however minimal, to operate the aircraft satisfactorily, as well as the judgment and willingness to operate within safe limits. In retrospect, I now think that the government's recognition of how easy it was to learn to fly the Ercoupe, made public by the reduced flying time required to obtain a license, together with the placard about the freedom from spinning, made many pilots approach the Ercoupe with less concern and less respect than they approached the general run of airplanes. This led to a number of needless accidents.

It is easier for me to see this problem with hindsight, but even in the beginning I was worried about the Ercoupe's reputation. In a paper on the development of the Ercoupe published by the SAE journal in December 1941, I warned: "This does not mean, however, that the airplane is foolproof. Safe operation of the Ercoupe requires that the pilot know the capabilities of the airplane and operate within them, allowing a reasonable margin for unforeseen contingencies." This shows that my basic idea was much the same over forty years ago, though I would now put even more emphasis on the pilot. It is safer to fly with a very competent pilot in a tricky and hard-to-fly airplane than it is to fly with an incompetent pilot in an airplane that is easy to fly safely.

In April 1940 Henry Berliner flew an Ercoupe up to Philadelphia to let one of the editors of the *Saturday Evening Post*, Richard Thruelson, try it out. Soon thereafter, on December 21, 1940, Thruelson published a story in the *Post* covering his experience in the airplane. His article began:

> The sky was a clear blue, the fall sun pleasantly warm and the wind moderate from the west, when the little silver plane lifted itself from the horizon. It circled lazily around Philadephia's municipal airport, and drifted quietly down to the end of the long east-west runway. No one heard the thunderclap as it touched the ground, but there was one. For private flying in that instant came of age. Here, in the first non-spinnable, single-control, fool-resistant airplane was a promise for wings for all of us, arriving quietly and almost unannounced.
>
> Get ready today, groundlings, for tomorrow we fly. A tanned man

in brown tweeds climbed casually out of the cockpit and came across the runway. This was Henry A. Berliner, the business half of a two-man team which has produced the Ercoupe. The other half is Fred E. Weick, who has designed and developed this small private-owner airplane which marks the longest stride yet taken toward giving the man in the street a pair of wings. Let's look at it, not as another airplane, but as a new means of personal transportation.

Later in the article Thruelson listed five requirements that he said people wanted in an airplane, and argued that the Ercoupe answered all five demands. Then he added, fortunately, that the Ercoupe was "not a foolproof airplane, for the air, as does the highway, lays traps for any fool. There will always be bad weather to tempt the unwary, amateur pilot, and high trees and wires to trick the low flying exhibitionist who likes to give them a show." The last sentence of his article read, "The eagle is changing into the sparrow and uncounted thousands of us will be flying soon."[4]

Well, the thousands haven't multiplied so rapidly that we can't count them, but there are hundreds of thousands of people who do fly in general aviation.

After going into production with the Ercoupe, the company had no more use for the original experimental machine, so it gave the Jeep to four of us—Frank Lane, Bill Green, Ted Waggy, and me—who had worked on it. We flew it for our pleasure for several years, mostly from Queens Chapel Field in the Washington area, where we could keep the plane out of the way of ERCO business. Later, during World War II, when a civilian plane could not be flown within 150 miles of the coastline, we kept the plane at Frederick, Maryland. After the war we kept the plane in a good berth in a nice closed hangar on a little airport, Schrom Field, just north of College Park. Adjacent to this hangar was another hangar that had no doors. One night a powerful nor'easter tore through the area and lifted the roof of the open hangar clear up and over the closed one. A large timber went through the roof of our hangar and right through the middle of the Jeep. That was the end of our original airplane.

Before its demise, I had had only two questionable flying experiences with it. After a winter during which it was not flown, we all worked to put the Jeep in shape and start flying it again in the spring. After we considered it in shape, Ted Waggy, who was a company test pilot, took it up for a twenty-minute check. Everything seemed fine, and when he came down he asked me if I didn't want to take it for a hop. The plane had to be cranked by hand, so Waggy just left the engine idling and got out. I got in and took off. When I was over the edge of Queens Chapel Field, the engine started slowing down. Noticing that the oil pressure was down, I throttled back and teased it around to the point where I could make a landing in the direction in which I had taken off. When I throttled back for a final approach, the engine froze and stopped. Fortunately, I had just enough altitude to clear the wires at the end of the field and made a satisfactory landing.

Upon examination we found the engine frozen solid and the oil tank completely empty. The airplane had a two-gallon oil tank made of galvanized iron, and it had been filled with fresh oil right before the run with no apparent leaking. When we filled the tank again, however, we found a tiny hole in the bottom, which had apparently rusted through and opened up during Ted Waggy's check run. We later rebuilt the engine but had to use quite a number of new parts. In this case our mistake was obviously in not shutting down after Waggy's check to make a new complete inspection, including a check of the oil level in the tank.

The second questionable experience occurred in 1941, after my visit to the company in Baltimore that made the fuselages for our later all-wood Ercoupes (see the next chapter). On a brisk autumn day of that year, I had flown over to Baltimore's Logan Field (the same field that the Berliner-Joyce people had used to build airplanes for the navy back in 1929) with the Jeep, taking Julian Zenitz, one of the ERCO engineers, along. After an hour or so of work on the wooden fuselage project, we got in the airplane and cranked it up for the return flight. In those days it was the practice to run the engine on the ground until the oil temperature got up to 90 degrees F. That day, because the weather was rather cool, it took about ten minutes at part throttle for the engine to run up all right. I then began the take-off.

When we were about 100 feet high, the engine stopped. Logan Field was right on the Patapsco River, which was really just an arm of the Chesapeake Bay, and a new field, the new Baltimore Municipal Airport, was under construction just ahead, also on the river. There, at the new airport, was a lovely long black paved runway, if I could only reach it. In between Logan Field and the new field, however, was a little bay of water that was several hundred feet wide. I knew that I was not going to be able to make it all the way across, but was going to have to land in the water.

At the near edge of the new municipal airport there was a high steel sea wall that, of course, I had to avoid flying into at all cost. I started to turn to land in the water alongside the wall, all the time frantically pumping the throttle back and forth, hoping that something would start the engine again. And, miraculously, something did. The engine ran full throttle for about three or four seconds and then quit again, but the additional thrust was just enough to get me onto the new field and let me land on what seemed an infinitely long black runway.

The engine was still ticking over at idle when we stopped on the runway. When I opened the throttle, however, the engine would just cough, sputter, and stop firing for a few seconds at a time. With the engine still idling, I got out and opened the cowling. The entire intake manifold was covered with hoarfrost one-eighth of an inch long. We not only had carburetor icing, but the intake manifold was below freezing also. We did not know nearly as much about carburetor icing then as we do now. I had thought that rather than put the complication of an extra carburetor heater on the airplane I would simply draw off the carburetor air from a warm place inside the engine compartment and let that do the heating job of the carburetor, even if it cost us a slight amount of power. Obviously that turned out to be an oversimplification. In this case, the long oil warm-up run was just the wrong thing to do—for it in fact had set up the carburetor icing. We shut the engine off, let the temperature equalize throughout and the ice melt, and then took off quickly. We flew around the field until we had an altitude of about 3,000 feet and then returned home with no more trouble. But after that we used a regular carburetor air heater.

Notwithstanding these incidents, the Jeep on the whole made very favorable impressions. I remember in particular a flight later that Dorothy and I made that same fall (it was her first long-distance flight in a light airplane) to Rensselaer Polytechnic Institute in Troy, New York, where I was to lecture to the aeronautical engineering students on the stability and control research that I had been involved with at the NACA and at ERCO.[5] There was a strong wind with a very strong crosswind component as we landed at the Troy airport. In fact, no other airplanes were flying; they were all hangared because of the strong winds. Upon our touch down, two young men came running out to help us get into the airport. (With most of the light tail-wheel-type airplanes then in use, this practice was necessary under high wind conditions.) The young men were astonished when I cheerfully waved them off and taxied in without the need of any aid. They were impressed by the obvious advantage of the tricycle gear under those adverse conditions.

In August 1941, at the Muroc Army Air Field in California, the Ercoupe established a special sort of record: it made the first jet-assisted take-off (JATO) airplane flight in history. The army had equipped the Ercoupe with six solid propellant rocket engines, each producing 27 pounds of thrust. Together with the airplane's regular power plant, these rockets gave the Ercoupe a very quick take-off and very steep climb. Later, with twelve small rocket engines and the propeller removed, the Ercoupe made an all-rocket take-off. These trials were made for the air force by Aero-Jet General, a company that had been started by professors Theodore von Karman and Clark Millikan of Cal Tech. Millikan, whom (as readers may remember) I got to know during my days with Hamilton in Southern California, was the person responsible for selecting the Ercoupe for these tests; he chose the Ercoupe because of its tricycle gear and easy handling characteristics. Before attaching the rockets to the Ercoupe in 1941, Clark had written to me for the plane's structural details.

I'll close this chapter on the Ercoupe with a story I call "The Unexpected Flight of Mrs. Freed." As I remember it, there was a club of five men in Moline, Illinois, that owned an Ercoupe, and one Sunday morning in November 1942 it was the turn of one of these men, a Mr. Brazil A. Freed, to fly the airplane. Mr. Freed took his wife, Dorothea, with him on a flight to Galesburg, Illinois, which had a nice grass field with a hangar and some airplanes on it. The couple visited around for a while, but when they were ready to go home there was nobody around to spin the propeller (in those days the Ercoupes did not have electric starters). Mr. Freed saw that his wife was seated and strapped in the right-hand seat—which in those days had no control wheel—and then he went around and started to crank the engine.

The engine started, but it was turning too fast to please him, so Mr. Freed stepped to one side and called to his wife to close the throttle, "that knob in the lower center of the instrument panel." Mrs. Freed was an automobile driver, but she knew nothing about airplanes other than that she had fun flying around in the Ercoupe a couple of times with her husband. In those days, automobiles had hand throttles as well as foot throttles, and one added power simply by pulling the throttle out. She therefore closed the airplane throttle by pushing it all the way in—which was the *wrong* thing to do.

The engine roared at full power, and the airplane shook a bit in the pulsations of the slipstream. Mrs. Freed, thinking that the airplane was creeping forward a little in the grass, made a wild grab for the brake to pull it on tighter. (The Ercoupe had a hand brake that you pulled out and then turned to lock.) She merely unturned it, releasing the brake, and the plane jumped forward. It started accelerating toward the hangar, and Mrs. Freed reached over to the pilot's control wheel on the left side and turned it just in time for the plane to miss the hangar. (This operation worked because with the Ercoupe the control wheel turned the nose wheel and steered the plane on the ground as well as in the air, which was not true with other airplanes.) She then found herself headed toward a couple of airplanes, but managed to steer around them, also. Finally, the airplane had nothing but open field ahead of it, and Mrs. Freed sat back and relaxed a bit. But the airplane was still accelerating at full throttle, and after a bit things felt different. Mrs. Freed couldn't feel or hear the ground rumble any more.

At this point Mrs. Freed was still expecting her husband to do something to help her, even though he had been knocked down as the airplane had jumped ahead and the wing had moved over him. The airplane kept going steadily higher and higher above the ground until Mrs. Freed realized that she was really on her own. In those days airplanes had no radios, so she could get no help or instruction from the ground, even if she had known how to use the radio. The airplane must have been trimmed for the climbing speed, and as she climbed higher and higher, she held a straight course by keeping her hand over on the control wheel on the left. Finally she decided that if she was going to have to fly this airplane, she better get over into what she called "the driver's seat." So she unfastened her seat belt and moved over. Then she started examining things to see what the instruments and controls looked like.

By this time Mrs. Freed was about 2,000 feet high and still going away from Galesburg. She started to turn back toward the town, but when she turned the control wheel, the plane "tipped," as she would later call it, as it started into its bank. This alarmed her, and she turned it right back straight. Eventually she found that she could tip it just a little bit and make a wide gentle turn, and for about twenty minutes she flew around the town of Galesburg at altitudes in the neighborhood of 2,000 feet.

She recognized some of the instruments, such as the altimeter and air-speed indicator, and began to experiment with the throttle in various positions. When she pulled it all the way back, things went very quiet, but she grew afraid that the airplane would stall. Her idea of a stall was that of the automobile driver; that is, she thought the engine might quit. So after that, she merely did all of her flying with the throttle more or less in an intermediate position.

When she had made her first turn back toward the town, the people on the ground thought that she might possibly get back to the field. Her husband immediately ordered a doctor and an ambulance in case of an emergency, and the airport operator put all the airplanes into the hangar and called out the fire department.

After flying around for about half an hour, Mrs. Freed decided she better try for a landing. Fortunately, she noticed a certain farmhouse over which, she remembered, Mr. Freed had flown on their approach to the Galesburg airport. She repeated the previous course as well as she could, always with partial throttle, and came in for her final approach to a landing. After passing over about a third of the field, she touched down, with only a slight bounce, and rolled along for some 300 feet. Everything seemed all right, so she closed the throttle again by pushing it all the way forward!

Again, the plane zoomed ahead and was soon going too fast to stop within the field. Mrs. Freed pulled back on the control wheel and got up into the air. She cleared the farmhouses at the end of the field and then made a number of circuits at low altitude, trying to think what to do. She finally decided to try landing again, and made another approach similar to the first one. This time she did not level off the flight path, but flew hard into the ground, bending the nose gear back and breaking the propeller, which was wooden. After a bounce or two, the airplane slid to a stop.

With the propeller broken the engine stopped, so it no longer mattered what she did with the throttle. When Mrs. Freed had moved over to the pilot seat, she had forgotten to fasten her safety belt and now she found herself on the floor, but with nothing but a bit lip and a couple of bruises.

The Freeds stayed in Galesburg until the next day when the CAA inspector arrived to record the incident. Everyone had some fun when the inspector recorded Mrs. Freed's previous piloting experience; he put down "Dual Time: 0" and "Solo Time: 0." She apologized for not making a better landing, but the inspector assured her he had seen good, experienced pilots make much worse landings than hers.

When I saw a newspaper article about the event, I wrote Mrs. Freed and asked her to tell me the whole story in detail, because I was particularly interested in the throttle operation. She answered very cordially, but unfortunately I have lost her letter. I do still have a little note that she sent me together with another newspaper article about the incident. In this note Mrs. Freed said, "As soon as the plane is repaired, I would surely like to learn to really fly it." I hope she did, but I never again heard from her. Obviously, she was a courageous and competent person. I worried about the throttle problem for some time thereafter, and on the later Ercoupes did manage to put a quadrant-type throttle located in the center of the instrument panel. Later on, however, and for the past many years, automobiles have not been provided with hand throttles. So the confusion no longer exists.

Peaks and Valleys of World War II

Already by January 1941, nearly a year before the United States entered World War II, we could get no more aluminum-alloy sheet or even aluminum-alloy extrusions for use in small commercial airplanes. The nation's entire production of these items was being used for military purposes, either to build up our own forces or to help those who would later be our allies. Except for the building of two more planes from the extra material we had on hand, our Ercoupe production was stopped completely. This made a total of 112 production Ercoupes.

From this time on, ERCO started doing a little military work. For example, we got a major subcontract from Boeing to design and develop spherical turrets for the nose, upper fuselage, and tail of its large XPB-1 flying boat patrol bomber, which at that time was still in an experimental phase of development. We also developed long elliptical egg-shaped turrets that would fit into the side of the XPB-1 and from which a gunner could fire straight down as well as sideways and straight up. The XPB-1 never got into production because the services found that they could fly the ocean more efficiently with landplanes. Our original turret development for the large flying boat was not wasted because the same basic designs were used on the PBY-2 and PB4Y-2, both of which were made by Convair in San Diego.

The United States was not yet in the war so we decided to start designing and building an experimental Ercoupe made of an all-wood structure. For its fuselage we used a plywood structure cemented together with a phenol formaldehyde cement, which we had molded under pressure and at high temperature in a form within a large tank. The center wing panel had a large solid laminated birch spar, which we had covered entirely with plywood. The outer panels had the same general form as the metal ones and were covered with fabric. We built one experimental structure just for static load tests and then made two flying airplanes of the wooden construction. These airplanes flew very well, and they were both smoother and quieter than the metal Ercoupes. However, with the extra paint that was required, the wooden airplanes weighed 50 pounds more, which meant baggage would have to be reduced by the same amount.

By the time we were ready to get the wooden Ercoupes approved for production, the Japanese had attacked Pearl Harbor. America was now in the war, and no light plane production for commercial use could be carried on.

Just before U.S. entry into the war another two-control spin-proof tricycle-geared airplane had come out. This was the Skyfarer, which had been designed by Otto Koppen, an aeronautical engineering professor at MIT. The Skyfarer was a high-wing airplane with a geared 75-HP Lycoming engine. (Both Lycoming and Franklin had come out with 50-to-75-horsepower engines a little while after Continental had done so.) Like the Gwinn Aircar, Koppen's airplane used ailerons alone for lateral control and possessed a very large and fixed vertical fin to overcome adverse yawing moments and to help prevent spinning. Though the large vertical tail operated satisfactorily in these respects, it proved to be a substantial disadvantage in high crosswind landings, since it made the airplane tend to weathervane and turn off the runway into the wind. The Skyfarer was made and sold under my patent, but only a few (possibly 15 to 20) were made before production was stopped by World War II. Production was not resumed after the war.

As soon as our country entered the war, ERCO's president, Henry

Berliner, immediately enlisted in the Army Air Corps. He was made a major and, because he had made numerous trips to Europe to sell machine tools and was thus quite familiar with industrial areas, was assigned to help Gen. Tooey Spaatz in his plans for bombing Germany. Berliner and Spaatz were old friends, having served together in the Army Air Service at Langley Field during World War I. From the time the war broke out in 1939 on, Henry and Tooey had been talking over the possibilities of air warfare with Germany in Henry's living room. At the time the United States was thrust into the conflict, Spaatz was a general in charge of the 8th Army Air Force. In 1942 the 8th Air Force was sent to England in order to bomb German factories. Berliner went along, and his help was so essential to General Spaatz's planning that Berliner soon became a full colonel, living with Spaatz's entourage in London.

Henry worked day and night for two to three years, until he finally wore himself down so completely that he was stricken simultaneously with pneumonia and meningitis. Later I had the opportunity to read the doctor's report on Henry's case. His heart beat so faintly that it did not force the blood through all of the members and his right arm became infected with gangrene. The doctor judged that the only way to save his life was to amputate his entire right arm. This was done. With the help of the newly available sulpha drugs, Henry finally pulled through and during the last year of the war he was sent home. But he never really recovered completely and died in 1970. He was awarded the Distinguished Service Cross for his valiant contributions.

Getting back to the beginning of the war, when Henry Berliner joined the service, Les Wells became ERCO's president, and I was made vice-president for engineering. This had to happen because, with the company filling government orders, Henry could not be in the service and be an officer of the company at the same time. Also, at the start of the war, Bob Sanders, who was a pilot in the naval reserve, went immediately into the navy full-time. Our Ercoupe sales manager, Harry Agerter, stayed on as the company's sales manager for the duration of the war. Our factory manager was Tom Queen, who had been with Henry Berliner for many years.

As stated in the beginning of this chapter, ERCO's main production during the war was in machine-gun turrets. We continued our production of propellers, but the output consisted mainly of all-compreg blades for the Stinson L-5. The factory also worked on the development of a hollow steel propeller blade fastened together by silver brazing. The silver brazing was done by induction, and the experimental brazing was carried out for us by a company in New York City. During the war I made many trips between Washington and New York for the purpose of overseeing this work, which, by the way, was carried out under a navy contract. ERCO's machine tool activities continued at an accelerated pace until about the end of 1943. Our production tooling also increased substantially with the addition of large hydropresses, stretch presses, and metal heat-treating equipment.

By the middle of the war the company had grown to about 2,500 people. The plant had been designed originally with possible expansion in mind, and during the war enough additions were made to make the plant's total area several times as great as that of the original manufacturing space. To help keep up the spirits and physical conditions of the employees, the company established an athletic program run by Andy Farkas and Turk Edwards, two of the Washington Redskins' football stars. We had baseball, softball, bowling, and tennis leagues, and even tried touch football for a while, until two of our officials broke their ankles.

When a Washington squadron of the Civil Air Patrol (CAP) was formed, several of us from ERCO joined, thinking that we might help the effort by the use of some of our airplanes. I became a first lieutenant. It turned out that the main use of light airplanes was in submarine spotting off the coast, and this duty required that a pilot leave his work and do nothing but sub spotting for at least six weeks at a time. This I could not do. I found myself teaching World War I–style foot drilling to a motley crew of CAP soldiers. This group included everybody from youngsters to women in their sixties. I guess I didn't have much of a military mind, but I couldn't see how it helped the war effort to have sixty-year-old ladies doing about-faces and to-the-rear marches in high heels. So I eventually withdrew from the CAP, partly because I was being considered to take charge of the entire Washington unit, and, for that, I didn't have the time to do a good job.

On February 18, 1943, Edmund T. Allen, who had been instrumental in the development of the large Boeing B-29 bomber, was killed when one of the B-29's engines overheated and the aircraft caught fire and crashed near Seattle. His death was a great loss to me. Allen had attended the University of Illinois both before and after World War I; curiously enough, he had originally studied agriculture. Allen was at Champaign-Urbana a little before my time, and I did not meet him until 1924 when I was working in the Bureau of Aeronautics and he was building himself a very small airplane with a Harley-Davidson motorcycle engine. I used to visit him and watch the construction during lunch hours. Allen, a World War I army pilot who weighed only about 120 pounds, had made the airplane as small as possible. In doing so, he had followed the square-cube law, where as you reduce the size, the volume and weight are reduced as the cube of the linear reduction, but where the area is reduced only as the square. Eddie finished the airplane and flew it a number of times from the naval air station at Anacostia across the Potomac from Washington.

When I first got to know Eddie, the bridge of his nose was missing, and he told me how that had happened. He said he had gotten used to flying Standard airplanes, and in making landings after higher altitude flights, he would usually spin down and make his landing out of the last turn. One day he changed to a Jenny and, not realizing that a Jenny lost more altitude in a turn than did the Standard, he had not been able to level out from his last spin before hitting the ground. Later Eddie had his nose built up again by plastic surgery.

In 1919 and 1920 Allen had done the NACA's first experimental flying at Langley Field. By 1934 he had become probably the country's best-known test pilot, particularly for trying out new airplanes. He did the first test flying for the Douglas DC-1, and this was what made his reputation. In connection with these early trials, he proved that the DC-1 could fly on only one engine by taking one propeller off and flying the plane all the way from Los Angeles to Albuquerque, New Mexico. For a number of years Eddie was chief of aerodynamics and chief test pilot for Boeing in Seattle, where he had a great deal to do with the development of their large planes. His death in the experimental B-29 was not only a loss to me, but a loss to all of aviation.

The B-29, incidentally, was the first Boeing airplane fitted with a tricycle gear. The first military airplane fitted with a tricycle gear was the Bell P-39 Airacobra, which was designed by Bob Woods, who had been in Eastman Jacobs's wind-tunnel section at the NACA Langley about the same time that I was working there on the low-drag engine cowling and later when the W-1 was tested. Lockheed's P-38 was also fitted with a tricycle gear at almost the same time as was the P-39.

In October 1944, with World War II still raging on, I presented a paper in Los Angeles at the annual meeting of the Society of Automotive Engineers (SAE); the subject of my paper was the four-year flight history of the Ercoupe. Among the assertions I made during this talk were that (1) "after four years of general use, no case of an Ercoupe spinning has come to our attention"; (2) "there is no indication that there has been a single accident caused by lateral instability or lack of lateral control"; and (3) "there appears to have been no accident associated with a turn in flight." Considering that most serious light plane accidents were associated with stalls in turns, this appeared to me to be a pretty good record.

There had been a number of unnecessary Ercoupe accidents, I advised the SAE audience, such as pilots landing in rough, unprepared fields, or taking off from such fields without knowing whether they could clear the fences or other obstacles. But there had been only one fatal accident. This had occurred when a pilot, who was taking a sixty-five-year-old judge for a demonstration ride, hit a lone tree during the climb following the take-off run. In a steep climb, the pilot of an Ercoupe (as was the case for pilots of nearly all airplanes) could not see the horizon straight ahead because of the nose of the plane. In the case of this fatal accident, one wing had caught on the tree and the plane had hit the ground nose down. The pilot survived, but the judge, who was heavy-set and suffering from diabetes, died three days later from his injuries.

On the trip to California to give this paper, by the way, I had my first ride in a Douglas DST, "Douglas Sleeper Transport." The DC-3 was originally designed for American Airlines in 1935 as the DST; the twenty-one-seat DC-3 was "discovered" later by taking out the sleeping compartments. It would have been a good idea to have built the DST with tricycle gear, because when the airplane, which employed the old tail-wheel-type gear, landed at night all the sleepers slid down toward the tail end. (The little-remembered Douglas DC-4 did employ the tricycle gear, but sleepers had gone out of use. Its production facilities at the El Segundo plant were taken over to expedite dive bomber production.)

On that trip to the West Coast I stayed over a day in Phoenix in order to see how our turret project was getting along at the nearby

Convair plant, which was in Litchfield Park, Arizona, just west of Phoenix. I found that the Convair people were putting the finishing touches on the turret installation for the PB4Y-2 airplane, which was built in San Diego. When I got off the airline at Phoenix and had a bit of time before the baggage was available, I drifted over a few hundred feet to the area where the small private planes were located, and I stumbled right off the bat into my friend Doug Robinson, the nephew of President Roosevelt, who had been one of the first buyers of an Ercoupe. Doug was living in Tucson at the time, but he had his plane at Phoenix to get some service work. He suggested that when I returned from my meeting in Los Angeles I stop off back in Arizona where he could introduce me to the unique joys of mountain flying, western style.

I had never done any flying in the Rockies, and the idea of it appealed to me. So after giving the paper in L.A. and stopping for a few days at the Convair factory in San Diego, I returned to Phoenix, where Doug Robinson met me with his Ercoupe. He insisted that I pilot the plane the 100 miles to Tucson. After taking off I noticed that there were no maps or charts in the cabin. I asked Doug what course I was supposed to follow. He pointed to a mountain peak straight ahead and said, "Aim for that," which I did. When we had been on our way for a while, I said, "And after we pass that mountain, what's the next landmark?" "Oh, when you get there," Doug said, "you just glide down and land in Tucson." That was an entirely new kind of flying to me, with visibility of 100 miles.

In Tucson I met Doug's friend, Rocky Nelson, who owned an Interstate airplane and later became an Ercoupe dealer in Phoenix. The three of us flew Doug's Ercoupe and Rocky's Interstate to the town of Nogales, which is due south of Tucson on the Mexican border. Actually, we flew to a pasture near Nogales and had our lunch in Mexico. The following day I got a real taste of western mountain flying during a trip to Safford, Arizona, which is located in a river valley of the Pinaleno mountain range. The highest peak in that range is Mt. Graham, which is nearly 11,000 feet.

I didn't get my first really serious lesson in mountain flying, though, until 1944. By the end of that year, ERCO's orders for war materials had fallen off substantially, and people were in general sensing the end of the war. In expectation of a postwar boom, manufacturers of light planes were beginning to reorganize their sales and distribution organizations. One of the arrangements

The end of our transcontinental flight in an Ercoupe, January 1945. This photo was taken by a newspaper reporter right after my wife, Dorothy, and I landed at Grand Central Airport in Glendale, California.

ERCO made during this time was for a Maj. C. C. Mosely to become the Ercoupe distributor for Southern California. Mosely, who was running flight-training schools for the military services and at some distance from Grand Central Airport in Glendale, California, wanted badly to get ahold of an Ercoupe, partly just to get familiar with it, but partly because he could use it to good advantage going from place to place in his operations. ERCO still had three planes at the plant and wanted to get one to Mosely. Management was moaning, however, about the chore of taking an airplane apart, crating it, and shipping it across country during wartime.

I had been working hard for a long time and had been told by my doctor to take a vacation. I then had the brilliant idea that I could save the company the chore of crating and shipping the airplane by flying it myself out to the West Coast, taking my wife, Dorothy, along, and thereby getting my needed vacation. Such a notion would not have occurred to me had I not done the mountain flying in Arizona just a little while before. My idea suited ERCO fine, and the arrangements were made. I went down to the Department of Commerce building in Washington and got thirty-five section charts to cover the whole route. (Each one covered only half the territory of the section charts presently available.)

After waiting three days for sleet and ice storms to clear the Washington area, we finally left for California on January 10, 1945. The plane had a low-frequency radio receiver but no transmitter. It also had the then-optional equipment of an extra gas tank in the right wing, so we had a total of 23 gallons (138 pounds) of gas. With our optional equipment, we had only 17 pounds legally left for baggage, which was rather tough on Dorothy, but she managed.

Our flight plan took us from Washington to Greensboro, North Carolina, where we stopped for fuel and lunch. It was snowing heavily by the time we finished, but the Greensboro airport officials let us get off before they closed the field (which, by the way, had been busy with military air traffic). Our next stop was Atlanta, where we landed at the city's main airport. At the time this airport was just a large grass field with two hangars on it, and there was not much action. It turned out that the people occupying the hangars were going to be Ercoupe dealers after the war, and they took very good care of us, getting us a room in a little hotel that was right on the airport. The little field grew into what is still the main Atlanta airport, but of course, it is now extremely large and one of the busiest airline hubs in the country.

The next morning we flew over Birmingham down to Tuscaloosa, Alabama. Because we had a tail wind, factory smoke from the steel mills obscured the atmosphere all the way. In Tuscaloosa we had lunch at a Parks training center. Oliver Parks of East St. Louis, Illinois, had flight-training schools for the services in Alabama, Georgia, and parts of the Midwest. Parks was also going to be an Ercoupe distributor after the war, and we stayed half the afternoon going over future possibilities. The last half of the afternoon was spent flying on without incident to Jackson, Mississippi, where we spent the night.

The next day we flew on to Port Arthur, Texas, where we were planning to stay the night with friends. Because we had strong headwinds, I decided to fly low, most of the time in the neighborhood of only 1,000 feet. Going over mile after mile of Louisiana swamp was very uncomfortable, and I eventually chose to go up a little higher where I didn't have to look down and see the bare poles of tree trunks and branches sticking up out of the dark brown water. This was the most uninviting country that I had ever flown over.

After spending a day with our friends (and giving each of their three children an airplane ride), we left for Waco, Texas. We enjoyed bright sunshine until we got near the town of Navasota, which is about halfway to Waco. Then we ran into a layer of low clouds and fog that ran clear to the ground and directly across our course. During the war the CAA weather people did not give hourly broadcasts, and I could not contact the little Navasota airfield that did have a CAA weather station on it, because I had no transmitter, just a receiver. There was a navy field about 35 miles on our right, but it looked as if it would be right within this same fog area, which stretched as far as the eye could see. Also, considering how busy military airfields were during this time, I feared that it could take days to get away from the navy field once landing there. It didn't seem very sensible to go back where we had come from because presumably the bad weather had already moved in all through that area.

I knew that the fog might go all the way to Waco, and I didn't want to fly over that stuff in a single-engine airplane that I was duty bound to deliver in one good piece. We remembered that on the way to Navasota we had flown over a paved road that had had no telephone lines or poles on either side of it. So I decided to follow the road back to Carpentersville, the nearest town, which was about 12 miles away, and land on the road as near to the town as possible so that we could get to a telephone. I managed to do this without much difficulty since there was no automobile traffic on the road at that time. I did have to hold the plane off, though, to clear two big black hogs before setting down.

We then turned off on a little road leading to a cemetery close to the town. Before long, a black man appeared, followed by another and another. Then two white men came by on horseback. I guess I got in bad with these two right away, because I asked them where I could go to a telephone, and they had to admit there was no telephone in town (that may have explained the lack of telephone lines along the road!). Finally, a young couple came along in a little

Chevy coupe headed for Navasota, and they stopped to see the airplane and were quite excited by it. I then gave a dollar bill (which still had a little purchasing power in 1944) to the oldest black man in exchange for him watching the airplane while we went on to Navasota to find out what we could about the weather.

The young couple took us to town in their Chevy coupe, Dorothy sitting on my lap, and we called the weather man at the local airport. He told us that the fog continued for about 40 miles and that it should clear up by mid-afternoon, which is what happened. We returned to the airplane, which was still being watched by the black man, took off, and finally got to Waco in the evening.

After spending the night with a friend I had known in Washington who was now in charge of the maintenance of all the army's airplanes at the Waco depot, we set out in cold clear air for Big Spring, Texas, which was some 90 miles almost due south of Lubbock. There were supposed to be two airfields in Big Spring, a little one for commercial use and a big one for the army and the airlines. After almost landing at the little one, which we thought abandoned, we flew on to the army field, which, by the way, was where I had landed on my airlines trip to the West Coast a little while before. I figured that if the airlines could land there, we could too. Moreover, there was a lunchroom right at the airport and we were hungry.

When we landed, though, a noncommissioned officer came right up to us and said that no civilian airplanes other than the airliners were permitted to land, and that I had better get off right away if I didn't want to stay a long time. So I just opened up the throttle, took off, and went back to the little field, anyway. We found that it was not quite as abandoned as we thought and did get a ride into town for lunch and back again.

That afternoon we flew on to El Paso. The Texas mountains and desert around Guadeloupe Pass looked very forbidding to Dorothy, but to me, who had had a couple of days flying in the western mountains before, it was just old stuff. According to our maps there were also two airfields at El Paso, one army and one commercial, only about three miles apart. The two fields had grown so much during the war, however, that they now ran into each other, and the army was using both. We watched unsuccessfully for a green light from the tower but finally found a chance to duck down between two army airplanes on an unused end of a runway under repair. We managed to get service at the commercial end of the field and stayed overnight in an El Paso hotel. The Weather Bureau was not too helpful about the approaching weather, but the next morning the skies were fair so we took off for Tucson.

En route we kept an eye on a little one-track railroad running fairly close to the Mexican border, but we were trying also to follow the regular radio beam between El Paso and Rodeo, a little place not quite halfway to Tucson. About 30 or 40 miles beyond the Rodeo radio and weather station, there was a range of mountains, the Chiricahua, that would provide the highest terrain over which we had to pass. Both to the right and to the left of our course were mountains over 8,000 feet high, and directly on our course was a pass at about 7,000 feet.

As we passed over Rodeo, we were flying at about 10,000 feet because I wanted to clear the path by a reasonable margin, and the legal flight levels going west in those days were in even thousands (6,000, 8,000, 10,000, 12,000 feet, etc.). I didn't like to fly that high because we had a headwind, but being conservative, I did. With my earphones on, I was following the old low-frequency aural beam—"A" on one side, "N" on the other—and after passing the Rodeo station, heard the message, "Dangerous pass, very dangerous pass ahead." Not knowing whether they had seen us, I wasn't sure the message was meant for us or someone else, but at any rate we did have that pass, that dangerous pass, just ahead of us. Then, still before getting to the pass, we got the message, "Icing, dangerous icing in the clouds at 10,000 feet."

Observing some fairly shallow clouds right ahead of us, I got us down below the 10,000-foot level, and being a good but stupid boy, went down all the way to the next legal level of 8,000 feet. This happened only five miles or less before we got to the pass. Until we actually got into the pass, I could have turned right and gone north about ten miles to a less difficult pass no more than 6,000 feet high, but in the rush of the moment I decided to stay the course.

Things then started to get tight. We sank below the 8,000-foot level, and even with full throttle and the best climbing speed, we were just barely able to hang on within 200 feet of the 8,000. This was because we were in the downdraft on the lee side of the mountain. The twisting, winding road that went through the pass looked pretty close, but we still had 700 or 800 feet clearance and were just maintaining our altitude. This was rather hairy. Suddenly, however, as we got to the windward side of the range, we were boosted up, even with a good speed and very little power, to 10,000 feet again.

So I had my first serious lessons in mountain flying. First, it would have been common sense to come down just enough to stay under the clouds with their icing, regulations or no regulations. Second, if I had wanted to come down, it would have been better to go ten miles farther north to the lower and less violent pass.

Thank God, the rest of the flight to Tucson was routine. After spending the night with Doug Robinson, we then set out for the West Coast. Because the authorities had no record of our arrangements to fly into the restricted coastal area, it took over a solid hour of telephoning to get permission to fly within 150 miles of the Pacific Ocean.

We had heard about the smog in the Los Angeles area, but we were not prepared for the severity of it. Mind you, this was in 1944, before the Los Angeles valley had become as highly industrialized as it has long since become. From Riverside on, even though flying only a couple of thousand feet above the ground, we could not see a thing except for a little bit of land straight down. We followed one of the main highways as well as we could, but fortunately I had anticipated difficulty and in the last stages of the flight had noted landmarks every five minutes or so. These included the Santa Anita Racetrack, the Rose Bowl, and the almost completely dry basin of the Los Angeles River. We followed the river channel all the way to our landing at Grand Central Airport in Glendale. Even though the field was not very long, the visibility was so poor that we could barely see from one end of it to another. Upon landing, we were met by Major Mosely who, because he had been informed of our flight plan, had known about when to expect us. He had photographers and reporters ready for us so that he and ERCO could get some publicity out of our transcontinental flight.

After staying in Los Angeles a few days with my brother Herb, we returned to Washington. We took the train because civilians could not get airline reservations at that time during the war. Though even the ordinary Pullman berths were all booked up, with Major Moseley's help we were able to get a drawing room on the Union Pacific from L.A. to Chicago. This was the most pleasant railway ride that we ever had. Because we were in a beautiful drawing room in a brand new car, facilities were excellent, and the mountains and the country in general were always lovely, interesting, and varied. I finally got the good rest my doctor had ordered.

During the flight to California, Dorothy had shown her first strong interest in aviation. It was a triumph for her when on the third day out she was able to spot airfields before I did. She was amazed at the wealth of detail given on the section charts and the accuracy with which features on the ground could be located on them. From that time on, she helped with the navigation and felt that she was part of the crew. I teased her a lot about it subsequently, though, passing off her contribution to other people by saying, "So she tells me where to go."

In late 1944 ERCO called a sales conference with its proposed postwar Ercoupe distributors.[1] At this meeting Henry Berliner outlined the company's Ercoupe policies and future plans. Les Wells talked

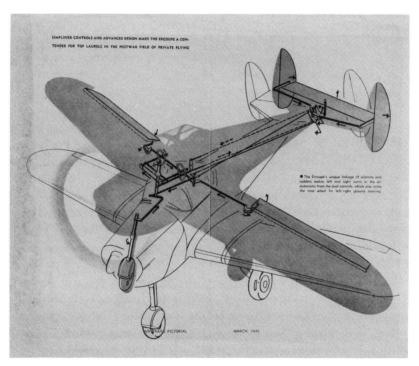

This diagram, which appeared in Air Trails *magazine in March 1945, showed the Ercoupe's unique controls system. The caption at the top reads, "Simplified controls and advanced design make the Ercoupe a contender for top laurels in the postwar field of private flying."*

The CAA's Non-Scheduled Flying Advisory Committee, 1945. Standing, left to right, Ed Williamson; yours truly; Doug Robinson; Bill Mara; Bevo Howard; Art Boreman; Bill Piper, Sr.; Harry Playford; John Groves; and Jim Johnson. Seated, left to right, Bill Burden, an aviation financial analyst from New York City; Henry A. Wallace, secretary of commerce; and Ted Wright, administrator of the CAA.

about production problems, and I talked about engineering problems and future possibilities in design. The real sales push was made by Oliver Parks, a very dynamic man, who was to be the airplane's distributor in eight midwestern states. Most everyone expected a big postwar boom, so spirits were high.

In the latter part of 1944 the government, too, started making plans for postwar aviation. The secretary of commerce was Henry A. Wallace and the new administrator of the CAA was Theodore P. Wright. Previous to his appointment with the CAA, Wright had held a high government position involving the procurement of strategic materials for wartime aircraft production. Wright immediately reorganized the CAA, dividing it into administrative, operational, and developmental departments. He hoped that streamlining the beginning of a program would eliminate a lot of red tape, and for a while I believe his plan worked.

To help in the area we now call general aviation, Wright established a Non-Scheduled Flying Advisory Committee. This body, which met three or four times a year, usually for two days, was made up of ten men who were selected with the idea of covering all of the main facets associated with general aviation, including manufacture, design, sales, flight training, airport operation, fixed base operation, and the private plane user. There was even one representative from the airlines, who was there to protect their interest, if necessary. The original members of this committee were chairman Art Boreman, who used a number of small airplanes for his own transportation; Ed Williamson; Doug Robinson; Bill Mara; Bevo Howard; Bill Piper, Sr.; Harry Playford; Jim Johnson; John Groves; and yours truly, Fred Weick. All ten of us were pilots.

In stating his general program, Secretary of Commerce Henry A. Wallace (best remembered for being FDR's secretary of agriculture from 1933 to 1945) had said in early 1945 that "the less government has to do in postwar aviation the better."[2] This was exactly in line with Ted Wright's view as the administrator of the CAA, and every member of his Non-Scheduled Flying Advisory Committee agreed with it. We worked hard to reduce the number of regulations and requirements for being a pilot, and we were successful in certain areas. For example, following one of our recommendations, the CAA ruled that a private pilot could have his physical examination done by his own family doctor. This ruling held for a number of years until, after the Wright administration, the old guard medical staff of the CAA got its way again and convinced the agency that the exam needed to be made by a CAA-approved designee.

As the Non-Scheduled Flying Advisory Committee's engineering representative, I met with a group of engineers from just about each of the light airplane manufacturing companies in regard to possible revisions of the regulations concerning the airplanes themselves. These representatives from industry said they also wanted the least possible government in the postwar period. When a simple general regulation was suggested, however, that would place more responsibility on the manufacturer, they each wanted the regulation spelled out in greater detail. This meant that the responsibility fell back on the government again, so nothing was really gained.

We did help a little, though, with respect to getting approval for handicapped pilots who could prove that they could operate an airplane satisfactorily. In spite of the one-eyed Wiley Post being one of the greatest aviators of all time, the old guard was inclined to eliminate one-eyed persons as pilots entirely. Our committee asked

From Boy's Life, *December 1945.*

the CAA to dig up whatever statistics there were regarding the flying experiences of pilots with only one eye. It turned out that their safety record was on the average slightly better than was the record of pilots with two eyes. The reason for this was, I believe, that handicapped pilots were conscious of their disability and thus did a more careful job than the general run of pilots.

Our committee also recommended that some arrangements needed to be worked out by which the manufacturers could follow government regulations to certify their own airplanes. Ultimately the Delegation Option Authorization, or D.O.A., system was worked out to accomplish this. When I say that our committee recommended this or that, however, I don't mean to imply that our committee was necessarily the first to think of these things, but only that our committee did make the recommendations, regardless of where the ideas originated.

In spite of the fact that Secretary of Commerce Henry Wallace, CAA administrator Ted Wright, the Non-Scheduled Flying Advisory Committee, and the light airplane industry all felt that the government's role in postwar aviation should be limited, the CAA and other government controls have, of course, grown enormously. It seems unthinkable that there should be one government employee involved in the federal administration of aviation for every two airplanes flying in the United States, but that's the way it has been for over twenty-five years now.

In the fall of 1946 I attended a demonstration of a new form of air navigation and air traffic control known as Teleran, a development of the Radio Corporation of America; the demonstration was held at the RCA laboratories in Princeton, New Jersey. In principle the Teleran system worked something like our present automobile traffic control system, wherein all available roads were definitely identified and all the traffic laws were well publicized. The duty of the ground controllers was to act like police traffic officers: to make sure that all operators stayed within the correct limits.

I liked the idea of Teleran at the time, and even today prefer the principle of its operation over that of our present system. Teleran gave the pilot all the information he needed to operate safely, but left the flying to the pilot himself, instead of giving direct control to people on the ground. A small number of ground controllers were available but only to provide help when it was needed.

Essentially the Teleran system employed a ground search radar that surveyed the air space of interest and displayed the information received on a cathode ray tube on the ground. This radar depended on line-of-sight contact, with projecting stations about as close together as the present OMNI or VOR stations.[3] The radar presentation was then viewed by a television camera that had a superimposed line map of the area, and the combination picture was broadcast by a television transmitter. A receiver in the airplane reproduced this picture so that the pilot saw his plane as a spot of light or blip moving across a map. Other planes appeared as different spots of light, each moving according to its actual course. Each spot representing an airplane had an elongated teardrop form that indicated the direction in which the airplane was traveling. The pilot could tell which blip represented his airplane because a radial line from the center of the map passed through it. The pilot, therefore, always had a simple chart in front of him something like the en route low-altitude charts used for present instrument flying, with all the main airways and airports marked on it. To fly safely, the pilot merely had to fly his blip along the established airway he desired, keeping on the right-hand side of it as you would on a highway. Flying at a suitable altitude, he saw the blips representing all of the other airplanes within a reasonable range of that same altitude. He did not have to bother seeing those that were flying at much higher or lower altitudes. When he wanted to land, he simply left his airway and flew his blip to any spot on the map he desired. As the terminal airport was approached, the pilot switched to a close-in radar map that covered a radius of some 30 miles; and for the final approach, he switched to one that did just about what our present instrument landing system does. There was even an option in the system for fully automatic landings. Weather information, such as ceiling and velocity and direction of the wind, was at all times available on the television receiver, thereby eliminating the need for much of the two-way communication that is now required, and which limits the amount of use that can be served.

All in all, Teleran seemed to me at the time to be about the most comprehensive of all the proposed air navigation and control systems, and one that should be developed very vigorously.

For light planes, however, RCA's Teleran had two distinct disadvantages: its cost and its weight. The necessary equipment included a television set receiver, transponder, and communications radio; at the time, in an electronic world full of vacuum tubes, the price of the electronics would have been great; with today's solid-state microelectronics it would be pretty reasonable. At that time over forty years ago the equipment weighed about 90 pounds, which for most light planes would be too heavy; by today's standards the weight of such equipment, with the development of transistors and so forth, would be dramatically less.

Unfortunately, instead of pushing RCA's more comprehensive

line of development, the CAA pushed its own VOR and OMNI systems. These systems, besides being less expensive at first, did become a highly satisfactory means of navigation for all airplanes, including the light ones. But I would still have liked to have seen the development of Teleran because it permitted pilots to do more of their own flying. Also, a great deal more traffic could have been handled satisfactorily with Teleran than with our present system, which is based directly on the capacity of ground control operations. I still think the system is worth developing; perhaps it's just waiting to be reinvented.

During the war years, and particularly toward the end of the war, I was fortunate to have a number of job opportunities offered to me. I felt duty bound to stay with Henry Berliner and ERCO, however, and so could not accept any of them. The first one, I remember, was an offer in 1942 from Henry John Heinz, grandson of the founder of the Heinz company in Pittsburgh, with its 57 varieties, mainly pickles. Mr. Heinz, who was then the company president, had a large woodworking shop for crating the Heinz products, which was busy changing from a wood to a cardboard operation. Mr. Heinz wanted to use the old woodworking shop to make cargo- and troop-carrying gliders for air service in the war. He thought that after the war his firm might even expand into the light airplane business. The prospect of being chief engineer for the "pickle plane company" struck me in a somewhat humorous vein. I recommended my friend Ralph Upson (who later worked at Boeing and taught aeronautical engineering at the University of Minnesota) for the job, and he took it.

Another job offer came to me from Cessna Aircraft Company in Wichita. Even with the war going on, Cessna and many of the other light plane companies had done a large amount of advertising, not only in the aviation magazines but in the general magazines as well. Most of these companies were doing war work more or less on a cost-plus basis, and advertising could be thrown in as a legitimate expense. One of the best known advertisements of the period was for Cessna's Family Car of the Air, which was to become available after the war.

One evening in early 1945 I answered the telephone and it was Dwane Wallace, Cessna's president and general manager, calling from Wichita. I was surprised to hear Wallace invite me to come with Cessna for the purpose of designing the Family Car of the Air.

This was an offer I hated to turn down, but at the time I felt that I had to. Don Flower, Cessna's sales manager, had been a fellow member of the Non-Scheduled Flying Advisory Committee and was thoroughly familiar with my work on the Ercoupe. In fact, Cessna had bought two Ercoupes in order to study the design carefully.

It looked as if Cessna, in developing the Family Car of the Air, might follow the line of the Ercoupe's development, but when the war ended Cessna actually came out instead with the 120 and 190 models, both of which were conservative tail-draggers. Later, following the general trend, Cessna came to use tricycle gears on its aircraft and has since become the most successful of all the light airplane companies.

I wonder how different both my life and the history of light airplane development might have been if I had accepted Dwane Wallace's offer in 1945.

Also in 1945, James S. McDonnell, with whom I had been friends since helping him with the NACA cowling and propeller for his Doodlebug entry in the Guggenheim Safe Airplane Contest of 1929, asked me to become his company's chief engineer. McDonnell understood and appreciated my commitment to ERCO, but left me a standing offer to go with his organization any time the situation changed.

Another good offer came to me from Paul W. Litchfield, chairman of the board of the Goodyear Tire and Rubber Company. Goodyear had made dirigibles in the 1920s and 1930s and still did a certain amount of aeronautical work involving aircraft tires, wheels, and brakes. Litchfield wanted to get into the light airplane business after the war and offered me a job as the engineer in charge of that activity. I didn't take it but figured anyway that it would not be a very secure position: Goodyear's light airplane project, I thought, because it would be only a small part of a very large organization, could be turned off just as quickly and easily as it could be turned on. What I didn't realize at the time was that with ERCO I was really in the same boat already, but on a somewhat smaller scale.

One other job offer worth mentioning was in connection with the Luscombe Airplane Corporation, maker of the Silvaire two-seat all-metal monoplane. Leopold H. P. Klotz had just taken control of the Luscombe company and was in the process of establishing a factory a little north of Dallas, Texas, to produce the Luscombe airplane. Klotz wanted to come out with a new four-place plane, and he invited me to become his chief engineer. The job was eventually taken by Eugene W. ("Gene") Norris, whom I had known when he had worked for the NAA. (Norris had also worked for Glenn L. Martin and for Beech; he later went with Boeing and was for many years in Boeing's Washington, D.C., office.)

In 1945 I also got offers to develop postwar personal plane programs at Lockheed and General Motors. It is too bad that all these opportunities came at a time when I felt that I shouldn't take advantage of any of them.

I'll close this chapter with a short story about the difference between the engineering of airplanes and the engineering of people.

Soon after the war's end, I got to know Dr. John G. ("Jack") Jenkins, the head of the psychology department at the University of Maryland. We met because of a study he was making on the nervous tensions that airplane pilots experienced under various flight conditions.

With the assistance of one of his doctoral students, Dr. Jenkins, who had served as a navy psychologist during the war,[4] fitted the control wheel of one of our Ercoupes with devices for measuring the tenseness with which the pilot gripped the wheel and then tried out people covering a wide range of piloting experience, temperament, and age. Jenkins and his assistant found that an experienced pilot could go repeatedly through the entire range of taxiing, taking off, making various ordinary air maneuvers, approaching, and landing without ever squeezing the control wheel very hard. A student or a highly emotional pilot, on the other hand, tended to grip the wheel very hard. It was obvious from their results that good instruction was that which kept the new pilot in a light, free and easy, but of course alert, state of mind. Any good instructor would have known this without scientific confirmation, but it was interesting to see the physical results actually demonstrated.

Besides acquainting me with the field of aviation psychology, Dr. Jenkins also introduced me to the field of scientific management. While teaching classes at the University of Maryland and doing research in aviation psychology, Jack had also built up a consulting practice in which he helped industrial officials to get ideas across to their employees more successfully. Part of this work involved teaching those officials a simple, direct English that could be understood by the employees they wanted to reach. He used a method developed by a Dr. Rudolf Flesch that divided English into different grade levels, eighth grade, tenth grade, and so on.

In 1946 I had been poring over the results of five years of flying with the 112 Ercoupes produced before the war and had written up a paper for Ercoupe pilots that listed six or eight suggestions for flying these planes soundly and safely. I thought I had done a simple and straightforward job of it, but I asked Jenkins to go over it and grade it on the basis of the Flesch method. Jack did this and concluded that the language of my paper rated the seventeenth grade; that is, to understand it easily a person needed not only four years of college but also one year of graduate work. I then asked Jenkins to put my paper into words suitable for an eighth grader, which he did. It came out not only much shorter than my version but was also a much more powerful and direct piece of writing. Whereas I had tried to give a little background and reasoning so that human judgment would itself lead the pilot to do the correct thing, Jenkins had come out directly and told him to do it or not to do it, in the manner of a military command. His statements were not always 100 percent correct or complete, but they were forceful and for most people, I suppose, more effective.

Personally, however, I rather like to do the correct thing because I understand the situation rather than because I have been told to do it. Engineering airplanes is one thing, but engineering human beings is another thing all together.

10.

A Boom Goes Bust

By the spring of 1945—less than six months before the war ended—there was a good deal of activity in the light plane industry regarding the possibilities of its postwar market. The Aeronca Company of Middletown, Ohio, for example, was busy developing a two-place airplane that was just about a dead-ringer for the Ercoupe. It was to have the same tricycle gear, limited control, nonspinning, two-control operation of the Ercoupe, as well as the same kind of tail with twin vertical surfaces. The main difference was just that entry to the cabin was to be by means of an automobile-type door instead of the window hatches that we had in the Ercoupe. Only one of these Aeronca airplanes was built, and it was licensed under my patents. I think I got a total of $15 in royalties.

As mentioned in the previous chapter, ERCO had increased its plant size and facilities substantially during the war years. The company had also built up a large tool design department. When the war orders started dwindling, these people had very little to do. We therefore put them to work on the design of a whole new production and tooling system for our postwar Ercoupes. This system was to incorporate an assembly line capable of producing ten airplanes in a regular eight-hour working day. Since ERCO made automatic punching and riveting machines, and since the Ercoupe had been designed for the use of the machines wherever feasible, the new production line was arranged so that we had riveting machines available right on the line without having to move the parts to a special riveting area.

As it first came out, the postwar Ercoupe was very similar to the prewar model except that it had a Continental engine with 75 HP instead of the original one with 65. The extra power enabled us to include a starter, generator, and battery so that the plane would no longer have to be cranked. These parts added a total of 65 pounds. Fortunately, however, a new classification of airplane had come along—the so-called Normal Category airplane—which, according to the civil air regulations, could have a lower load factor if it were to be flown without aerobatics of any substantial kind. This new classification allowed us to increase the Ercoupe's gross weight from 1,260 to 1,400 pounds. The postwar Ercoupes also came out with two wing fuel tanks, plus the original header tank, as standard equipment. Together this gave a total of 23 gallons (138 pounds) of fuel. With the additional power and fuel, the Ercoupe had a fair range and cruising speed of at least 100 or 105 MPH. With a reasonable allowance for baggage, it was now a much better cross-country airplane.

By the time the war ended in August 1945, ERCO was ready for both Ercoupe production and Ercoupe distribution. The first airplanes started coming off the line in October and by January 1946 were actually coming off at the rate of ten per day. Almost immediately after the war, however, we started working on a number of major additions to the Ercoupe. The first of these postwar improvements was the development of a tricycle ski arrangement for operations in harsh northern climates. The second involved adding Edo floats and making the Ercoupe into a seaplane. The third was the addition of a retractable landing gear.

Late in 1945 some of our customers in northern states asked us about the possibility of fitting the Ercoupe with skis for wintertime operation. This interested me greatly, because no one had tried a tricycle ski arrangement. Sometime before Thanksgiving, I got in touch with Federal Ski of Minneapolis, Minnesota, and asked whether the company could lay out a suitable ski arrangement.

The ski manufacturer agreed to try, and before long it provided two standard skis for our airplane's rear wheels and a small ski for the front one. The company selected a small ski for the front wheel not only because the static load on the nose gear was lower than that on the rear wheels but also because its ski experts thought it would be wise to keep the ski behind the plane of the propeller.

By early December we got word that the skis were ready to be test fitted to an Ercoupe that was in the hands of our Twin Cities dealer, and I started out to ferry an Ercoupe that needed to be delivered to the same dealer, taking my nineteen-year-old son, Donald, along. A year earlier, Donald had enlisted as a cadet in the navy's V-5 pilot-training program; the navy had put him in school for a couple of semesters at Emory & Henry College in Virginia and had then sent him to the University of North Carolina for preflight education, and when the war ended he was discharged and transferred to the University of Maryland so he could be close to home. He came with me to Minnesota because he had spent his freshman year at Carleton College—which is about 35 or 40 miles south of Minneapolis—and wanted to visit some of his old friends, particularly one young lady. We flew the new Ercoupe to Pittsburgh where we had lunch with a dealer before continuing farther west. Originally we had hoped to get to Chicago that evening so that we could stay with my folks, but because of heavy headwinds we couldn't make it. Flying the railroad tracks, we stopped at Van Wert, Ohio, and in getting there barely eased ahead of a fast freight. The next morning we were detained by weather, but managed to get out just about noon in a severe snowstorm, with the knowledge that Fort Wayne, Indiana, which was not too far away, was clear.

This was my first experience with flying in a snowstorm so severe that you could see down fairly well if you didn't fly too high, but you couldn't see ahead at all. I was glad that the stormy weather had been coming from the west and that we would soon be in the clear. In the meantime we kept our nose on the railroad track.

That night in Chicago with my folks, the temperature was three degrees below zero. Fortunately, the new Ercoupe was a tight little airplane with an adequate cabin heating system. My mother, knowing that we were going up to Minneapolis where it would be still colder, disappeared upstairs. She came back down with my suit of long, woolen underwear that I had used in Illinois and Iowa during the winter of 1922 when surveying emergency landing fields for night air-mail use. This underwear came in very handy for the next couple of weeks.

By the next morning the winds had pretty well dissipated, and we flew all the way from Chicago to St. Paul in one hop without stopping for fuel. After delivering the airplane to the Twin Cities dealer, my son Donald started off for Carleton College and I went right over to the Federal Ski factory in Minneapolis.

After I inspected them, the experimental set of skis were fitted onto the Minneapolis dealer's Ercoupe by Federal Ski's mechanics. The dealer's pilot, George Mallinson, who was accustomed to airplane ski operation, tried them out, and so did I. Unfortunately, field conditions were not very good for ski trials. The temperature was down near zero and there was no more than one inch of snow on the ground. On the runway there was no snow whatsoever, and on the grass areas that we used, grass blades were sticking out through the snow. Even with good conditions, the drag of skis is roughly equivalent to the drag of smooth rubber tires on an airplane on a grass field with the brake half on. Put technically, the coefficient of friction is close to 0.25. It was no doubt higher with only the very light snow covering. With the skis dragging back at ground level and the high propeller thrust pulling forward, the nosing-over moment was so great that with the limited elevator control of the Ercoupe we could not get the tail down far enough to get the wing up to an angle suitable for take-off.

After a few days of adjusting the spring tensions that held the skis at a certain angle and blocking the nose gear down so that the airplane's nose was two or three inches higher, we were finally able to get satisfactory take-offs and landings both with one and two persons in the airplane.

I got ahold of some good Canadian data on the drag of skis from the Federal Ski engineers and did some computing. I was surprised to find that at the start of a take-off run, even though the static load on the nose wheel was much less than that on the main wheels, the nose ski had a greater load than either of the rear skis. This was because, with the drag of the skis down below and the propeller thrust up above, the load on the skis was shifting from rear to front. Knowing this, I insisted that we try a regular full-size ski on the nose wheel as well as on the rear ones, even though the front of the forward ski would have to extend ahead of the propeller. When

Ercoupe fitted with skis, December 1945.

we did this, the operation was better than with any of the previous arrangements. The standard-size ski actually gave the propeller some protection when running through high drifts, but it did require having an absolutely sure support linkage so that the ski would never get up into the path of the propeller blades.

We flew the airplane up to St. Cloud, Minnesota, where the snow was a foot deep and had about an inch of heavy crust on top of it. This gave us a good test, and we found that we could operate quite satisfactorily under these conditions. After making one or two runs through the snow, packing down a track, take-offs were easy. And with the castering of the nose ski, steering on the ground was equally good. The first successful installation of a tricycle ski arrangement had been accomplished.

During the next few years, skis were used for winter operations on a fair number of Ercoupes in the northern United States and in Canada. As time went on, though, more and more northern airports kept their runways open all winter, and the use of skis on Ercoupes declined to the point where it is now negligible.

The ski situation got me thinking about tricycle gears with wheels operating on soft field conditions. Back at ERCO I made some experiments. We dug out a hole a yard wide, four yards long, and a foot deep, and in it we put various types of soft terrain material, such as dry loose sand, soft mud, thick mud, and so forth. We

Ercoupe equipped with Edo floats, 1946. In the large photograph, the seaplane is flying over the East River near Manhattan.

then used a pickup truck to drag an Ercoupe so that the airplane's nose wheel ran through the soft area. We ran a cable forward from the propeller hub to the truck and supported the front end of the cable on a scale so that we could measure the force that represented propeller thrust.

Doing this with two different sized nose wheels, we got a fair amount of data—some of which were rather hard to use. For example, especially with the smaller wheel, if the mud was soft enough the nose wheel would ultimately sink down to where the earth was hard. From this I concluded that, for use of soft fields, the nose wheel of a tricycle gear needed to be as large as the rear wheels, because at certain times it would get at least as large a load. Because the nose wheel would get the most severe treatment, its size was what should determine the size of the wheels all around. From another viewpoint, if one was always operating on a smooth hard surface, such as a paved runway or firm and even turf, the rear wheels needed to be no larger than the nose wheel. This was no doubt an oversimplification, especially if applied to large transport- or bombing-type airplanes, which have groups of wheels instead of just one in each location. But it was a general principle that I have upheld for many years.

Our second major postwar project to improve the Ercoupe involved making it into a seaplane by adding Edo floats (named after Earl Dodge Osborn, the founder of the company that has since become synonymous with airplane pontoons). This made a relatively neat package and at first looked quite promising. With the Ercoupe's sliding windows and the walkways on either side, one could get off on either side and down onto the floats either fore or aft of the wing. And with the seven degrees of dihedral, even the low wing position was not a terrible disadvantage in docking, because the tip of the wing was only a foot or so lower than the tip of an ordinary high-wing airplane. Thus the wing could be brought in over a low dock, though not over a high one. With its low wing and relatively "widetrack" floats, the plane felt solid on the water and could be handled very easily in strong winds.

As produced after the war, however, with only the two-control system, the Ercoupe had a severe disadvantage on floats. Floats did not have the stable taxiing characteristics of tricycle landing gear and did not work well with two-control operation in strong crosswinds, either landing or taking off. Under ordinary conditions two-control operation worked very well, but for strong crosswind conditions, three-control operation was really necessary with the floats. But ERCO was no longer building the airplane with the option for three-control operation. Before the war the company had produced the airplane with both two and three controls; after the war, however, management decided to save about $25 per plane and produce all the new Ercoupes as two-control airplanes. Of the 900 orders for Ercoupes that had come in before the war (only 112 of which were produced), only 6 had asked for the full three controls. Four of these were the first 4 that went to the CAA. And after trying them out, the CAA had even removed the pedals and flown the planes with two-controls.[1]

The elimination of the rudder pedals enabled the installation of a foot pedal for the brake (in addition to the hand brake), which was a nice new feature. Based on later experience, however, I believe that eliminating the rudder pedals as an option was a big mistake. After the war there were thousands of pilots who had flown planes with rudder pedals but who did not know how to handle the two-control Ercoupe satisfactorily. A two-control plane had to be handled in a special way. Ex-military pilots assumed incorrectly that they did not need any special instruction to fly this "simple, easy-to-fly" airplane. So they often embarrassed themselves, and us at ERCO, too.

The third item under development for the postwar Ercoupe was a retractable landing gear, which would have increased the plane's top speed about 15 MPH to 140 MPH. Before Ercoupe production faded out in 1948, we completed the main design, installed it on one experimental Ercoupe, and made preliminary flight tests. The main wheels folded inward up into the center wing section. The nose wheel folded back to the point where it was almost completely enclosed. The gear doors and closing elements were never completed on this project, so the full maximum speed potential was never attained. The gear was operated by means of a single hand lever, and the weight of the gear was balanced by springs. The gear worked reasonably well—though its mass and inertia made it stop with a hard jerk if it was brought up too suddenly. We planned to correct this with some sort of damper, but then all Ercoupe production stopped. All in all, the addition of retractable gear had looked very promising. One member of the ERCO staff, Bill Green, had even suggested that we add a "Sup" to the front and call our new retractable model the "Supercoupe."

Another experimental development for the Ercoupe carried on during 1946 and 1947 was the development of a special muffler. This shows that a quarter of a century before policing the noise of the airplane became fashionable, aeronautical engineers were quite conscious of its desirability. We had a young physicist on the staff who went into the problem quite thoroughly. After a fair amount of both theoretical and experimental work, he finally developed a muffler that attenuated both the high and low frequency sounds from the engine exhaust. Because the muffler was quite large, it was very difficult to fit it into the Ercoupe cowling. We did finally manage it, though, and made flight tests that measured the sound level at the ground as the airplane passed over. These tests showed that with the new muffler, people on the ground should not be bothered very much by the noise of the airplane going over. We then obtained a four-bladed Sensenich propeller, whose diameter was somewhat smaller than the Ercoupe's conventional one, and tests with it showed a slight further reduction in the noise level. However, the airplane's performance was not quite as good with the different propeller.

In general, we were pleased with our noise reduction efforts from the standpoint of the people on the ground. However, we still had the tough job of better insulating the cabin from the noise of the engine and propeller. This of course has since been done fairly satisfactorily for large jet planes and small private planes. It would have been harder with the Ercoupe than for most planes, though, because of the large amount of Plexiglas in the canopy. Our efforts would surely have improved later Ercoupes, though, had their production been continued.

During the war years, when I was taking the train back and forth between Washington and New York quite frequently, I had thought quite a bit about how airplanes could be improved further, particularly for private use. It seemed to me that closer to the best possible performance could be obtained, and with fewer stall-type accidents, if the airplane could be made to help the pilot fly always at a suitable angle of attack and always with a good margin from the stall. One approach might be, I thought, to design the airplane so that it would tend to hold firmly any angle of attack for which it was set or trimmed. With such an arrangement, the pilot could set the control directly for the angle of attack desired; the airplane would then continue to fly at that angle of attack and at the corresponding indicated air speed. The trim indicator could be marked off directly in terms of indicated air speed, and the positions for optimum flight conditions could be designated. Then if the pilot wanted to fly at the speed that would give him the best rate of climb, he would merely set the trim indicator for the point so marked, and the plane would fly at that speed. In like manner, the air speed giving the best performance could be set for the maximum angle of climb or for the flattest glide. The trim control would then become the basic speed control. Moving the elevator control from this firmly trimmed position could be made to require the overcoming of a certain acceptable break-out force. The pilot would presumably have to do this only for getting the tail down to cause rotation at a high angle of attack in the take-off, for flaring off the flight path in a landing, for making emergency movements in the air, or possibly for overcoming the effects of violent gusts.

It happened that this automatic control system was easy to try out experimentally for one speed at a time on the Ercoupe, because for it there was a given elevator position, and corresponding fore-

and-aft control wheel positions, for each of its indicated air speeds. (The indicated air speeds varied with the center of gravity locations, but the cg locations changed very little with various loadings.) Also with the Ercoupe, the trimmed air speeds remained very nearly the same regardless of whether the power was on or off. These factors made the Ercoupe ideal for the automatic arrangement. All I had to do was select an indicated air speed, find the position of the control wheel for that air speed, and then block it so that it could not go forward from that position, but could come back or could turn for lateral control. Then, by setting the longitudinal trim tab full forward, the control wheel would always tend to rest up against the stop. And it would take a certain force to pull it back from that position.

I made a set of easily removable stops that covered the speed range reasonably well, and set out to make some flight trials. I found that for any one of the speeds selected, the indicated air speed would remain the same within very small limits—from full power in a climb, through cruising at horizontal flight, down to a power-off glide. And the same indicated speeds held good at altitudes up to 10,000 feet. Of course, maintaining a constant air speed under all of these conditions depended on the natural longitudinal stability of the airplane, and if a disturbance occured, phugoid oscillations would be set up and would have to damp out. Fixing the elevator in this way, however, gave a greater damping than with free elevator controls and thus helped some in this regard.

Before making a cross-country flight in my Ercoupe in late 1947 I taped on a control wheel stop that would give an indicated air speed of 102 MPH; I kept it on the entire trip. The system seemed to work reasonably well, even in moderately gusty air or VFR flight. All in all, the general idea seemed promising.

As mentioned earlier, by early 1946 the Ercoupes were coming off the assembly line at a rate of 10 per day, and this was the output of just one daylight shift. The demand for the airplanes was great, and in the early spring the company established a second shift that worked from 4:30 in the afternoon until one o'clock at night. This doubled our production to 20 airplanes per day. Even with that, our orders were backing up; so in the late spring a third shift was created. By working around the clock, we were now building 30 new airplanes each day.

After the end of World War II our manufacture of Ercoupes really got going.

This made for a difficult type of operation. Except for weekends, there was no shutdown time whatsoever for repairing tools or taking care of any production difficulty. Even so, for about a month, our production was squeezed up to 35 a day. Because there was only one model of Ercoupe with very few options, the postproduction check-testing procedure was relatively simple. Still, with it taking three days for an airplane to be check-tested, readjusted, and flight tested again when necessary, the increased production meant that there were usually 100 Ercoupes or more on the field being tested or waiting to be flown away by dealers or owners.

In the summer of 1946 Henry Berliner announced that because of rising demand the company would have to step up production to 50 planes a day. To get the main items such as engines and aluminum sheets, we began ordering this material many months in advance. Then suddenly, during a single week in September, the airplanes on the field built up from 100 to 300. The dealer's pipelines had filled up and they just could not handle any more volume. Emphasizing the abruptness of the reversal in the demand versus supply situation was the fact that Oliver Parks, our aggressive St. Louis distributor, had called up the same week asking for more airplanes. What exactly had happened to cause such a flux in the light plane business?

At the close of World War II many service people and business-men possessed a fair amount of extra spending money because during the war the production of so many desirable civilian items, such as automobiles and housing, had been curtailed. With so many people having been involved in one or another aspect of aviation during the war, there was a lucrative postwar market for private airplanes. By the summer of 1946, however, the boom had already peaked; the pent-up demand for small airplanes like the Ercoupe had been mostly satisfied, and demand for further production would be at a greatly reduced rate. Most of the other light airplane companies were not hit as hard so soon as was ERCO, because they also built trainers that could be used in the civilian-training program sponsored by the government.

As a result of this recession, ERCO had to lay off first the grave-yard shift and then the earlier night shift. Then the regular day shift had to be pared down substantially. ERCO was in a very bad situation because the large orders for future delivery of engines and aluminum had to be canceled, at a substantial cost. For example, the Decker Company of Chicago, an automobile parts supply firm, had been given an order for control wheels for 5,000 airplanes—which made, since each plane had two, a total of 10,000 control wheels. Unfortunately, Decker had purchased all the materials and had already cut the parts to size, awaiting assembly. Thus the cost to ERCO on that order was a large part of the total cost of the finished wheels.

For ERCO the boom had busted, and Henry Berliner had a very tough time saving the company from ruin.

The general stoppage of light airplane work at ERCO that began in late 1946 was one of the greatest disappointments in my entire career. For one thing, it brought an end to a project to develop an experimental four-place Ercoupe that, although it had just gotten under way, was about 75 percent finished. This model was basically a more powerful (150- to 200-HP) Ercoupe with a beefed-up retractable gear. It hurt me a lot to see this airplane dropped, but it hurt still more to see another one of my pet projects dropped. This project was a twin-engine light airplane that I had been working on for about five years. We called this plane the Ercoach.

In the spring of 1941 I had made some computations regarding a twin-engine airplane that would have at least some of the characteristics of the Ercoupe. For the next few months I worked, with help from a couple of my young engineers at ERCO, to develop the new plane concept. December 7 stopped the project dead in its tracks. I thought that the entire venture would have to be put off until after the end of the war, but an interesting situation developed.

Some excellent foreign-born engineers had applied for work at ERCO in 1941 and 1942, but because of wartime security considerations, we could not take them. One of these men was Dr. Felix Nagel, who had been born and educated in Germany but had been working in this country for ten or twelve years at the Martin and the Douglas company plants. Though Dr. Nagel was an American citizen, his mother still lived in Germany, and the FBI would not permit ERCO to hire a person in that situation.

We then formed another little company called the Aircraft Development Corporation which, though wholly owned by ERCO, operated in an entirely separate area about two miles away from the main plant. As the president of this new company, I hired Nagel, along with an Italian-born engineer who, incidentally, had married the daughter of a United States senator, and a Canadian mechanic who for some reason also couldn't be used on war work. An auto dealer in College Park had gone out of business because of the war, and I rented his office and shop area for our company's activities.

The main activity of our Aircraft Development Corporation was to design the Ercoach. During 1942/43 I put in full time at ERCO on our war efforts, spending also many evenings and weekends there, but went over daily to the little unit in College Park an hour before work started at ERCO to keep in contact with what was going on with the twin-engine airplane.

The design had some unique features and, I believe in retrospect, that if the Ercoach had been built it would not only have been the first light twin to be produced after the war, but could have had performance and flight characteristics that would have been hard to beat for a few years. We designed it to have two engines of at least 150 or 160 HP each, even though at the time the only two models available in a light form had only 125 HP. One of these was a four-cylinder Lycoming and the other was a six-cylinder Continental. We were counting on the power of these engines to be boosted within a short time, however, to between 145 and 160 HP, which they were.

In order for the plane to fly satisfactorily with at least four people on only one of these 125-HP engines, I gave the Ercoach a large 45-foot span and tried to make it as sleek and aerodynamically clean as possible. To do so, I stayed as close as possible to the form of the best contemporary sailplanes and gave the design fully retractable landing gear. It had a tapered wing that was thick enough in the center to house either of the engines completely, since they could be furnished with fuel-injection systems and would not have carburetors hanging down below. Because the oil was housed not below in a sump, but in a separate tank, the vertical dimension of the engine could be made to fit completely within the contour of the wing itself. For the wing section, we used one of the NACA's new low-drag or so-called laminar-flow airfoils, which had the thickest part of the wing near the center of the chord. The center panel of the wing incorporating the engines was straight, but from the engines out, the wing was tapered in such a way that the planform gave very nearly an elliptical loading for both the wing and airplane as a whole. With the 45-foot span, it should therefore have had a very low induced drag and been able to do reasonably well even with just one of the 125-HP engines operating.

The general configuration of the Ercoach was a little more like the W-1 than the Ercoupe, in that it had a high wing and used pusher propellers. The tail surfaces were very similar to both of my previous designs, with a horizontal surface between two vertical ones. The horizontal surface was supported on the fuselage, though, as with the Ercoupe. In this case the vertical tails were directly behind the propellers so that by setting the fin at a slight angle we could get a certain amount of correction against the yawing tendency of a single engine, when a single engine was in use. With this arrangement, it would have been relatively easy to get approximately the same trim for a given control wheel position through the entire speed range, regardless of whether the power was on or off. This would have made it easier to limit the elevator movement so that it served both the power-on and power-off conditions.

By the summer of 1945, the preliminary design work on the Ercoach had been completed, and a wooden mockup of the fuselage, landing gear, and other parts had been built. After the war ended in August, the Aircraft Development Corporation was abolished and its activity moved into ERCO itself.

The airplane had two features that needed extra development. One was the cooling of the pusher air-cooled engine entirely submerged within the wing; the other was the development of a suitable extension shaft arrangement for the propellers. This shaft was necessary because the propellers were located about two and a half feet in back of the engines to give reasonable clearance from the wing.

We made engine-cooling tests, both at ERCO and on a dynamometer at the Lycoming plant in Pennsylvania. At ERCO I used inlets in the leading edge of the wing, like those that the NACA had worked out, in front of each row of cylinders and tried exhaust ejectors for pumping cooling air through the engine's baffles. We finally obtained satisfactory cooling at full throttle on the ground, but the baffles that we had installed did not last very long and cracked. Because of the pulsations that were in the cooling air as it was pulled through by the exhaust ejector cooling pumps, we could not use any flat surfaces in the baffling that did not vibrate to the point of failure. In the middle of 1947, when ERCO ended its light plane work, this problem still needed development, but I am sure that it could have been worked out satisfactorily. We also made ground runs with the propeller extension shafts, but this matter had not been worked out satisfactorily by the time the work was permanently discontinued because of the general stoppage of the light plane industry at ERCO.

As stated earlier, not being able to complete the Ercoach project and see it in actual use was one of my greatest disappointments. Compensating for the professional disappointments was my family's growing shared involvement with airplanes and flying. In August 1945, when World War II ended, our sixteen-year-old daughter, Betsey, started taking flying lessons. She wanted to be able to fly any kind of airplane and not be limited to Ercoupes, so she took her flying lessons in Cubs. Her instructor was ERCO's experimental test pilot Everett Hart, who during the war had been an instructor at the Parks Air College in East St. Louis. The lessons, which took place in rented Cubs at the College Park airport, went along rather slowly, because Betsey had had motion sickness when she was young and still could not take much bumpy air. Hart told me that during their lessons he would watch Betsey, and when her lips turned green he would call it a day and head for home. I remembered that when I gave Betsey her first ride in an airplane several years before, she had tossed her cookies after only a couple of take-offs and landings. Betsey soloed in April 1946 and got her pri-

My family, about 1947. Left to right, Betsey (Elizabeth Jane), Dickie (Richard Fred), Donald (Victor), Dorothy, and me.

vate license four months later, after she had turned seventeen. Subsequently she also got checked out in Ercoupes.

The following summer (1947) Betsey helped to sell and demonstrate Ercoupes in a Hyattsville, Maryland, showroom. She spent most of the day telling people about the plane's characteristics, but she also gave flight demonstrations to prospective customers. She attracted quite a bit of attention in the mornings and evenings when she taxied, with a police escort, a wingless Ercoupe from the nearby field to the display room. Her most interesting experience came, however, when, with less than one hundred hours of flying time, she gave a flight demonstration to an airline pilot. After telling her how amazed he was by what the airplane could do, he made his landing approach at 90 MPH! He got it down, held it off, and landed satisfactorily, but Betsey wasn't too happy with what had happened.

Our son Donald, who as I have mentioned was disappointed that he had not been able to become a navy pilot, also took private instructions. He obtained his private pilot's certificate also in the summer of 1946.

With both Betsey and Donald flying, I decided that I would like to have an Ercoupe of my own, so I put in a written order to our sales department, hoping to get a distributor's discount. Sales immediately took up the matter with Les Wells and Henry Berliner, and Henry came to me and said, "We can't sell you an Ercoupe, Fred." And I said, "But I'd like to have one for my very own." So he said, "Well, I'll tell you what we'll do. We'll assign you one for your very own, and we'll maintain it for you and keep it filled with fuel." So Ercoupe N2439H was mine, at least for my own personal use.

But what about my wife, Dorothy? Was she left out of the flying? In the early summer of 1947 I returned from a business trip in my Ercoupe and landed on the north-south runway at ERCO field. Rolling to a stop, I was much surprised to see an Ercoupe on the grass off the runway with Oscar James, a company pilot, in it, along with Dorothy. During the period before the company's really bad times began, ERCO had set aside three Ercoupes for any employees or their immediate family members who had their licenses or who wanted to learn to fly. Without letting me know anything about it, Dorothy had been learning to fly and was well on her way toward soloing. She wanted to surprise me by telling me after she had soloed. She surprised me all right, a little ahead of time. Dorothy did solo soon thereafter and got her private license in the fall. It was very good after that, flying around the country with Dorothy, to know that she could handle the airplane very well entirely by herself. Before long, Dorothy even became a member of the 99's, an organization of women pilots that had been initiated by Amelia Earhart and some of her friends about 1930.[2]

And I can't leave out our youngest son, Dick, who a few years later, as a senior at Texas A&M, would win first prize in the Minta Martin Aeronautical Student Fund Contest. This contest was a national competition sponsored by the Institute of Aeronautical Sciences (IAS).[3] Original papers were presented to fellow students in a given class, and the best of that group was selected by the class. The winner then presented his or her paper at one of eight regional conferences throughout the country. Each regional winner's paper was then sent to a committee of eminent scientists that selected the national winner. These scientists were Dr. Jerome C. Hunsaker, chairman, professor of aeronautical engineering at the Massachusetts Institute of Technology, and a member of the National Advisory Committee for Aeronautics; Dr. Hugh L. Dryden, director of research, National Advisory Committee for Aeronautics; Dr. Clark B. Millikan, director, Guggenheim Aeronautical Laboratory, California Institute of Technology; and Dr. Theodore P. Wright, then vice-president of Cornell University.

Dick was a double-major in aeronautical engineering and English. In the spring of 1956 he submitted to the contest a paper entitled "Preliminary Design Study of a Turbine-Powered Executive Airplane." Dorothy and I were happy when his peers selected his presentation as the best paper from Texas A&M. Dick then presented his paper at the regional conference in Dallas and won first place there. One of the other contestants had given a paper that Dick thought was probably at least as good, but he was not able to present it very well, particularly when it came to answering questions about it. Dick thought that his studies in English had helped him in that regard. Then his paper was awarded the first prize for the entire nation, which made us prouder and happier still.

Ironically Dick, like Betsey, had always been subject to motion sickness. When he was a little child and we were driving in the car, we always had to be ready to pull over to the curb and stop and let him toss his cookies. He wanted to go with me on airplane trips, however, and survived them by taking dramamine and resting back in as horizontal a position as possible. Beginning in the late 1940s, I took Dick flying with me quite often and taught him to take off, land, handle the airplane in the air, and navigate satisfactorily.

Dick eventually became an aeronautical researcher at NASA's Ames Research Center in Moffett Field, California, south of San Francisco. In the early 1960s he worked on the control of VTOL aircraft. For this he wanted to know more about people, and he took night courses in physiology at nearby Stanford University. He developed such an interest in this field that in 1970 he obtained a Ph.D. in physiology. He then obtained a postdoctoral fellowship at the University of Pittsburgh. Eventually he established himself at the University of Western Ontario in London, Ontario, where he could do both teaching and research work in physiology.

In 1946 I was fortunate to receive the W. H. Fawcett Award, which was given annually by Fawcett Publications, Inc., for the past

In 1946 Capt. Eddie Rickenbacker, World War I flying ace and president of Eastern Airlines, presented the W. H. Fawcett Award to me in New York City on the CBS radio program "We the People."

year's greatest contribution to the advancement of aviation as a public service. Two of the previous recipients of the award were Donald Douglas, for the development of the DC-4, the first large airplane with a tricycle gear, and Donald Hibbert, Lockheed's chief engineer, for the development of the P-80 Shooting Star, this country's first fully operational jet fighter. My award, which included a nice $1,000 honorarium, was for the tricycle-geared, spin-proof, two-control Ercoupe.

Earlier I was given the Sylvanus Albert Reed Award for my Ercoupe design. This award was presented to me in 1945 by my old mentor and good friend, George W. Lewis. Lewis had directed research for the NACA from the end of World War I, when it employed less than a hundred people and Langley was its only research facility, through the end of World War II, when it employed over six thousand people and had two or three other major facilities scattered from coast to coast. George Lewis died in July 1948 after many years of illness. He had had an immense influence on

In this photo, Dr. George Lewis is presenting me with the Sylvanus Albert Reed Award in 1945; I cannot think of anyone from whom I would have preferred to receive it.

my life, and I missed him sorely. Although he had a retiring nature and was not well known to the public, he was well known in aviation circles.

In the summer of 1947 Sanders Aviation, Inc., purchased all the drawings, tools, parts, and materials that ERCO had on hand for the Ercoupe, as well as the rights to distribute the Ercoupe worldwide. This corporation had been started a few months earlier by Bob Sanders and some of his close family members. After returning to the company from wartime service in the navy, Sanders had been in charge of the Ercoupe service department, including the sale of spare parts. Sanders Aviation set up an office, hangar, and shop on the field and operated from the field as a fixed base. At first the company assembled and sold Ercoupes from parts already on hand. The production continued on a limited basis until, by August 1948, the five thousandth Ercoupe was produced. In addition, Sanders had the four-place Ercoupe and the twin-engine Ercoach, both of which they sold to two Piasecki engineers in Philadelphia.

In all, however, Sanders sold only about 200 airplanes between 1948 and 1952. Minor improvements to the Ercoupe were made during this period, including a shoulder harness arrangement, the first in the light plane industry (offered as optional equipment); a seat for infants not over 75 pounds in the baggage compartment in lieu of baggage; and a plexiglass bubble windshield.

In 1954 Sanders would sell all of the rights to the Ercoupe, including the tooling and drawings, to Univair of Denver, the main business of which was to furnish parts for airplanes that were no longer in production. Then, in April 1955, the Forney organization in Fort Collins, Colorado, would purchase the entire Ercoupe package, including the approved type certificate, from Univair, and change the name of the plane from Ercoupe to Aircoupe. Forney had a thriving business with a number of different branches, the main one involving the manufacture and sale of portable welding machines used by farmers who did not have electric current available to them. Another branch produced short motion pictures for commercial use. Forney had about six hundred salesmen scattered over the country, and some of them were using small airplanes, including some Ercoupes, to cover their territories. It appeared that they could make airplanes for their own salesmen as an entree into the light airplane business.

Though production of Aircoupes would begin in a small way in 1955 and 1956, Forney had no real concept of the amount of engineering that was required to manufacture aircraft; his entire engineering staff was the part-time service of an assistant mechanical engineering professor at Colorado A&M. Nor did he appreciate the extent to which government regulation and bureaucracy was involved in the aviation business. Their enterprise would not last very long.

But this gets me ahead of my story. In late 1947 there was a meeting in Los Angeles of the NACA's Industry Advisory Committee. About a week ahead of that, there was a meeting in Dayton of the Institute of Aeronautical Sciences (IAS) on general aviation subjects. Dorothy and I had decided to fly to both meetings in my Ercoupe. This was the cross-country flight on which I had taped on a control wheel stop to give an indicated air speed of 102 MPH.

At the IAS meeting in Dayton I talked with many aviation notables, including Orville Wright. This was the last time I saw him before he died in early 1948. And James S. McDonnell was there too. The McDonnell Aircraft Corporation, which had been organized in St. Louis, Missouri, right before the start of the war, had grown rapidly during the war but was now reduced some to about three thousand employees. All of its orders had been for the military, and it was at the time of the IAS meeting actively producing Phantom and Banshee jet fighters for the navy. McDonnell was also working for the navy on helicopters.

James ("Mac") McDonnell was of course aware of the depression in the light plane industry and of the fact that ERCO was suffering from severe financial difficulties and struggling along with a skeleton crew. In that connection, all of us ERCO officials were going along on greatly reduced salaries and in fact had not been paid anything for the last couple of months. I was still hoping, however, that ERCO would pull through and resume its aircraft manufacturing activities. At any rate, Mac invited me to visit him at his plant in St. Louis on our way to the West Coast, and he invited Dorothy and me to stay at his house for a few days.

So, the day after the IAS meeting, we flew to St. Louis and landed on Lambert Field, which was the main St. Louis airport and the field on which the McDonnell plant was located. This was the same field, incidentally, on which Hans Hoyt and I had landed in a Jenny for the 1923 National Air Races—and with only enough fuel left to taxi a few feet. The field was entirely built up now and quite active—quite a change from the grass field with the two hangars on it in 1923. I was taken to the McDonnell plant where I noticed that all of the employees referred to the company president in a somewhat familar but respectful manner as Mr. Mac.

As I explained earlier, during the war McDonnell had made me the standing offer to come see him anytime things were not favorable at ERCO. Now, during this visit in late 1947, knowing what he did about ERCO's difficulties, Mac offered me the job of director of research for the McDonnell Aircraft Corporation. I thanked him and said that I would be glad to consider it if (1) things did not work out at ERCO, and (2) McDonnell would get into light plane activities. Mac said that he too was interested in light airplanes and would take it up with his board of directors. He added, however, that he didn't think the board would go for it. He informed me later that it didn't.

While I was visiting the McDonnell factory, it was interesting to see Banshee jets that were to make flight tests in the St. Louis area zoom up to Chicago and back just to warm up for the flight tests. In 1923 it had taken Hoyt and me over four hours to fly a Jenny from Chicago to St. Louis one way. Also while at the plant, I witnessed a demonstration of "Little Henry," a small one-place helicopter whose power plant consisted of a ram jet on the end of each rotor blade. The man in charge of the jet-powered helicopter design was none other than C. L. Zakarschenko, who had done the structural design for Mac's Doodlebug in Milwaukee back in 1929.

After leaving St. Louis and getting weathered in for a couple of days in Rolla, Missouri, where the Missouri School of Mines was located, Dorothy and I squeezed out another hundred miles to Springfield and stayed for an evening and a day at the home of Jim Johnson, one of the members of the CAA's Non-Scheduled Flying Advisory Committee. The Johnsons lived right on the smaller of two Springfield, Missouri, airports in a one-story building, part of which was used as the airport office. During our stay, the office door opened and in walked Bill Piper, Sr., and his wife Clara. The Pipers were on their way by car to the same NACA meeting that we were going to in Los Angeles. Bill Jr. was in Southern California trying to help sell Piper airplanes in those hard times, and Bill Sr. was driving his son's car to him. We had a good visit with them before they left late in the afternoon. When the weather cleared we flew on to California without incident.

After the meeting of the NACA's Industry Consulting Committee, or rather as part of it, H. M. Horner, a committee member and president of United Aircraft Corporation, flew the whole committee in his DC-3 to see the Convair plant in San Diego and back again.[4] We flew from the Lockheed terminal in Burbank, the same field that I had worked on with Hamilton Standard in 1929 and 1930 and had flown with Lindbergh. But how different the field was now, only seventeen years later! Instead of an open grass field, it was covered with paved runways and aprons and was surrounded by factory buildings. When I had set out the five-mile speed course in 1930 following five miles of railroad track between Burbank and Van Nuys, there had been only one farmhouse close to it. Now the old course was enveloped by a major metropolitan area.

One day early in 1948, after I had returned from the West Coast, Henry Berliner called me into his office for a talk. He told me that he was sorry but he had decided to get out of the fickle light plane business entirely. This was a terrible blow to me. I had thought that ERCO had a chance to pull through if we all tried hard enough and that we had some very good features for airplanes that would be coming along in the near future. Henry was firm in his decision, however, so that was that.

I thought that I could no doubt return again to the NACA, but it was now an organization of many thousands of people, and it was working in the area of high-speed aerodynamics, even leaning toward rocket research. Langley, the NACA laboratory I knew best, hadn't done anything in the light airplane field since before World War II. And I wanted badly to stay in the light plane field.

What to do?

Helping the Flying Farmers

(1948–1957)

11.

Texas A&M and the Ag-1 Project

For the light plane industry 1948 and 1949 would be bad years. Only three light plane manufacturers—Cessna, Beech, and Piper—would manage to survive this difficult period, and Piper in particular would barely be able to do it. In the early 1950s Sanders Aviation, Inc., ended its Ercoupe operation. It sold all of its drawings, toolings, and leftover parts to Univair of Denver, a company that supplied spare parts and materials to owners of discontinued airplane models.

A few days after Henry Berliner told me that ERCO was going out of the airplane business, I got an invitation from the dean of engineering at the University of Maryland in College Park, right where we lived, to start a new aeronautical engineering department. Although I could have possibly worked into a position where I might have been able to do a little research in the field of light airplanes, I did not particularly want to get into a primarily administrative job at an academic institution. I had turned down two opportunities of that nature before.

In February 1948, out of the clear blue sky, I got a letter from Dr.

Howard ("Bud") Barlow, dean of engineering at Texas A&M College, wondering if I would be interested in joining his staff. Dr. Barlow emphasized that I would be able to carry out aeronautical research in pretty much whatever manner I most desired. He invited me to come down to College Station at the school's expense to talk over the situation and see if something could be worked out.

This looked like a real opportunity to me. I had gotten to know Bud Barlow back in the late 1930s when we were both on the contest board of the National Aeronautic Association, and he was a real go-getter. (I had been on the NAA board ever since and had been chairman for the last few years, but Bud had dropped out.) I was also a good friend with one member of Bud's faculty, Bob Pinkerton, who had worked under Eastman Jacobs in the variable-density tunnel when I was at NACA Langley. So I did go down and spend a couple of days in Texas, talking over the situation with Bud, Ed Brush, the head of the aeronautical engineering department, and Gib Gilchrist, the college president.

They offered me a dual rating: one of distinguished professor, under which I might do some occasional teaching; and the other of research engineer, under which I would spend most of my efforts. I outlined a number of possible research topics, some of which, I said, could probably receive financial aid from the NACA. Things looked satisfactory to me, so I told the school officials that, if Dorothy agreed with the idea when I got back home, I would start at Texas A&M in April, which was only two months away.

Dorothy was not too happy with the idea of leaving our home in College Park, but she agreed to the move. In April I drove our 1939 Buick, loaded to the gills with technical books and reports, down to College Station, Texas, and started living in a motel. Dorothy stayed at the house until mid-June so our three youngsters could finish their school terms. (Donald and Betsey were at the University of Maryland and our younger son, Dick, was finishing junior high.)

When I had first received the unexpected letter from Texas A&M inviting me to come and talk over possibilities of doing research work, I had wondered how in the world they had happened to get hold of enough information about my situation at ERCO to make such a suggestion. But I had a sneaking suspicion. A year or two before, I had talked at some length with George Haddaway, editor and publisher of what was then *Southern Flight* (later *Flight*) magazine, at an aeronautical meeting in Washington. Like me, Haddaway was a member of the CAA's Non-Scheduled Flying Advisory Committee. He was also an ardent promoter for Texas, and while we were walking away from that meeting in Washington, George had asked me whether I would consider coming to Texas if an arrangement could be made where I could continue working in the light airplane field. I had replied that I was committed to staying at ERCO, but if that fell through in some way, the situation he suggested would interest me.

I had forgotten all about this conversation with Haddaway, but was reminded of it just before I left for my new job in Texas. George telephoned and asked if I could stop in Dallas on the way to College Station; some kind of party had been planned for me, with city officials and local aviation people, including many members of the Texas Private Flyers Association (a body I later joined). So I did stop in Dallas, where there was a dinner for about fifty people in my honor at the Baker Hotel. The dinner had been arranged by Haddaway and Jack Nelson, who was then a member of the aviation committee of the Dallas Chamber of Commerce. I was made an honorary citizen of the city of Dallas and was given a plaque signed by the city secretary, city manager, and mayor. And I then knew for sure how Texas A&M had gotten the idea. It's wonderful to have good friends, especially when you need them.

The aeronautical engineering department at Texas A&M was housed in what had been an old laundry building. The college had a fine airport, Easterwood Field, with mile-long runways, about three miles southwest of the main campus. I had an office both in that laundry building and in the new wind-tunnel building on the airport. The wind tunnel, whose test section measured five-by-seven feet, had been approximately completed, but had not yet been made to operate satisfactorily. My main activity was to be at the airport, where I was to head what was originally called the Personal Aircraft Research Center. Later, "Personal" was dropped.

Finding suitable housing in College Station turned out to be a problem. The town at that time had only about three thousand inhabitants in addition to the students, although it was adjacent to the city of Bryan with about twenty-five thousand inhabitants. During my first month I found three possible rentals and three possible purchases, one of which was a half-completed new house, but none of them looked very desirable. In May 1948 I took a commercial airliner to Washington, where I attended an NACA committee meeting, and then flew with Dorothy back to Texas in our Ercoupe. (When I left ERCO, Henry Berliner had agreed to let me buy my Ercoupe—which I did for the going rate of a used model, $1,500. I did not have to pay cash, because the price of the plane was taken out of the back pay the company owed me. Incidentally, the back pay finally came through a couple of years later.)

The only house Dorothy found suitable was the half-built one, but she said that its construction would have to be stopped temporarily so things on the inside could be rearranged. I had met a young professor of architecture at the college, William W. Caudill, and got him to go out with us one Saturday morning to look into the possibilities for modifying the house. He decided that it could be done, but said, "If you're going to do all this, why don't you just build a house of your own? It would take only about a month longer than to do this one all over again, and you could get just what you want." I said I would be willing to consider such a possibility if we could get a place on the edge of town where I could have the house adjacent to a pasture and could make arrangements to fly a plane right from home. I had been musing about such an ideal situation for some time.

Bill Caudill said he knew of such a place, a farm just south of town that was owned by a former professor in the economics department. One section of this property, called "the Knoll," had been subdivided by members of the architecture department with the idea of building homes on it sometime in the future. Nothing had been built on it yet. A portion of the Knoll was adjacent to the farm's pasture, and another portion of it was adjacent to a different pasture.

We drove right out to look the situation over and found that two or three of the lots would satisfy us if the proper arrangements could be made. We then went to see the owner of the property, who agreed that if we would build the first house in his subdivision, he would permit us to fly the airplane from the pasture—at least until he developed it, and he had no immediate plans for that. By mid-afternoon we had purchased a lot at the corner of the pasture. As it turned out, Bill Caudill and two of his associates, who were doing some commercial work on the side, designed the house for us. We moved into it about five months later, in early October. In the meantime we resided in the home of Sherman Crites, a professor in

Forget the horse! All a man needs to be happy in Texas: his son (Dick), his dog, and his airplane. I would also include "his wife," but unfortunately she is not in the picture.

the aeronautical engineering department. Our house was built, incidentally, by a company owned by former Texas A&M football stars Herschel Burgess and Marion Pugh.

Our pasture had something less than fifty acres and was not quite rectangular. By running diagonally from our house to the opposite corner, however, I could get 1,800 feet of runway for my plane, but with 25-foot trees at each end. The pasture was rough, and it cost me $35 to get a man with a road scraper to smooth off a strip 50 feet wide and 1,800 feet long. There was a dip in the center, which meant that a stream ran through it after heavy rains, and it cost me another $35 to put enough gravel in this dip to take care of it in all weather. I kept the plane parked and tied down close to the house but in a position ready to take off on the runway. Cows occasionally were pastured in the field and near the plane until I ran electrified wire across in front of the plane to keep them away. Before starting off for a flight, I simply had to disconnect the end of the electrified wire, let it lie on the ground, and unsnap three tie-downs that were always in place. I could then fly away in the plane about as easily and quickly as we could drive away in a car.

As time went on, I found I was spending almost all of my time at my office in the wind-tunnel building at the airport. Because I could park my plane at Easterwood Field just outside of my office, I soon made a practice of flying to and from work and even flying home for lunch. I kept this up for most of the nine years we spent at College Station. I did this mostly for fun, of course, because it saved only about two minutes to fly rather than to drive by car.

Incidentally, our Ercoupe was a two-control model with no rudder pedals, and it is interesting to note that never in all my flying from the pasture, with only its single north-south landing strip, did I have to abort a landing because of the wind. And I made some landings in crosswinds that were reported by the nearby airport as high as 40 MPH. It is thus surprising and somewhat painful to me that, even now, half a century after the W-1, most pilots are still not aware of what the tricycle gear will do for them in a crosswind landing.

Although I always made satisfactory landings under all wind conditions, the same was not true for take-offs. In very strong crosswinds, there was not enough traction on the nose wheel—even with the elevator control held full forward—to keep the airplane from weathervaning and running off the 50-foot-wide smooth grass strip. After one experience in which I bumped off over into rough ground, I decided never again to take off if the crosswind was above 25 or 30 MPH; I would drive the car to work instead.

After flying around the various parts of Texas a bit, I learned the length of flight necessary to make an airplane really worthwhile as a regular means for family transportation. If we flew to Houston, which was 100 miles away, it took an hour for the flight and then it would take forty-five minutes to land and put the airplane up, get a taxi, and ride into the center of town. If we drove, it took two hours to get from home to the center of Houston—only fifteen minutes longer. And the convenience of having our own car for local transportation more than offset the extra fifteen minutes. So, we soon resolved that all of our trips to Houston would be by automobile. If we went to Dallas, Fort Worth, or San Antonio, however, which were 150 to 180 miles away, we found that it saved a significant amount of time to take our plane.

My research program at Texas A&M, as first laid out, was divided into three main categories: (1) the speed range of light airplanes, (2) the safety of light airplanes, especially during flights into adverse weather conditions, and (3) the reliability of the power plants for light airplanes. Naturally, my objective was to find ways to improve or increase each.

For the first research category, the speed range, I immediately got the sponsorship and financial support of the NACA to make an analytical investigation of the effect on take-off performance of high-lift flaps. At the conclusion of our study, which was the first project undertaken at the new Personal Aircraft Research Center, we selected a single-slotted, full-span flap as the high-lift device best suited for a four-place private owner–type airplane. Along the way we found that the shortest take-off distances could be obtained with low span loading, low power loadings, and low aspect ratios, and that air drag and ground friction were relatively unimportant aerodynamic factors at these low loadings. In sum, our analysis indicated that considerable improvement in take-off performance of light airplanes (including reductions of roughly 25 percent in the distance required to take off and climb to 50 feet) was possible by the use of suitable high-lift flaps.

As I state these results now, more than thirty-five years later, the general run of production light airplanes now on the market has made use of only a small portion of this possible improvement. The rest is still available to be taken by designers if they want to take the trouble.

Regarding the second category, though airplanes like the Ercoupe were already available that were easy to fly safely in good weather, there was still a dire need to improve the odds of safe airplane flight during times of poor visibility. It was extremely important for private pilots to be able to fly their airplanes blind, I thought. (This was in 1948, before VOR and present flying capabilities.) They shouldn't try to fly through thunderstorms or extreme turbulence, but they should be able to fly almost regardless of how well they could see the terrain until the final landing. If the airplane was ever really to become a useful means of private transportation, pilots had to be able to make a date two weeks in advance and then leave late enough to take advantage of the speed of the airplane and to get there with reasonable assurance. Blind flights required the use of instruments, of course, and safe use of instruments required specialized training and practice. A competent instrument pilot had to do a lot of things at the same time.

At Texas A&M, I planned to explore ways to make light airplanes as easy to fly on instruments as feasible. I felt that a good step would be making the airplane so that it would fly straight if you let go of it. That would also help to prevent the fatal spiral-dive accidents caused by spatial disorientation.

The third line of proposed research was to improve the reliability of the power plant of the light airplane so that these blind flights could be made with assurance. Eventually what we tried in this regard was to improve a single engine to the point where it had about as much reliability as a twin arrangement would have.

In November 1948 I delivered a talk in Cleveland, Ohio, at a joint meeting of the National Aviation Trades Association and the Aviation Distributors and Manufacturers Association. After outlining our proposed research program at Texas A&M, I focused on the subject of safety. In particular I discussed possible improvements in cockpit design for protection in crashes and told about a simple shoulder harness arrangement that I had worked out and was using in my own Ercoupe. (This harness was then available as optional equipment for the Ercoupes produced by Sanders.) At the same time I tried to give credit to the crash-injury research that had been conducted by Hugh DeHaven at Cornell University Medical College in New York.[1]

One of the most important things needed in the late 1940s and early 1950s for improved light airplane safety was improved power plant reliability; I have already indicated that this subject was part of my original research program at Texas A&M. Shortly after starting at the college I obtained detailed information from the CAB's Bureau of Safety Investigation on all of the airplane crashes that had been caused by engine or power plant failures during the year 1947. I spent several weeks analyzing and cross-analyzing all of the statistical information before publishing them in a report by the Texas A&M Engineering Experiment Station. This report, "An Analysis of Personal Aircraft Power Plant Failures during 1947 with Some Suggested Remedies," was reprinted in its entirety in the March 7, 1949, issue of *Aviation Week*.

As stated in my article, there were 1,353 accidents listed that year as caused by power plant failures. Nearly all of them, 1,286, had resulted in forced landings. A breakdown of the 1,077 failures with determined causes offered the following striking divisions:

Fuel system	920
Engine structure	53
Lubricating system	47
Propeller assembly	19
Ignition system	18
Control system	12
Miscellaneous	5
Engine accessories	3

The startling fact revealed by this study was that seven-eighths of all light plane accidents with known causes in 1947 had been brought on by some failure of the fuel system.

Obviously, then, the fuel system was the most important part of the power plant needing to be improved at that time. Of the fuel system failures, half of them could be ascribed to ineffective carburetor heat or improper application of heat. These failures, I wrote, could have been overcome by an effective fuel-injection system. (Since the late 1950s, failures of this sort have been largely overcome, partly by fuel injection, partly by improved carburetor air heaters—both of which have produced a greater amount of heat—and partly by better operation by pilots.) It appeared that many of the rest could have been avoided by duplication of the fuel system and duplication of the lubricating system.

I then laid plans for conducting work of that nature. One interesting item involved fuel valves. I said in the report that fuel valves, either through failure or mishandling, had caused 69 of the accidents listed. Three of these accidents had been fatal. Twenty-six had been caused by the failure of the pilot to switch from an empty tank to a full one. In 14 cases the pilot had taken off with closed or partially closed fuel valves, and in 13 cases the pilot had confused the fuel shutoff valves with the carburetor heat controls.

From these records it appeared to me that the private pilot would be far better off if he had no fuel valve within his reach. The reason that had always been advanced in favor of having a fuel shutoff valve within reach of the pilot was that he needed to be able to shut off the fuel flow in case of fire in the air. For 1947, the year of my statistics, however, there appeared to be no record of a power plant fire during flight that would have been helped by shutting off the fuel. There were 69 accidents, three of which were fatal, though, that had been caused by mishandling of the fuel valves.

After studying my report, the Aircraft Owners and Pilots Association, or AOPA, sent the following recommendation to the Civil Aeronautics Board: "that those portions of the civil air regulations requiring personal plane manufacturers to install fuel valves in the cockpits be eliminated and that those manufacturers now be permitted to equip their aircraft with a continual flow fuel system, similar to that now used in automobiles." However, because the old guards in the CAA and the CAB did not agree with that viewpoint, the recommendation was either turned down or ignored.

In the late 1940s three particularly interesting airplanes came out. One was the Anderson Greenwood AG-14, which was really just an updated W-1A. The AG-14 was a two-place pusher with the tail support on booms, and it was powered by a 90-HP Continental flat air-cooled engine. Unfortunately, the AG-14 came out during the light plane slump, and only a few of them were made before production was stopped. The Anderson Greenwood plant was at the Houston airport, and as soon as Ben Anderson and Marvin Greenwood heard that I had moved to College Station, they began to use me as a consultant. I was sorry to see that they could not carry their project through to a successful commercial conclusion.

Another interesting airplane to come out during this period was the Bauman Brigadier 250. Except for the single vertical tail and rudder, this plane had the same configuration as our unfulfilled twin-engine, five-place Ercoach, including tricycle landing gear. The Brigadier was powered with two 125-HP engines driving pusher propellers that were just back of the wing. These engines were in good-sized nacelles, however, and not completely buried within the wing, as ours were. Also like our Ercoach, the Baumann airplane had space for five people, with two individual seats in the front for the pilot and copilot and one wide seat in the rear for three passengers. The rear seat was only 50 inches wide, however, whereas the width of our seat had been 54 inches.

In 1947 Jack Baumann had had the opportunity to look over our plans for the Ercoach very thoroughly. In that year the Convair Company of San Diego had thought about taking over ERCO as part of its own organization, and it had sent Baumann, along with two other men, to investigate our plant operations. During his visit

Baumann had demonstrated a particular interest in our Ercoach concept, and I had even gone over my plans for it with him in great detail. I don't suppose I'll ever know what influence this may have had on Jack's design.

Shortly after his visit to ERCO, Baumann had left Convair for North American in Los Angeles. He then had started building the Brigadier as a moonlighting project, hiring engineers from the local airplane companies to help him design the airplane and giving them stock in the company for their reward. While I was on the West Coast for a meeting late in 1948, Jack took me out to the Van Nuys airport to show me his prototype airplane. He kept the Brigadier project going for several years but did not make a commercial success of it.

The third interesting light plane to come out during 1949 was the Koppen-Bollinger Helioplane. This was an extreme effort in the STOL (short take-off and landing) direction and a successful one. The designer of the Helioplane was Dr. Otto Koppen of MIT, who had previously designed the Skyfarer. The business end of the venture was run by Professor Lynn Bollinger of the Harvard Graduate School of Business Administration, a former airline pilot and fixed-base operator.

Though Koppen built the prototype around a Piper Vagabond with an 85-HP engine, by the time he had finished the Helioplane, he had created an almost entirely new airplane. The aircraft had full-span slotted flaps and automatic leading edge slots. The rudder was divided into upper and lower parts that operated independently. The lower part was connected to the flaps when they were used differentially as ailerons and served to overcome the adverse yawing moments of that type of lateral control. The upper part was connected to the rudder pedals. At less than 30 MPH the airplane could fly at full control, and it was clean enough aerodynamically to cruise at least at 100 MPH. The plane's stall angle was 14 degrees above the angle used to fly at 30 MPH, meaning that the airplane was both stall-proof and spin-proof. The ground take-off and landing runs were both well under 100 feet.

The speed range and STOL performances of the Koppen-Bollinger Helioplane were truly remarkable, but the airplane was not yet developed in a form suitable for commercial production. For one thing, it had a large, slow-turning propeller that, though very effective for the purpose desired, was not commercially feasible because it was driven at low RPMs by means of a multiple V-belt drive. In the fall of 1949 Hugh DeHaven of Cornell University Medical College flew me to the airport at Norwood, Massachusetts, where the Helioplane was built and test flown. Koppen and Bollinger came out and demonstrated the Helioplane for us.

In the May 16, 1949, issue of *Aviation Week*, an article congratulated Koppen and Bollinger on their design and suggested that the Helioplane might have a large effect on the future of light airplane activities. The article stated that the Helioplane, even in its earliest test stage, appeared to be "the most important new idea in light planes since the pre-war Ercoupe."

Originally, Koppen and Bollinger had thought that the Helioplane could be produced for only about $500 more than the price of the ordinary run of light airplanes. The commercial version finally came out, however, as a larger, four-place, and relatively sophisticated and expensive airplane. It was a highly specialized airplane suitable for certain purposes only. For this reason, production was on a very small quantity basis. Still, the Helioplane was the only one of the three new light planes of 1949 that is still in production—although in all, only a small number of the planes have been made over the years.

After I arrived in Texas in the spring of 1948 it soon became apparent that the use of airplanes in agriculture for dusting, spraying, seeding, and fertilizing had already become important in the production of food and fiber and that its importance was steadily growing. I started feeling around for ways in which our experimental work might help in that particular field.

During the winter of 1948/49, the National Flying Farmers Association held a meeting in Chicago at which agricultural aviation was to be discussed thoroughly. I attended this meeting and found that there was a general desire for an improved airplane particularly designed for this work. The airplanes then in use were all converted trainers of one kind or another. In addition, there was a need to know more accurately how uniform the distribution of the agricultural materials was, how to measure it, and how to improve it. We then made arrangements for a cooperative program with the Rice-Pasture Laboratory at Beaumont, Texas, which was connected with the Texas A&M College system. Together, we would measure the distribution of the rice seed and later of fertilizer over nine different cross-section portions in a seventy-seven-acre field. The distribution was accomplished by a local commercial applicator firm, M&M Air Service, using a Stearman airplane. The crop turned out to be successful, but the distribution of both the seed and fertilizer was still far from uniform. There was still plenty of room for improvement. (M&M Air Service grew to become one of the most outstanding aerial firms. Its current head, George Mitchell, the son of one of the firm's founders, is a past president of the National Agricultural Aviation Association.)

In August 1949, Texas A&M got a telephone call from Del Rentzel, who had succeeded Ted Wright as administrator of the Civil Aeronautics Administration. Representatives of the National Flying Farmers Association had been in Washington, D.C., pestering the hell out of the officials of both the CAA and Department of Agriculture in an attempt to get aid from the government for the development of an airplane especially suited to agricultural uses. The government wanted to help but did not feel that it should carry on the project itself and did not want to give it to an individual manufacturer, because with a development of this nature, it would be difficult not to show favoritism.

Rentzel wanted to know if I might be available to spearhead an effort to develop a special agricultural airplane. (I was told later that someone in the Fort Worth region of the Flying Farmers organization had suggested that, since I was down at Texas A&M, with shop facilities available, and had experience both in research work and in the design and construction of commercial airplanes, I might be the one to carry out the proposed agricultural airplane project.) The university administrators, after discussions, informed Rentzel that such a project could be carried out by the Aircraft Research Center under the auspices of the Texas A&M Engineering Experiment Station and that they would be glad to go into the matter further.

On August 23, 1949, Rentzel flew to College Station in a DC-3 full of CAA and Department of Agriculture people. We then spent a couple of days in the rooms of the Texas A&M board of directors, exploring the various possibilities. It was determined that the project should go ahead. Texas A&M would provide my services and those of the personnel at our Aircraft Research Center, plus shop facilities in the wind-tunnel building on the airport. The CAA would provide a grant of $50,000 and loan to the project the services of those aeronautical engineers from the various CAA regions that could be spared. A steering committee of nine men representing the various government, commercial, and academic interests would be formed to guide the project. This body was to include Bill Berry and C. W. Von Rosenberg of the CAA's Fort Worth region; Harold Hoekstra, the CAA's chief engineer of aircraft development in Washington, D.C.; and Frank Irons, head of the USDA's Agricultural Experiment Station near Toledo, Ohio. My friend George Haddaway, publisher of *Southern Flight* in Dallas, was not exactly on the committee, but he counseled us in regard to all of our public relations releases. I served as the committee's chairman.

The new agricultural airplane program was announced a few days later in Fort Collins, Colorado, at the annual meeting of the National Flying Farmers Association. In fact, Del Rentzel and his group had flown right on to Fort Collins from their meetings at Texas A&M. As he was climbing up the steps of his DC-3 to leave for Colorado, Rentzel had turned around to shake hands and had said, "So long, Fred. You've got the ball now."

We initiated two lines of activity immediately. One line was to get as much information as possible from the 1,600 or 1,700 aerial applicators who were then operating across the nation. We did this by sending questionnaires to every known operator in the various CAA regions. In addition, we visited the operations of many of the aerial applicators within a distance of a few hundred miles.

One thing that became apparent as the returns came in was that most operators wanted airplanes similar to those that they already had and knew about. For example, those that had Cubs or Aeroncas thought that a high-wing monoplane was the best type of agricultural airplane. Those flying Wacos or Stearmans thought it should be a biplane. It was obvious that they had not thought out the problem of an ideal airplane for agricultural aviation to any great extent at all. It was obvious, also, that no single-size airplane would cover all of the various uses desired.

The other activity that was initiated immediately was the paperwork necessary to procure the $50,000 from the CAA. The Department of Agriculture officials informed us that it would take no less than about three years to get the money appropriated and approved by Congress. Del Rentzel of the CAA was a businessman, however, and he set about to find a way of getting the money immediately. His people found that there had been a rather large appro-

The signing of the contract between Texas A&M and the federal government for the development of the Ag-1. Right to left, Bill Berry from the CAA's Fort Worth office; Bud Barlow; Bob Pinkerton; Ed Brush; and yours truly, all from Texas A&M; and George Haddaway, editor of Southern Flight *magazine, who helped the Ag-1 project throughout its history.*

priation made for a certain medical research activity that was apparently not going to be used up within the present fiscal year. Fifty thousand dollars of that appropriation, they believed, could be transferred to our agricultural aviation project. To do this required approval of the Bureau of Budget and action by each house of Congress. Rentzel gave Bill Berry of the Fort Worth region of the CAA the job of greasing the bureaucratic and legislative machinery, and Bill worked hard in Washington with all of the parties involved until the transfer was actually made. By December 1949 a contract was executed, and the money was made available to us.

Immediately following the completion of the original meetings with Rentzel in College Station on August 23 and 24, 1949, I had started to work on the initial preliminary design. As had been the case with the W-1 and the Ercoupe, some of the requirements were obvious from the start. With the pilot flying back and forth low over the crop and needing to clear trees, electrical wires, and other obstacles at the end of most runs, the field of view from the cockpit, both forward and downward, had to be excellent. Between swath runs, the pilot would want to turn back in the shortest possible time, and he would need to be able to see clearly where he was going. The inside wing of a high-wing monoplane or the upper wing of a biplane was likely to blank off a portion of the area toward which the pilot was turning. A low-wing monoplane was better in this regard. The quickest turns were made at low flying speeds near the stall—and in this type of flying there were likely to be more stalling accidents and collisions with obstacles than occur in ordinary flying. At the low speeds near the stall the airplane should obviously then have both excellent field of view and excellent lateral control and stability.

Fortunately, because this type of accident occurred at a relatively low speed, the pilot, with proper crash protection, could survive with little or no injury. In most airplane crashes, the tail surfaces and the rear portion of the fuselage were damaged the least. Thus, the safest place for a pilot in a crash appeared to be well back in the fuselage and behind all heavy weights such as the engine or the load.

Another desirable feature for an airplane of this type was for the hopper door to be free of all obstructions and easy and quick to load, either by hand or by machine. After considering all feasible locations of the pilot with respect to the hopper load to the rear, to one side, and above, I concluded that the best arrangement was a low-wing monoplane with the pilot behind the hopper and located high enough so that he could get the desired field of view. With this general arrangement, I then made preliminary performance estimates for various amounts of load carried, engine powers, and airplane sizes.

On September 8, 1949, only two weeks after the original meeting with Rentzel at Texas A&M, I called the first meeting of the agricultural airplane steering committee. At this time, we got the design concept off to a good start. In particular, there was a lot of discussion about engines. All of the new engines being manufactured were of the flat type, and these gave a better view over the nose. The flat engines were then available in powers up to about 200 horsepower, but the manufacturers said that all engines in the future under 400 HP would be flat engines (which turned out to be the case). No radial engines were currently in production, but surplus radial engines from about 225 to 450 HP and up were still available at relatively low prices. More than half of the agricultural airplanes in use at that time were in the very light category, consisting of Piper Cubs, Aeroncas, and Taylorcrafts. Most Stearmans and N3Ns had 220- or 225-HP engines. A few were equipped with 450-HP Pratt and Whitney Wasp Juniors, and they were considered very powerful. But no one expected these surplus engines to be available for very long. The entire committee finally agreed that the first experimental airplane should carry a payload of 800 pounds and be developed around a flat engine from 185 up to a maximum of 300 HP.

As it turned out, we chose for our first engine a 225-HP flat six-cylinder engine from Continental. Bill Berry went to work on the procurement of the engine and managed to get Continental to donate it to the project. We anticipated that if an engine of 300 horsepower became available later, the airplane's payload could be increased from 800 to 1,200 pounds. With the original 800-pound load and 225-HP engine, it appeared to be possible to fly the airplane out of a one-quarter mile long field; or, in other words, the plane should be able to take off and get to a height of 50 feet in only one-quarter of a mile (or 1,320 feet at sea level). Under favorable enough conditions with longer runways, even the heavier 1,200-pound load could be carried with the original 225-HP engine.

When Harold Hoekstra got back to Washington and told the CAA officials there that I was thinking in terms of a low-wing monoplane, they were greatly disturbed. All of the agricultural (or "ag," for short) planes they knew about were converted high-wing monoplanes or biplanes. The CAA officials thought that low-wing monoplanes were likely to be tricky to fly, as some in fact had been, and they apparently did not keep in mind what the Ercoupe had shown. At any rate, they sent Hoekstra back down to College Station to spend a couple of weeks with me and get me in line. Harold and I then went over the entire procedure again of putting the pilot in every feasible place with respect to the load. Fortunately, he finally agreed that the arrangement I had come up with was the best. Now, thirty-nine years later, a fair number of airplanes especially designed for agricultural use are on the market, and all but one follow the configuration of the "Ag-1," which is what I called our design.

At first some of the Flying Farmers wanted an all-round airplane,

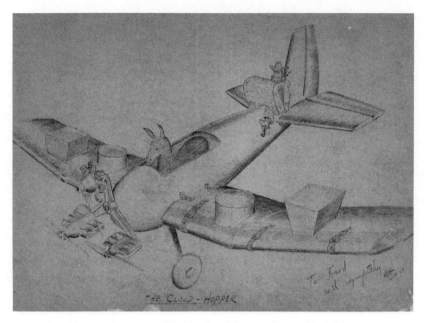

Harold Hoekstra's drawing of "The Cloud-hopper," October 1949.

one that they could use to dust and spray crops, but that they could also use to fly a calf to market, go to another town for a tractor part, or even to take the family out for a Sunday picnic. Fortunately, our steering committee agreed with me that we should confine the use of the new plane to the dispersal of agricultural materials.

After spending two weeks with me on the project, during the evening before he left to go back to Washington, Harold Hoekstra drew me a picture that I later framed and still have up on the wall. He entitled it "The Cloud-Hopper," and it shows our airplane, but in the form desired by the Flying Farmers. In his drawing, the plane has spray tanks and dusthoppers mounted on the top of the wing whose leading edge was removable and easy to replace in case it was bunged up by trucks or fence posts. Both radial and flat engines are mounted on the nose. The pilot sits astride the fuselage just in front of the tail with his spurred feet on the rudder pedals sticking outside of the fuselage, and with a folded mattress in front of him for protection. There is a large open cargo or passenger compartment in front, in this particular case housing a donkey, which could supply some plant food, if needed. The picture was

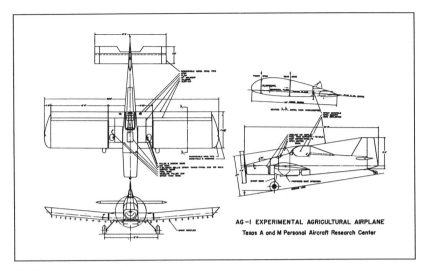

AG-1 EXPERIMENTAL AGRICULTURAL AIRPLANE
Texas A and M Personal Aircraft Research Center

Outline drawings of the Ag-1.

signed "To Fred, with Sympathy, H.D.H. 10-19-49." Although this represented a touch of humor, the easily replaceable leading edges have actually been incorporated in our latest Piper Pawnee Brave agricultural airplane.

After the meeting of the project steering committee in September, the design work began to proceed in earnest. The specifications were very demanding, and special means had to be used to attain them. The plane was to take off from a soft field and climb to 50 feet of altitude in 1,320 feet. The range of safe operating speeds for dusting and spraying was from 60 to 90 MPH. In order to make safe low-speed operation and short take-off and landing runs possible, the stalling speed with full load was 45 MPH or less. To cut the time lost between loads and facilitate ferrying of the airplane, the maximum speed was more than 100 MPH. And to avoid having to use an excessively large wing to obtain the low-speed characteristics with full load, I decided to use a very high lift coefficient and go to full-span slotted flaps. The center panel of the flap would go clear across the bottom of the fuselage and have a maximum deflection of 45 degrees. The outer portions would deflect to only 25 degrees but then would deflect differentially as ailerons. To ensure a very rapid rate of control comparable to that of a pursuit plane, which was desirable for maneuvering close to the ground, a form of spoiler or slot-lip aileron, as I called it, was added just ahead of the slotted flaps. These slot-lip ailerons were quite narrow and were deflected up to a very high angle. Thus, they gave favorable yawing moments that offset the adverse ones of the aileron deflection. The slot-lip ailerons also gave very rapid control at low speeds, particularly when the flap was deflected.

In the early fall of 1949 the CAA sent Herman S. Workentin, an engineer from its Fort Worth region, down to help us, and he spent the entire Ag-1–design period with us at College Station. Also I engaged the part-time services of Professor Bennett B. Hamner of the aeronautical engineering staff at Texas A&M, and he took care of our structural strength computations and tests. These two men, Workentin and Hamner, had worked together previously on the design of the Globe-Swift airplane, and they were good friends. As time went on, more people were added to the design staff, and in all four other CAA engineers from four different regions worked with us from three to nine months each. In addition, we hired some full-time draftsmen and had some part-time student help.

The structure of the Ag-1 was almost entirely of aluminum alloy, partly sheet and partly extrusions. Directing the structural construction was young George A. Roth, who was in charge of our experimental shop. Roth was a veteran of World War II and had been an airplane and engine mechanic in the air force. Our wind-tunnel building, including offices and shops, was on Easterwood Field, the college airport. A couple of small airlines, including Trans-Texas and Continental, had stops at the small terminal building just across the road from us. George was very competent and reliable, and when the airlines' DC-3s occasionally had engine trouble, he would be called over to fix them up.

The wind-tunnel shop in which we were going to build the Ag-1 was only 40 by 60 feet, and in it there was light equipment for making scale models. George Roth started rearranging the shop for the construction of the airplane, and among the equipment he added was a sheet-metal foot-operated ERCO shrinker. He then started making some of the jigs and fixtures on which the parts of the plane would be made. The structure was to be very simple, rugged but simple, and inasmuch as we made it with such simple tools, we figured that most operators would have at least as good tool equipment as we had and that they could easily repair the airplane, if necessary, in service.

George Roth in the cockpit of the Ag-1, with me holding the hopper door partly open, in December 1950. The organizations that contributed to the Ag-1 program are listed on the side of the plane.

In late 1949 I visited Hugh DeHaven in New York City. As mentioned previously in this chapter, DeHaven had been studying airplane accident statistics and crash injuries to the occupants at Cornell University Medical College since the early 1940s. By 1949 he had become the outstanding authority in this field. I had kept in touch with DeHaven for the last two or three years and wanted to make full use of his findings in the design of the Ag-1.

While I was visiting DeHaven in New York, he introduced me to a pilot, Howard Hasbrook, who had just recovered from a very serious accident while crop dusting in a Stearman airplane. Hasbrook was understandably very interested in improving the safety of the pilot and occupants in crashes, and Hugh wondered whether I could not add him to my staff at Texas A&M. I had no funds available for this, except on a very temporary basis, but fortunately

Hugh managed to find funds to have Hasbrook working with him in his crash-injury research at Cornell. The three of us spent a couple of days going over Hugh's results, finding ways to apply them to improve the safety features of the Ag-1. Both Hugh and Howard worked with me all through the design period of the Ag-1 and ultimately came up with a list of items that I will mention later in some detail.[3]

Both the design and the construction work on the Ag-1 continued throughout 1950. The size of our staff of mechanics and sheet-metal workers who constructed the airplane varied from one in the first part of January 1950 to a maximum of fifteen six months later. By the time the airplane was ready, the staff size had tapered off to seven.

The quality of the workmanship was exceptionally high, considering that only one experimental airplane was constructed, and it was all done with very limited facilities. As the various parts were completed, strength tests were made under Professor Hamner's supervision. All of the critical limit loads were applied on the fuselage, wings, flaps, tail surfaces, and control systems, and deflections were measured in each case.

When the airplane was nearing completion, the CAA, particularly Bill Berry of the Fort Worth region, wanted to make a big show of the first flight, with the press and important government and political personages on hand. The airplane was highly experimental, however, having many unusual features, including an exceptionally powerful flap and an unusual and completely untried lateral control system, consisting of slot-lip ailerons in combination with differential control of the flaps. My desire was therefore to go at the flight testing very gradually and to do quite a number of tests before showing it to the public at all.

The CAA was adamant, however, and we finally agreed on a date for the first flight. I insisted, though, on scheduling the flight far enough ahead so that we would have time at least to make some ground runs beforehand. Because we had insufficient wind-tunnel test data to know just what the lateral control forces would be, I wanted to make sure that these forces would not be overbalanced.

After getting the power plant to work satisfactorily, we made numerous tests of the ground-handling characteristics. As an extra precaution against the chance that the airplane might get out of hand, temporary centering springs were installed. At this stage all of the piloting of the Ag-1 was done by Ted Von Rosenberg, who was the CAA's chief of the aircraft division at Fort Worth. By taxiing the plane around, Rosenberg got thoroughly familiar with its ground-handling characteristics in all kinds of wind conditions; he even made sharp turnarounds in crosswinds with the flaps set in various positions. Easterwood Field had three mile-long paved runways, and after a bit Rosenberg would even ease the control stick back a little and make some rather fast taxi runs, lifting off a little from the ground. Lightly loaded as it was, the Ag-1 could make a number of touchdowns during the mile length of one runway. After a bit, the high taxi runs were enough above the surface to permit shallow banks and turns and trying out of slipping and skidding. As time went on, we made a few minor adjustments and Ted got quite familiar with the handling characteristics of the plane. By the time our taxi tests were finished, we felt reasonably comfortable with the idea of making a first flight around the airport and landing.

The date selected for the first flight was December 1, 1950. It was a gray, cloudy day, and the winds recorded at the airport were about 30 MPH with gusts up to 40. An audience of a couple of hundred people, including the press and many officials, were waiting for the airplane to take off on its first flight. With the wind conditions that existed, which were not lined up with any runway, it would have been utterly stupid to have made a first flight before such an audience without Ted Von Rosenberg having become familiar with the operation of the airplane. As it was, he felt confident that he could accomplish it satisfactorily.

Rosenberg took off, climbed to an altitude of about 100 feet, and then landed on the same runway from which he had taken off. With the strong wind and the light loading, the plane, after touching down, ran along only a couple of lengths before it came to a stop. He then turned back and made another take-off, this time climbing to the pattern height of about 800 feet, turning and coming back at high speed, and then making another landing with a very short roll. Everyone was happy with the performance, particularly considering the adverse conditions.

The subsequent test flying, which covered a period of several months, was done by Rosenberg and John Paul Jones of his staff. The flight tests fell into two main categories: one, those to complete the development of the aileron system, for which insufficient

Ag-1 making its first demonstration flight, December 1, 1950, at Easterwood Field, College Station, Texas.

basic wind-tunnel data were available; and, two, those required to prove airworthiness under CAA regulations. For lateral control we first tried the flap ailerons alone. We found that they did very well for the high-speed condition with the flap up, but at low speeds, particularly with the flap down, they were completely inadequate. The yawing moments were quite noticeable and undesirable. We then tried the slot-lip ailerons alone and found that at the high-speed condition, they barely gave a minimum amount of control;

at the low speed, however, they were quite good. And with the flap down they were excellent.

The problem, then, was to find a linkage that would combine them properly and give good control throughout the entire range, flap up or flap down, and with satisfactorily low control forces having a smooth gradient. To accomplish this I designed bell cranks with various holes for pivot points so that a wide variety of differential linkage arrangements could be tried. Each combination was put through a standard set of tests, and after a couple of months of testing we finally arrived at a satisfactory combination.

The effect of the flap was so great that I was afraid to use a control that could be changed suddenly. If a pilot was flying at low speed with the flap fully deflected, and then suddenly retracted the flap, he would lose a great deal of altitude or have to pick up a substantial amount of speed before he would be flying satisfactorily again. I therefore arranged a crank linkage that required about twenty turns to go from zero flap setting to the full 45-degree setting for the center flap. This required too long to make the change, though, and we finally found a satisfactory arrangement that required only nine turns.

The change from zero flap to full flap also required a very large trim change. To relieve the pilot of the need to change the trim, we connected the flap linkage to the adjustable stabilizer, which made the trim change automatic. The regular longitudinal trim control was then superimposed upon this linkage.

This arrangement worked out very satisfactorily. In the tests to prove satisfactory airworthiness under CAA regulations, it was found that the five degrees of dihedral that I had given the wing was not quite sufficient to raise the low wing in a slip. I cured this by changing the form of the wing tips. The original wing tips were made of two single pieces of curved aluminum sheet, one of which came down from the top, and the other up from the bottom. The new wing tips had the upper surface of the wing extend out in its original form, with all of the tapered portion coming up from the bottom, giving in effect greater dihedral. At the same time I extended the span a little, making it an even 40 feet. This modification took care of the wing slip situation satisfactorily. At this point we considered the airplane satisfactory enough to go on to the next stage of our two-stage program, which was installing and testing the equipment for dispersing spray, dust, seeds, and fertilizer.

Note the upswept wing tips of the Ag-1 in its final form.

On the flat plantation owned by Texas A&M just west of the Brazos River, we had just begun to establish a station for measuring the spray patterns of various types of agricultural airplanes. Several different forms of measurement eventually were used, but the main one turned out to be a novel direct method in which we weighed the material directly where it fell. The weight measurement was accomplished by the use of a number of delicate platform scales. Each scale was made up by reworking an analytical balance, so as to have a light platform or pan about 16 inches square at the top. The dust or spray fell on the platform and was weighed in place. These scales were placed 5 feet apart over a lateral distance of 100 feet. In order to get results quickly, the balances were reworked to become dial scales that gave readings directly in terms of pounds per acre.

We used this measuring station for a period of years in order to study the swath distribution and to improve it wherever possible. At the same time that construction of our measuring station was started, we also put our first spray equipment on the Ag-1. Then, as the measuring station became operational, we experimented with different nozzle arrangements to obtain the best possible spray pattern. This was difficult, partly because of the effect on the pattern of the twisting propeller slipstream under the center portion of the airplane.

In late February 1951 the Third National Agricultural Aviation Conference of the National Flying Farmers Association was held in

Memphis, Tennessee. The meeting was well attended, and most of the talks were on agricultural subjects such as insect control, weed control, seeding, mesquite control, and fertilizing, all of which could be done by airplane.

The Ag-1 was flown to Memphis for the meeting, where it was demonstrated and its characteristics discussed. (George Roth and I flew to the meeting in my Ercoupe.) The weather was quite cold, and the 500-mile trip to Memphis was enough to make the pilot complain bitterly about the discomfort in the open cockpit. We later provided an enclosure for the pilot that could be used when needed.

Bill Piper and his first son, Bill Jr., attended the Memphis meeting in order to present to the Flying Farmers a new Piper Tri-Pacer. The Tri-Pacer, which had just started into production, had been converted from the Pacer, by changing from the tail-wheel-type gear to a tricycle gear and by connecting the ailerons and the rudders together with a flexible spring linkage. I was naturally pleased when Bill Piper, Sr., in presenting the Tri-Pacer at the meeting's main banquet, stated that his company had followed the characteristics of Fred Weick's Ercoupe wherever it could.

The testing and minor improving of the Ag-1 continued through the spring of 1951. Because many of the agricultural planes in use had had contact with electrical wires (in fact, many of the Stearmans were then showing creases in their landing gear fairings because of contact with electrical wires that they had broken), we decided to sharpen our plane's spring steel landing-gear legs to a point, so that they could more easily break through any wires that might be contacted. In addition, we designed two fairly large sloping tubes into the turnover structure to guide wires over the cockpit, in case they slid back along the upper cowling. Also, because many airplanes had had their vertical tail surfaces catastrophically damaged by wires, we mounted a cable from the top of the cockpit to the top of the vertical fin, so that the wires would be guided over the fin and not harm it. Thus, some bad crashes were to be avoided.

Another innovative feature of the Ag-1 was an instrument panel mounted so far ahead that the pilot's head would not come in contact with it in a crash. Since we had allowed one foot for the stretch of the pilot and safety belt, this would not happen even if he did not wear a shoulder harness. I soon realized that this was not a practical solution, however. With my long arms I could reach the instrument panel to make adjustments, but most shorter pilots could not reach it at all with the seat belt fastened. It thus became necessary to use a shoulder harness to keep the pilot's head from striking the instrument panel in a crash.

We provided the Ag-1 with a standard navy seat belt and shoulder harness strong enough to support a 200-pound man with an acceleration of 40 g, or a momentary load forty times the man's weight (or 8,000 pounds). It had been demonstrated that a man can withstand accelerations of this order when properly supported. Since the history of safety-belt failures had indicated that accelerations from 15 to 25 g were likely to be obtained in crashes of the kind under consideration, we felt that a harness capable of withstanding a 40-g acceleration was warranted, and that adequate support for the harness was, of course, also necessary.

We came up with a novel arrangement that combined the shoulder harness with the seat belt. As originally installed, the harness had the usual loop at the lower end of each shoulder strap, which the pilot had to slip over a portion of the belt clasp before fastening the belt. Thus there were four loose ends—two for the shoulder straps and two for the belt—that had to be located and assembled before the harness could be fastened. This was a time-consuming operation, which probably explains why many duster pilots, who got in and out of their airplanes every few minutes, often did not bother to use a shoulder harness, even when it was available. The only final change made to the Ag-1 installation was the permanent attachment of each shoulder strap to its respective side of the seat belt. Thus there were no loose ends to hunt for. Now, over thirty years later, the arrangement is still used in some of the new agricultural airplanes.

The shoulder straps of the Ag-1 were supported on an inertia reel, which gave the pilot freedom to move as far forward as the seat belts permitted. If the airplane were given a deceleration of 3 g or more, such as would occur even in a mild crash, the inertia gear would lock the harness in the position it had been in at the start, and the pilot's shoulders would be restrained from going forward while the airplane came to a stop. At that time the inertia reel had just come out, but at the present time it is in fairly general use.

During the entire design and construction period of the Ag-1 I had been working closely with Hugh DeHaven and Howard Hasbrook of the Crash Injury Research Unit of Cornell University Medical College. As the plane approached completion, DeHaven and Hasbrook came out with the following ten recommendations for making an agricultural airplane crashworthy.

1. Design forward fuselage and cabin structure to resist nominal crash loads as well as flight and landing loads.

2. Design aircraft structures to absorb energy by progressive collapse.

3. Design tubular structure to bend and fail outwardly away from the occupants.

4. Locate the passengers and pilot seats as far aft in the fuselage as possible, behind the wing.

5. Locate fuel tanks in or on the wings, not between the fire wall and instrument panel.

6. Provide space between the instrument panel and fire wall or nose section to permit forward displacement of the panel and the instrument casings.

7. Design the instrument panel to be free of sharp rigid edges in range of pilot's head.

8. Fabricate the instrument panel of ductile material and/or use an energy-absorbing shield on the panel face.

9. Mount instrument cases on shearpins as low on the panel as possible.

10. Provide shoulder harness, safety belts, seats, and seat anchorages of sufficient strength to resist failure up to the point of cabin collapse.

The Ag-1 was made to conform to all of these recommendations except number five, which called for locating the fuel tanks in or on the wings and not between the fire wall and the instrument panel. My study of crashes had shown that many had occurred because of mishandling of the fuel system or failure of the fuel system. Putting the fuel tanks in the wings meant extra complications, I thought, in the form of fuel pumps, valves, and fittings. In my opinion the overall safety picture would be better with the simplest possible gravity-feed fuel system draining directly to the carburetor, and this required a position in the fuselage up back of the engine.

12.

Ups and Downs of Aerial Application *

From July to October of 1951, the Ag-1 airplane was taken on a demonstration tour by CAA personnel. The tour covered most of the agricultural areas of the United States. At each stop the airplane was demonstrated by a CAA pilot and was then flown and evaluated by other pilots, largely duster and sprayer operators. In all, over 650 pilots flew the airplane. Considering that the Ag-1 was a single-place airplane and that there was no opportunity for these

---

*A generally used term for aerial application to crops and forests is "cropdusting." But this term has come to have a certain stigma attached to it. Immediately after World War II, when many trainer planes were available as surplus, trained pilots who were looking for jobs often purchased surplus planes, added spraying and dusting equipment to the planes, and went into the cropdusting business. Some of them moved from place to place and made a reputation for not being entirely reliable. Cropdusting therefore got a bad name. Many of the cropdusters stayed in one place, however, and became stable in their operations, serving the same customers year after year. They did not like the stigma of cropdusting attached to them and preferred to be called "aerial applicators." This went along with their formation of statewide and national organizations. It was this group of professionals that I worked with at Texas A&M in the 1950s.

pilots to receive special dual-control instruction or to be checked out by a pilot familiar with the airplane, the mere fact that the Ag-1 survived this treatment and returned to College Station in one piece vindicated both its handling characteristics and its ruggedness.

Before each pilot flew the airplane, though, he did receive a typed sheet of paper with information from the CAA regarding the airplane's special characteristics. Afterward each pilot was asked to record his opinions on thirty-seven individual items listed under the main headings of performance, flight characteristics, controls, ground handling of materials, protection, and maintenance and repair. In obtaining a pilot's opinion of the airplane, it would have been desirable of course to have had his judgment only after he had become used to the plane and had had considerable experience with it. A pilot's first impressions, such as were obtained in the one or two flights possible for each pilot during this tour, were often different from his impressions after he had become familiar with the airplane.

Nonetheless, the first impressions of several hundred pilots were of substantial value. When averaging all of the ratings, 98 percent of them were satisfactory or better; 67 percent were excellent; and only 2 percent were unsatisfactory. Of the thirty-seven characteristics evaluated, the worst two were considered unsatisfactory by only about one-seventh of the pilots who checked them. In general the pilots' approval ratings for the Ag-1 were higher than expected, especially considering the plane's unusual features, such as the high position of the pilot and the unusually powerful flaps. It is likely that some of the pilots thought they were receiving a favor in the opportunity to fly the airplane and were therefore less severe in their ratings than they might have been otherwise. I thought that on the whole it was probable that more weight should have been given to the unfavorable comments than to the favorable ones.

Before starting on the demonstration tour, the Ag-1 had been fitted with its first installation of spraying equipment. After the tour, the plane was returned to us for an extended period of experimental use at the Texas A&M plantation measuring station.

At about the same time we started a new investigation, which was sponsored by the NACA, on the lateral control of light planes near the stall. Initially this work involved flight testing with a light high-wing Taylorcraft monoplane having various amounts of washout and various lengths of leading edge slot. We found that satisfactory lateral control occurred consistently, even under conditions simulating extremely gusty air, at angles of attack approximately two degrees below that for the maximum lift coefficient (or the stall of the wing as a whole). To explore the dangerous possibility of entering spins, we made supplementary tests on control at high angles of attack under actual gusty air conditions.

During the period when we were testing spraying systems on the Ag-1 and studying lateral control near the stall for the NACA, I served on an advisory committee to the Texas Aeronautic Commission. One day in January 1952, Asa Burroughs, who worked for the Aeronautics Commission, called on me at our Texas A&M Aircraft Research Center to see if the commission could help sponsor a joint project of some kind that might attract additional public awareness to the future of aviation in Texas. I told Burroughs that I was planning to set up an annual conference on the use of airplanes in agriculture, starting about a year later, after we had some worthwhile results from the measuring station. Asa was enthusiastic about the idea but couldn't wait until the following year. And so, only two months later, with the generous help of the agricultural departments at the college, we held the first conference.

We held our meeting, which we optimistically called the First Annual Texas Agricultural Aviation Conference and Short Course on Pest Control, on March 31 and April 1, 1952. It was sponsored not only by Texas A&M, but also by the Texas Aeronautics Commission and the Texas Flying Farmers Association. The first day included a morning of papers on insect control, a short talk by me on the Texas A&M agricultural aviation program as a whole, followed by an afternoon demonstration of the Ag-1 airplane and the operation of the measuring station. In the evening there was a dinner meeting chaired by E. M. ("Tex") Anderson, president of the National Flying Farmers Association, and with talks by Dr. R. B. Lewis, director of the Texas Agricultural Experiment Station, and Ralph E. Young, president of the Ohio Flying Farmers and the agricultural aviation coordinator for the Ohio Aviation Board.

The next morning there was a panel of papers on weed and brush control, defoliation, and state laws and regulations. In the afternoon Ted Von Rosenberg, our pilot for the Ag-1, explained the CAA's agricultural aviation program. Finally, there were papers on the fundamentals of plant disease control and the essentials of seeding and fertilizing by airplane.

The attendance at the first conference was good, even though many operators in the Rio Grande Valley had not been able to come because they had already started their spring work, and nearly everyone there recommended that we make the meeting an annual event. We did continue the conferences, and they thrived for as long as I remained at Texas A&M and for a few years afterward.

At the 1953 conference I gave a talk in which I presented a general picture of agricultural aviation activity in the United States. During 1951, I said, one-sixth of the country's total land area was under cultivation and about one-tenth of that, or some thirty-nine million acres, was being treated from aircraft. (A much greater proportion is treated now.) The number of airplanes used in the distribution of agricultural materials had increased from a few hundred in 1942 to about 6,500 in 1951. The large increase was made possible partly, I stated, by the surplus military training airplanes that were available at a very low cost following World War II—the supply of which appeared to be about exhausted in 1951. On record there were 1,725 aerial applicator firms; these firms averaged between 3 and 4 airplanes each, with only a few firms having over 20 airplanes and only one having over 40. At that time, about 30 percent of all the aerial application work was done on cotton, about 15 percent on wheat, 6 percent on rice, and lesser amounts on tobacco, alfalfa, corn, tomatoes, peas, and fruits.

At the same meeting George Roth gave a paper on the work that we had done at the rice pasture experiment station over the period of the last three years. It is interesting that at that time there were as many as six different types of aircraft applications that could be made effectively on a single rice crop. These included (1) sowing of the rice seed, (2) application of a chemical fertilizer, (3) spraying of a herbicide for weed control, (4) application of an insecticide, (5) a second application of fertilizer, and (6) spraying of a desiccating agent for preharvest drying. There were other papers, delivered by faculty from the college's school of agriculture, discussing such topics as grasshopper control on the ranges, defoliation and preharvest drying, and toxicological hazards and care in the use of the chemicals.

In early 1953 we made our first installation of dust-dispersing equipment in the Ag-1. At the same time, additional tests on the airplane's performance and handling characteristics were made as the program permitted. In this connection, the distance required to take off and clear a 50-foot obstacle was measured for various flight and load conditions. As I remember it, the Ag-1 with its original gross weight of 3,000 pounds actually did take off and climb to 50 feet well under the quarter mile (or 1,350 feet) that we had originally specified.

In addition, I personally made a series of tests to find the airplane's roll response in lateral control. I rigged up a high-speed movie camera in the plane and pointed it forward so that it could take a picture of the horizon but in addition could also take pictures of a stopwatch and some of the instruments, including the air-speed indicator. From these tests we confirmed that the airplane actually did have excellent lateral control, far more than the ordinary run of airplanes.

As additional test information and experience were obtained, we made minor improvements wherever possible. It was obvious to us that if good short-field performance were to be obtained with the larger 1,200- instead of the original 800-pound load of spray or dust equipment, the airplane would have to have more power. Continental Motor Company was developing a flat six-cylinder, 300-HP engine, and as soon as it was sufficiently developed, we made arrangements to get one for the Ag-1.

During the course of the two and a half years that the Ag-1 had been flying, it had been demonstrated at various meetings. Most of these demonstrations had been made by "the Admiral," as we called him, John Paul Jones of the CAA's Fort Worth region, who had also done much of the original test flying on the airplane with Von Rosenberg. The Admiral ordinarily flew the plane light (i.e, with a light load of seed and spray) and gave quite a demonstration. In his own words: "Normally, when the aircraft reached 50 MPH indicated air speed on the take-off run, a wing tip would be lowered until it almost touched the ground, and at this moment, as the air speed passed 55, I would pull the plane into an abrupt, climbing turn. At the top of this turn, about 50 feet high, and in a bank of approximately 45 degrees, the air speed would be 45 MPH, and this would fall off to 40 MPH as the plane was held at the same height and the turn tightened. Roll-out would be at the 180-degree point of the turn, unless crowd location, terrain, or other obstructions dictated otherwise." Most of these demonstration flights had been made near sea level.

On June 26, 1953, John Paul Jones made a demonstration flight

John Paul Jones in the Ag-1. I am holding open the door to one of the spray tanks.

for the purpose of showing the aircraft to members of the National Cotton Congress at Texas Technological College in Lubbock. The elevation at Lubbock is about 3,200 feet, and the density altitude that day was probably between 5,000 and 6,000 feet. The Admiral made one of his regular demonstrations, including several duster passes, at the main Lubbock airport. And the only peculiar thing he noticed was that power appeared low on the sharp pull-ups and turns. This was normal and expected, however, due to the altitude.

Later, the Admiral flew the plane to a special strip that had been prepared on the experimental farm at the west edge of the Texas Tech campus. From a report that he prepared later, he appears to have thought that the operating area was much larger than it actually was. He stated in his report that "a strip about 100 feet wide and 1,600 feet long had been smoothed off with a grader, making a very good duster field. It lay north and south, with a power line across the north end, but with a clear south approach of 1,500 or more additional feet." Subsequently, I went to Lubbock and measured those distances. From my pacing, the distance between the power line on the north and south ends of the grading was only 1,000 feet instead of 1,600, and from the end of the grading to some buildings several stories high was a distance of only about 300 feet. In other words, the total distance from the start of the run to buildings that could not be cleared was only 1,300 feet, meaning that a turn had to be completed within that distance. Also, there was another 13,000-volt power line running parallel to the strip that was only 600 feet to the west of the strip, instead of about a quarter mile, as the Admiral had stated in his report.

For the campus exhibition, Jones had roughly 100 pounds of maize seed in the hopper to demonstrate seeding and also a little over 200 pounds of water in the spray tank to demonstrate the spraying operation. In the AG-1 these two operations could be accomplished independently. The load was still relatively light, but it was a couple of hundred pounds more than the Admiral usually had with his demonstrations.

He took off to the south, left the ground at just about the point where his audience was standing, and climbed satisfactorily to a height of about 50 feet. He then had to make an unusually tight turn, even for his demonstrations, in order to change his course by 180 degrees and still be inside of the power line that was only 600 feet from his take-off strip. The airplane would not hold its altitude throughout this sharp 180-degree turn. Though the pilot thought that it was losing power, the engine operated smoothly without interruption, and later tests showed that it was still in good operating condition. When Jones saw that he could not maintain altitude and was heading toward one of the poles supporting the power line, he throttled the engine and put his right wing down, so that the left wing hit the pole a few feet outside of the fuselage. The left wing sheared off at the point of contact. The right wing hit a fence post underneath the power line, which was very heavy because it supported a gate and was made of a railroad tie. Then the plane flipped over on its back and slid along to a stop about 60 feet from the fence. The pilot was supported by his seat belt and shoulder harness and released himself and got out of the plane immediately. He then waved to his audience to show them that he was all right, for they were running toward the plane to help him if he needed it.

The crash of the Ag-1 in 1953 from which pilot John Paul Jones walked away virtually unhurt.

He was in fact unharmed, except for a sore thumb on the hand that was on the control stick.

Later on, I made some rough calculations that showed that in order to make a 180-degree turn within 600 feet and have a little room to spare, an angle of bank of more than 45 degrees was required. Under those conditions, the airplane was flying a little above its ceiling and could not be expected to hold altitude. The conditions were made even more difficult by the fact that the last half of the turn was a downwind turn with a wind of about 15 MPH. This naturally made the pilot tend to tighten the turn even more. So as I saw it, the pilot was trying to make the airplane do more than it was capable of doing.

The next morning the Admiral gave a talk to the National Cotton Congress and started by saying that he was thankful to be alive. He also said, "I am completely convinced that the specially designed cockpit and other safety features of this plane were responsible for the fact that I lived through this crash. It appears highly improbable that any other plane used in agricultural work could have been crashed as this one was without killing the pilot, and it appears beyond reason that such planes could have sustained this crash and left the pilot unhurt."

I would have been delighted to have believed his statement, but unfortunately I couldn't. The accident was not of the type where the nose hit the ground at a steep angle and the deceleration was very great. The Admiral's accident, the type where the airplane flipped over and slid to a stop in some distance, was not the type that gave the highest decelerations and not the type that was most likely to be fatal. I would have preferred to have had the pilot come out unscathed from a severe nose-down accident, for then it would have given better proof of the crashworthiness of the airplane. The airplane gained a wonderful reputation this way, but unfortunately it was not founded on fact. On the other hand, I believe it would have done well in a severe nose-down accident also, especially at the speed at which it was traveling.

One point of interest is that the seat belt of the Ag-1 was supported by means of navy dynamometer rings, which in a crash would show how much load had been put on both the right-hand and the left-hand attachments of the seat belt. In this case the dynamometer ring on one side showed no permanent deflection at all, which meant that the load on it had not been over about 500 pounds. The ring on the other side, however, showed that it had sustained a load of 3,000 pounds in the crash. The pilot was therefore thrown around in a very unsymmetrical manner. The Admiral weighed 200 pounds, and if the total load had been taken in a symmetrical manner, it would have represented a deceleration of over 15 g. So it appears to have been a good thing that he was well supported and that the cockpit did protect him satisfactorily.

In 1952, after the Ag-1 had been completed and tested to a certain extent, the technical data regarding it were made available to those who desired it for the cost of reproduction, which was then $50. Included in the sale were about fifty blueprints, specifications, and technical reports covering the general design information, strength computations, and load tests. As I remember it, about twenty-five sets were delivered to various manufacturers.

One man who bought the Ag-1 data was George Wing of the Los Angeles area. Previously, while working as a designer for North American Aviation, Wing had invented a new kind of fastener, which he had called a high-shear rivet. Ordinary bolts were likely to be loaded in shear and in tension. Some bolts, however, were required to take shear loads only, and for these the ordinary bolt head and nut were heavier than necessary. Wing furnished his high-shear rivets with a strong steel body and replaced the old bolt head with a small flange. Wedged over the end of the nut was a light aluminum ring to hold the fitting in place.

This concept was accepted immediately by the designers of sophisticated aircraft. George Wing then made arrangements with North American to set up a small plant for manufacturing not only the high-shear rivets, but also the tools for making them, which he leased out to others on a royalty basis. His plant grew and his income rose so rapidly that he was soon able to do development work for what he called "11-cent dollars." Under these conditions, he purchased the Trans-Land Company, which was a small outfit making hoppers, spray equipment, dust-distributing equipment, and other items suitable for use on agricultural airplanes. He then expanded this activity to include the production of the agricultural airplanes themselves. This enterprise led him to purchase the blueprints and reports for the Ag-1.

After the Ag-1 crashed at Lubbock, Wing wanted to purchase the wreckage. It was therefore put up for bids, which he won, and the wreckage was shipped to his plant in Torrance, California, where he used it, together with the drawings and technical information on the Ag-1, as a guide in designing a similar but more powerful agricultural airplane. The wing for his new airplane had powerful flaps with connected slot-lip ailerons, essentially similar to those on the Ag-1, which gave the plane an unusually effective lateral control system. Wing had to strengthen his wings (pardon the pun), though, to take care of the heavier weight that the airplane carried.

Wing called the new machine the Ag-2. The original design called for a power plant consisting of a 450-HP Pratt and Whitney engine, but by the time the development was completed, the engine used was a 600-HP Pratt and Whitney R-1340 engine.

Wing used me as a consultant on the project, and in January 1954 I made a trip out to the Trans-Land operation in California. We went over the entire project in detail with his staff, and I stayed overnight at George's house. It was interesting that he had a drafting table in one room, and during nights when he couldn't sleep he spent a lot of time at the drafting board musing over new designs. It was also interesting that his wife's maiden name was Cessna and that she was related in some way to Clyde Cessna.

George had a surplus military plane that he kept for his own use. (I forget whether it was PT-13 or an AT-6.) When our work was finished, he flew me over to an airport near Arcadia where my brother Herb lived with his family so that I could have a visit with them before going home on the airlines. The entire trip was over a solidly built-up city area, and I marveled at how the private pilots around the Los Angeles area kept flying over that sort of thing at relatively low altitudes with single-engine airplanes year after year. I have also marveled all these years how they could do so much flying in the Los Angeles area in air they could barely see through. It has been work for me to navigate to the proper airport in that area ever since 1945, when the smog was much less dense than it is now. But there is more flying in that area than almost any other, and so they must find a way of doing it satisfactorily.

The development of the Ag-2 went on in a moderate way for a number of years. In 1955 the prototype was flown to Texas A&M's annual agricultural aviation conference, and I had an opportunity to fly it. I made some simulated duster runs with procedure turns and found that it handled very nicely, even though it was much heavier and larger than the other ag planes I had flown. The production model, with the 600-HP engine, finally came out with a nominal gross weight of 6,000 pounds. Under part eight of the civil air regulations for agricultural operation, however, it was possible to use it with a gross weight as high as 7,700 pounds. The plane had a hopper capacity of 53 cubic feet, and even with the 6,000-pound gross weight, it had a payload of 2,000 pounds. It would have fit very well into the present use of ag planes, which are larger in size. But over thirty years ago, it was well ahead of its time. Because only a few were sold, production was discontinued. Too bad it is not in production now.

In July 1953, Howard ("Pug") Piper, son of the founder of Piper Aircraft Corporation, visited me and looked over our operation at College Station. This was the beginning of an enduring and a happy relationship between Piper and myself.

My first project for him was as a consultant to design, build, and test a dust and seed distributor for a modified Piper PA-18 Super-cub airplane that had been fitted with a hopper for agricultural use. A good number of these modified Supercubs had been produced and were in service. We tried several different distributors at our measuring station, particularly for the distribution of rice seed. I presented the results of our research, which fitted into our college's general agricultural aviation program very well, at our third annual Texas Agricultural Aviation Conference in 1954. Eventually, the Piper company manufactured the distributors and sold many of them with the PA-18 agricultural airplane over the next few years.

I had pointed out to Pug Piper during his visit to College Station in July 1953 some of the results of my studies of the accidents that had occurred in agricultural aviation during the last few years. In general, I explained, there were two types of airplanes in use, both of which were two-place tandem training planes, with one person in front of the other. One type consisted of light, high-wing monoplanes in which the pilot was put in the front seat so he could see ahead reasonably well and the load was placed behind him in the rear seat location. The other type was made up of open cockpit biplanes, and in these cases the agricultural load was put in the front cockpit, ahead of the pilot. My count showed that the proportion of accidents that was fatal was more than twice as great for the airplanes having the load back of the pilot and in a position to help crush him than for the airplanes with the pilot located back of the load. This made a great impression on him, for the Piper PA-18A Supercub used in agricultural work did have the load in back of the pilot. It made him appreciate the extent to which we had gone, in the case of the Ag-1 agricultural airplane, to protect the pilot in a crash.

In a couple of weeks he telephoned me from the Piper plant in Lock Haven, Pennsylvania, to inquire whether I could make arrangements for our Aircraft Research Center to develop a new agricultural airplane under Piper sponsorship. The new plane was to have the special features of the Ag-1 so far as feasible, but it was to be somewhat smaller. Also, instead of the structure being mainly made of aluminum alloys, it was to have a steel tube fuselage and a fabric covering throughout. Also, it was to have the structural form and some of the actual parts of the Piper PA-18A and the Piper PA-22 Tri-Pacer.

I arranged for this project to be accomplished through our Texas A&M Research Foundation, and in September 1953, after attending an NACA Aerodynamics Committee meeting in Washington, D.C., I borrowed an Ercoupe from the Sanders brothers in Riverdale, Maryland, and flew the 150 miles north to Lock Haven, where Pug and I arranged the details of the new project. When I got back home, I started in earnest on the new design, which I called the

Ag-3. Professor Ben Hamner, who taught the structures courses in the Texas A&M aeronautical engineering department, helped me, and we made fair progress. Three months later, in December, I made another visit to Lock Haven, and we ironed out further details. For my return trip, Pug gave me ride in a PA-22 Tri-Pacer that he was delivering to the Piper dealer in Baton Rouge, Louisiana. In fact, he let me fly the plane on the last leg from Birmingham to Baton Rouge.

During this trip, incidentally, Piper made a direct comparison between the cruising performance of his lightweight Tri-Pacer, which had a fixed tricycle gear, and his new experimental airplane known as the Airsedan. The Airsedan was an all-metal, low-wing airplane with retractable landing gear. Both were four-place airplanes, but the Airsedan was a little larger and more powerful. The airplanes were flown together in loose formation at a cruising speed of 120 MPH, Piper piloting the Tri-Pacer and a man by the name of Stover piloting the Airsedan. (Because he flew with a cigar in his mouth, he was referred to as "Smokey Stover.") At each stop the fuel consumption of each plane was measured and compared. The comparison showed that the Tri-Pacer, even with its fixed tricycle gear, used slightly less fuel than did the Airsedan, with its retractable gear. The Airsedan was never put into production.

The other interesting item on the trip was that we stopped in Starkville, Mississippi, where we visited with Dr. Gus Raspet, head of the aerophysics department of Mississippi State University. Raspet was carrying out interesting and useful research, partly on boundary layer control of the air flowing over a wing. He had a two-place Schweitzer sailplane fitted with battery-powered boundary layer control with a myriad of small holes over the upper surface of the wings. He gave me a chance to try it out.

We were towed by a Stearman airplane up to 10,000 feet and then released. From this altitude we had ample time to fly both with and without the boundary layer control under various conditions. Though I do not remember the quantitative results, I do remember the impression that the boundary layer control was effective in influencing the sailplane's performance by reducing the drag.

During the flight, Professor Raspet mentioned that buzzards would sometimes fly in formation with him and that he could get a good measure of their performance by flying the sailplane at its maximum lift-over-drag ratio, where the buzzards could soar right along with him. This meant that a buzzard could attain a lift over drag ratio of more than twenty. This compares with an L over D of only about five or six, as I remember it, for a dead buzzard frozen with its wings stretched out in the flying position. (This type of test had in fact been made in the NACA's towing tank at Langley Field in the early 1930s.)

While design and construction work on the Ag-3 continued in 1954, I attended an SAE meeting in Houston for the purpose of hearing a paper delivered by an engineer from the Fram Filter Company on a new type of air filter for automobiles. With the new filter, the air going to the carburetor would pass through a large area of pleated but porous paper. With the large area, the pressure drop across the filter was supposed to be so low that very little power would be lost; this was true even though the air passages through the filter were minute.

At the meeting I heard that the efficiency of the pleated paper filter in removing dust and other material from the air was over 99 percent. This compared to an average of 85 percent for the oiled, wire-screen-type filters that had been in general use at the time. A fair amount of airplane dusting and spraying was done, of course, in dusty air close to the ground, and it appeared to me that the new filter could be a substantial help in increasing engine life. I, therefore, incorporated it into the Ag-3 design, which became, so far as I know, the first airplane to use a pleated paper filter. At that time the filter was just starting to be used in certain Chrysler automobiles; since then it has become standard equipment in just about all automobiles and airplanes using small piston-type engines.

In 1954 a group of people from western Europe visited the United States in order to investigate our use of airplanes in agriculture. One or two representatives each came from Finland, Sweden, Denmark, West Germany, France, Switzerland, Belgium, Italy, and the Netherlands. The trip was organized by Dr. W. J. Maan, of the Netherlands. Dr. Maan was what would be in this country the top official in the department of agriculture in charge of disseminating agricultural information to county agents. This group of visiting Europeans met first in Washington with personnel from the CAA and the Department of Agriculture and then were flown in a CAA DC-3 to various parts of the country to see aerial applications in operation and to note the experimental work that was being done at some universities and government experiment stations.

The group spent a couple of days with us at Texas A&M, where they learned about our special agricultural airplanes. We took them out to our measuring station where they saw a demonstration run of pattern measurement. We told them about our annual agricultural aviation conferences and gave them copies of the reports for the three conferences that had been held up to that time. We also showed them some of the local aerial applicator operations, particularly the Delta dusters, that were located nearby.

I then accompanied the Europeans on a trip to other parts of Texas and Oklahoma. In western Oklahoma they saw a B-17 bomber which was fitted to distribute grasshopper bait to kill the grasshoppers in the range land. The grasshoppers would sometimes swarm and devastate large areas of range land, making it worthless as feed for the cattle if they were not controlled.

In the cattle country west of Fredericksburg, Texas, we visited a Texas A&M experiment station that dealt primarily with cattle and sheep. The gentlemen from Europe had read about cowboys and had seen them in action in moving pictures, but they requested that they be given a demonstration of a live cowboy actually roping a steer. So one of the cowboys saddled his horse and went after a steer, roping it, throwing it, and tying it up so that it could be worked on. The horseman then rode back to the group, and he was introduced to them. His name was Schultz, which caused a great deal of hilarious laughter from the Europeans. Herr Schultz, a typical American cowboy?

What the European gentlemen apparently did not know was that about one hundred fifty years ago, in the early 1800s, many different groups of people immigrated into the spare parts of Texas from a number of European countries. This was at a time when they could obtain land by homesteading. A large number of people from Germany settled in the area west of Austin and north of San Antonio. A group from Italy settled in the Brazos River Valley near Bryan. And an area farther south was populated largely by Czechs. Thus the Texans of today have names that derive from many parts of Europe as well as from the British Isles. Many of the early professors at Texas A&M who have been honored by having buildings named for them had names like Sbisa and Guion. Of course the Spanish influence still prevails throughout all of Texas as illustrated by the Brazos River near Texas A&M, the original name of which was El Río de los Brazos de Dios, or the River of the Arms of God.

In 1951 Charles MacMillan of Edinburgh, Texas, had invited a number of the agricultural airplane operators in his area to meet and discuss the economic and technical problems they were facing. During this meeting MacMillan recommended that an organization should be created through which these problems and others like them might be met and dealt with collectively. This meeting led to another meeting in the home of Bill Cuby of Pharr, Texas, which furthered the plans for an aerial applicators association. This was followed by a general meeting of most of the operators in the Rio Grande Valley. As a result of the surprising accord that was demonstrated that day between the Rio Grande operators, who usually could not agree about anything, final plans for a formal organization of cropdusters was completed at that time.

At first there was just a simple agreement on business ethics and a pledge by the operators to work together for the advancement of the agricultural aviation industry. In time, however, a constitution was drafted and accepted. Following this effort the organization, the Rio Grande Valley Aerial Applicators Association, was recognized by county, state, and federal agricultural agencies.

Our first Texas Agricultural Aviation Conference and Short Course on Pest Control in early 1952 had given all the operators in Texas their first opportunity to get together in one place. At our second conference in 1953 they had organized state-wide as the Texas Aerial Applicators Association, and from then on through the time that I was at Texas A&M (through March 1957) they held their main annual meeting at our conference in a room provided for the purpose.

One thing that the Texas Aerial Applicators Association did during this period to improve the general state of agricultural aviation was to establish a fund with which the organization could help accident victims and their families. When this fund began to strain its finances, however, the association decided to concentrate on ways to establish safer operating practices. For one thing, it encouraged the use of shoulder harnesses by pilots. Small, high-wing monoplanes like Cubs and Aeroncas and commercial biplanes such as Wacos and Travelairs that had been converted to agricultural use did not come equipped with shoulder harnesses. The Stearman and navy N3N military-training planes did come equipped with shoulder harnesses originally, but most of the agricultural pilots did not use them. In some operations they had to get in and out of the airplane every few minutes to help with the loading, which made the use of shoulder harnesses an extra nuisance. By 1954, however, the value of the shoulder harness, as well as other safety items such as the crash helmet, was recognized, and the entire operation of being an aerial applicator took on a more professional nature.

Our Fourth Annual Texas Agricultural Aviation Conference was held February 21–22, 1955. This time it was sponsored by the Texas Aerial Applicators Association as well as by Texas A&M, the Texas Aeronautics Commission, and the Texas Flying Farmers and Ranchers Association. As usual, the subjects of insect control, weed and brush control, and plant disease control were brought up to date by professors from the college's department of agriculture. A cotton planter gave his experiences with insect control by airplane. Other papers were given on preventive maintenance for aircraft engines, full-flow oil and air filters, and the installation of a 450-HP Pratt and Whitney engine in a Model 75 Stearman airplane.

Besides overseeing a demonstration of the Ag-3, George Roth and I also gave a paper at this meeting. We discussed our spray distribution experiments and told about the problem we had encountered with corrosion caused by agricultural chemicals. The influence of the Ag-1 and other agricultural airplanes that were then being developed, like the Fletcher Utility, led me to say that it appeared likely that airplanes designed especially for agricultural use should be commercially available on a significant scale in the near future.

A very significant paper on safety was given at this conference by Gayle F. Hansen, a CAA agricultural specialist. I had met with him at a Texas Aerial Applicators Association meeting in Galveston the previous November and had had quite a discussion with him and the association's board of directors on the possibility of establishing an applicator-pilot–training course at a land-grant college like Texas A&M. At the Galveston meeting, the association had adopted, as one of its objectives, a resolution approving such a course.

At our Ag Aviation Conference at Texas A&M in February 1955, Hansen presented a study of the first 178 agricultural aviation accidents of the year 1954. Eighty-six "green" or rookie pilots and ninety-two experienced pilots had been involved. He found that the experienced pilots had a 2 : 1 survival rate over the green pilots in the accidents. His study also showed that pilots who wore shoulder harnesses had a 2 : 1 survival rate over those who did not. He recommended wearing crash helmets and special clothing to protect against poisonous chemicals.

The recommendation he stressed, however, was the establishment of applicator-training facilities in land-grant colleges. Of course, the Texas Aerial Applicators Association would have to insist that every new pilot be a graduate of the course before its members could hire him, Hansen said. "Just think of the precedent your support for such a course at Texas A&M could establish," he said, "because if you help to make a success of it, look how rapidly it could be adopted across the nation in other land-grant colleges."

Subsequently, the Texas Aerial Applicators Association did make a formal request of the Texas A&M system to establish such an agricultural-pilot–training course. The response of the college administration was favorable, and I found myself the professor in charge of the course. The course was planned and organized with the aid of a special committee appointed by the Texas Aerial Applicators Association consisting of Lloyd P. Nolan, chairman; W. A. Lewis; Ralph L. Crosnoe; Flint G. Fried; and Joe E. Jones, TAA president and ex-officio member. Gayle Hansen also helped by preparing the flight instruction portion of the curriculum.

The first course was offered that October, and it lasted for six weeks. Entrance requirements included a CAA commercial pilot's certificate and a minimum of five hundred hours of solo operation. The curriculum was divided into two substantially equal parts: one, field operation and flight instruction, which included thirty hours in the air; and, two, classroom and laboratory instruction in biological elements, care and handling of equipment, customer relations, and aviation law.

The first class was comprised of ten students, eight of whom took the full course. One man, who was already an experienced applicator pilot, took partial flight time, and another took the classroom and laboratory work but no flight time. The facilities and pieces of equipment used for the first class were furnished by various sources. A surplus navy N3N training airplane was available from our Aircraft Research Center at Texas A&M, but the following four other airplanes were loaned to the project by interested companies: a dual-control 125-HP Piper PA-18 airplane, loaned by Aero

Agricultural Service, Inc., of Alice, Texas; a 135-HP Piper PA-18 duster and sprayer, loaned by the Piper Aircraft Corporation, Lock Haven, Pennsylvania; a dual-control 225-HP Stearman airplane, loaned by Delta Airlines Dusting Division, Bryan, Texas; and a 220-HP Stearman sprayer, loaned by the Gulf Coast Dusting Company, Houston, Texas. Other equipment, such as crash helmets, special goggles, and radio sets, was loaned to the project by various companies.

The flight instruction was given partly from Easterwood Field, the college airport, but mainly from a flight strip at the pattern measuring station on the college plantation and on nearby strips used by applicator firms. The dusting and spraying runs were made over a number of typical fields on the college plantation and on the experimental farm.

The flight-training course was very thorough and included many details, including aircraft preflight inspections; between-load inspections; prestarting, starting, and taxiing for take-off; pretake-off checks; take-offs; climb-outs, departing take-off area; slow flight; powered turns; flat power turns; vertical reversements, both coordinated and snapped; applicator procedure turnarounds; stalls and recoveries with minimum loss of altitude; accidental spin entries; slips or other losses of altitude; surveying fields; checking for obstructions; applicator S turns at working level; forced and emergency landings; approaches and landings; taxiing after landings; and parking and tie-down. The course also covered checking the distance needed to become airborne and the distance needed to clear a 50-foot obstacle, plus checking the distance needed to stop from the airborne point. It also included maneuvering flat turns— which were used to avoid obstacles and in clean-up swaths—and simulated complete treatment of the field in dual instruction.

In the applicator aircraft the training also included familiarizing and repeating the above maneuvers with various loads, flying under and over wires, mapping out areas to be treated, and calibrating equipment during application. We designed the flight instruction for maximum performance consistent with safe flight practices in all phases of agricultural flying. Particular attention was paid to the angle of attack and its relation to the flight characteristics. Each airplane was fitted with a green light, which indicated the angle of steepest climb, and a red light, which indicated the proximity of the stall. In the instruction on stalls and recovery, typical accidental situations were closely simulated, and attention was given to the detrimental effect of sudden application of power. The course taught turnarounds between adjacent swath runs that were conservative, but could be made in close to the minimum possible time.

The flight instructors were Gayle Hansen, who was loaned to us by the CAA for two months to establish the flight training; Cleveland Riggs, an aerial applicator from Navasota, Texas; and Robert L. Hamm, the Texas A&M Aircraft Research Center pilot. Because of more favorable weather conditions, the flight instruction was given in the afternoon.

A tuition fee of $50 was paid at registration. The flight instruction was paid for in advance at $10 per hour for the Piper airplanes and $15 per hour for the Stearman and N3N airplanes. Lodging and meals were available at the college at nominal rates. Under Public Law 550 (also known as the Korean Bill), veterans taking the course had to pay only one quarter of the costs; they didn't have to pay anything if they were taking just classroom and laboratory work and not the flight training.

The college did not have to appropriate any funds for this short course. A donation of $500 by the Texas Aerial Applicators Association established an operating fund, and a short time later a contribution of $200 was added by the National Insurance Underwriters of St. Louis, Missouri. Thus an original total of $700 was available for the purchase of equipment and for the labor needed to prepare the course. We obtained the only other money directly available to cover the costs of the course from the tuition fees and charges for flight instruction. It happened that the direct expenditures were entirely covered by the money paid by the students and a balance of $748.44 was available to prepare for the next session.

Obviously, the course was a special sort of thing that did not go through the regular procedures of getting appropriations from the state government or the regular college administration.

We held our Fifth Annual Texas Agricultural Aviation Conference on February 27 and 28, 1956. At this conference I gave a paper reporting on the agricultural-pilot–training course. As usual, the subjects of insect control, weed and brush control, and fertilizing were brought up to date by the Texas A&M professor who specialized in that field. Included in this area was a paper by Richard Behrens of the United States Department of Agriculture on the effect of herbicide drop size on mesquite control.

In using herbicides for weed and brush control, it was very important that the herbicides did not drift away from where the application was intended and thereby damage valuable crops or flowers. Large droplets did not drift a significant amount, but very small droplets could drift extensively and cause substantial damage. In our aircraft research center we had constructed a whirling disk apparatus that produced droplets of uniform size. A cooperative program with Dr. Behrens had been arranged in which he furnished six-week-old mesquite plants in pots, which we sprayed with droplets, all of uniform size, at a rate corresponding to four gallons per acre.

Four sizes of droplets were selected: 200, 400, 600, and 800 microns. These four sizes corresponded relatively to drizzle, very light rain, light rain, and moderate rain. With the 200-micron size, 575 droplets were deposited per square inch, and this was reduced as the size increased to only 9 droplets per square inch for the 800-micron size. The results showed that about 75 percent of the plants were killed with the 200-micron size and that the kill was reduced as the droplet size increased to the point where it was very, very slight with 800 microns. Fortunately, the 200-micron size drifted a reasonably small amount, but the larger droplet sizes, which had been used extensively in mesquite and weed and brush control, were obviously very wasteful. Unfortunately, up to that time (and possibly up to the present) no nozzle arrangement had been developed that could give enough flow for use on airplanes in actual application with 200-micron droplet sizes that did not have a substantial number of smaller droplets going along with the flow.

Another paper at the conference was given by Wesley E. Yates and Norman B. Akison of the Department of Agricultural Engineering of the University of California at Davis. Their paper included the effect of nozzle type and droplet size on the possible drift. The authors recommended a solid, one-eighth-inch jet nozzle pointed to the rear that produced very few small droplets. They also studied the effect of microclimate, or the air movements between elevations of 6 and 60 feet above the ground, as well as magnitude and direction of the air currents produced by the airplane and their effect on the pattern distribution. The technique involved releasing small, four-inch diameter, gravitationally balanced hydrogen-filled balloons from the spray boom. The paths of the balloons were recorded by two movie cameras illustrating the air forces acting on the fine aerosol droplets. The downwash behind the airplane and the wing-tip vortex effect were made with several aircraft, including the N3N, a Fairchild Model 24, a Cessna 305-A high-wing monoplane, and a Bell helicopter.

The results indicated that for minimum drift with hazardous sprays, it was desirable to fly low, keep the nozzles out of the wing-tip area, and keep the boom as far from the wing as practical. In general, these findings agreed with theoretical analysis made by Wilmer Reed of the NACA in 1953 (NACA Technical Note 3032, "An Analytical Study of the Effect of Airplane Wake on the Lateral Dispersion of Aerial Sprays"). Reed's analysis covered the paths of droplets from 200 microns to 700 microns as dispersed from the Ag-1 airplane.

Also at this 1956 conference I was honored by being made a life member of the Texas Aerial Applicators Association.

The last agricultural aviation conference at Texas A&M for which I was responsible before leaving for employment with Piper was held in February 1957 (however, I did keep on attending the event for a number of years thereafter). The conference, as always, was held mainly in the Memorial Student Center, and on Sunday afternoon the Texas Aerial Applicators Association once again had its annual business meeting. This body had become quite active and strong, and talk was going around that it was leading other state organizations into the formation of a national aerial applicators association.

On the first day of the 1957 conference there were, as usual, sessions on insect and brush control. That evening there was a dinner in the ballroom chaired by Bill Lewis, president of the Texas Aerial Applicators Association. Among other things, he presented Dorothy and me with a hand-embroidered linen tablecloth with matching napkins, and I have a picture in my study here of the set being examined by Bill Piper, Sr., who attended the meeting, and me. Later a talk was given by Jim Pyle, administrator of the Civil Aeronautics Administration in Washington, D.C., on general aviation in the national picture. General aviation included, of course, agricultural aviation.

The next morning we had papers on our continued work on distribution equipment and spray and dust patterns. In the afternoon I told about agricultural aviation in western Europe and Scandinavia, which I had learned about firsthand during a three-month

William T. Piper, Sr., and I examine a present given to Dorothy and me by the Texas Aerial Applicators Association upon our leaving Texas to go with Piper in Vero Beach, 1957.

tour in the spring of 1956. We then went out to Easterwood Field for field demonstrations and a view of the new vertical wind tunnel under construction for the study of droplet formation.

Also at the airport a new agricultural airplane was displayed. Sometime earlier a young man by the name of Leland Snow had been a student in my course on flight test engineering. He had done well in the course, but nearly all of his questions had had to do with the design and construction of the Ag-1 experimental agricultural airplane that we were developing at that time. After Snow graduated he did some graduate work at the University of Texas using as a thesis the design of an agricultural airplane. He then built the plane and refined it for production, and I believe his first production model was the one on display at our 1957 conference. I was in agreement with nearly all of his design features and thought he had done a fine job except for one item.

In order to give the pilot a good view, Snow had put the pilot in front of the load, and this of course was not in accordance with my philosophy. After a couple of years he changed his mind and put the pilot back of the load, where in my opinion the pilot should be.

For several months prior to the 1957 conference, I had been working on a handbook covering aerial application in agriculture. In it I was attempting to summarize the most important developments in the field. Most of my information was from the papers of the five annual agricultural aviation conferences that had been held at Texas A&M since 1952, but some of it also came from other relevant publications. My information on aircraft, equipment, distribution, and the fundamentals of the biological subjects was applicable to aerial application in general, but the specific crop treatments that were recommended in the handbook were intended especially for the area in and around Texas. This area, though, included subtropical, moist coastal, medium rainfall, and high arid conditions. With the assistance of George Roth, I prepared chapters on aircraft, distribution equipment, distribution measurements, and operation of aircraft. Others from Texas A&M and the Department of Agriculture prepared chapters on insect control, brush and weed control, preharvest chemicals, plant disease control, fertilizing, seeding, and such general topics as customer relations, client-building, and accounting. The Texas A&M Short Course office printed 2,500 of these handbooks, and we presented one to each person who attended the 1957 conference. After a time they were all sold out. The handbook is now out of print, but there is still some demand for it, partly by attorneys who want to use it in court cases involving agricultural aviation accidents.

5.

Piper

(1957–1969)

13.

The Pawnee

In November 1956 I received a telephone call from Pug Piper in Lock Haven, Pennsylvania, inviting me to form a new development center for the Piper Aircraft Corporation. This center was to be located somewhere in the south to avoid the disadvantages of the Pennsylvania mountain winter and its effect on flying activities. I was to direct the design of new models, the construction and flight testing of experimental airplanes, and the production of prototype airplanes. Before handing any completed airplane over to a production facility for manufacturing, of course, it would first be necessary to obtain an approved type certificate based on production drawings.

The first project, Piper explained, would be to get the Ag-3 ready for production. The second project, which he also wanted to start immediately, would be to design a low-cost replacement for the obsolescent, fabric-covered PA-22 Tri-Pacer. The replacement was to be a modern, all-metal design. The production version of the Ag-3 would be produced in Lock Haven, he said, because the same sort of construction would be used as in the PA-18A and PA-22. When the all-metal replacement for the Tri-Pacer was ready for production, however, the new plant would produce it.

I enjoyed doing research work, but I was also enticed by the idea of seeing my designs out in actual use in large numbers rather than just having the results go out in the form of reports that other people would make use of in their design work. On the other hand, I also enjoyed the academic atmosphere and the friends we had made in the College Station area. After considering the pros and cons for a couple of weeks, the pros won and I said I would go with Piper.

The loss of our private strip where we could fly directly from home had some slight influence on my decision. Somewhat earlier in 1956, Dr. Clark, the owner of the pasture on which our airstrip was located, had decided to subdivide it and to sell off the lots. When he informed me of this decision, I thought I might buy the pasture and keep it to fly from until I could sell it as an investment. I had heard that farmland, which was not very good in that area, a little farther away from town, was selling for as low as $50 an acre, and thought that $100 an acre or $5,000 for the entire pasture would be a satisfactory price. When I approached Clark, he was willing to sell it all right, but his price was $1,000 an acre, or a total of $50,000. I thought that was extremely exorbitant, particularly before the work to subdivide it had been put in. As it turned out, it would have been an exceptionally good investment, even at $50,000, because the town grew to the point that that entire area is now built up. With Clark cutting roads across my runway, I had to keep our airplane at the college airport.

In mid-December 1956 Pug Piper telephoned from Fort Lauderdale and said that he and his father and the company treasurer, Charlie Poole, were going to be the next day in Vero Beach, Florida. Pug and his brother, Bill Piper, Jr., had flown all up and down both coasts of Florida, looking for likely locations, and had selected Vero Beach on the east coast and Venice on the Gulf Coast as the two most suitable. Pug asked me if I could take the airlines down immediately and spend a couple of days with them, helping his family to decide which of the two places was best for the new plant.

I told Pug I would join him as soon as possible and then tried to find "Zero Beach," which I had misunderstood Pug to say, on the map but could not find it. There was a Vero Beach, however, which I knew was somewhere near the correct location, as I understood it, and I did go there and joined them the next day.

I knew nothing whatever about the area, and when we were being driven around the town by a member of the Vero Beach chamber of commerce, I noticed a few orange and grapefruit trees in people's yards and asked innocently whether this was just for fun or whether there was some citrus activity in the outlying neighborhood. I was informed by our driver that "this was the heart of the Indian River citrus area." He said this stiffly and pompously, putting me in my place.

Vero Beach was a very attractive town of about seven thousand people and growing at a fair pace. The airport was an abandoned navy base that had been used during World War II. It had several runways, one of which was 7,000 feet long. The airport also had a CAA flight service station located on the field and a nearby VOR sending station. After a couple of days in Vero Beach, we all flew over to Venice in a Piper Apache that Pug had flown down from Lock Haven.

Venice had a field that had been built by the services for World War II. It had 5,000-foot runways and would have been quite suitable for our purposes. The town had less than half the population of Vero Beach, however, and there was no large population area nearby from which to draw workers. Also, Venice was a pleasant town, but, in my opinion, it was not as attractive as Vero Beach.

One evening, after spending a couple of days in Venice, we met in our motel to talk things over and vote on whether the plant should be built at Vero Beach or Venice. Charlie Poole, the treasurer, said it was immaterial to him, and so he did not vote. I was given a vote because I was to live there and be an original part of the enterprise.

As the discussion went on, it was apparent that Pug and I were both talking in favor of Vero Beach and that his father, Bill Sr., was bringing out all of the advantages of Venice. After a while he said, "Well, I can see that both of you are going to vote for Vero Beach, and so I'll just go along with you." I never will know whether Bill Piper, Sr., was actually for Venice or whether, being a wise and cagey person, he was just drawing us out to make us show the points in favor of Vero Beach.

When I got back to College Station, Pug phoned me and suggested that I sketch out a layout for the initial plant. I did this, giving only minimum measurements, and he fortunately enlarged my plans for the plant a bit. When we were in agreement, Pug made arrangements with a Vero Beach architect, Ellis Duncan, to design the buildings and arrange for construction. Pug also wanted the all-metal replacement for the Tri-Pacer to get started as soon as possible. It was out of the question for me, the only worker at that time and still finishing up my work at Texas A&M, to work effectively on both the agricultural project and the new all-metal Tri-Pacer replacement. So, I informed Piper that I could not start work at Vero Beach until April 1, 1957. This would allow time not only to clean up my work at College Station satisfactorily but also to supervise our next year's agricultural aviation conference in late February, the planning for which had already begun.

After the annual agricultural aviation conference, I spent the month of March 1957 cleaning up odds and ends and preparing to go with Piper to start the development center in Vero Beach, Florida. While talking to Pug Piper during this period, I happened to mention that we had two cars and an airplane and that inasmuch as I would probably need a car in Vero Beach from the start, perhaps I should first drive one car there, then after a month or so come back to pick up Dorothy and fly her back in the Ercoupe. In the meantime she would sell the other car.

Pug's response was, "Oh, sell the Ercoupe; we'll always have planes for you to fly while you're at Piper." On that basis I sold the Ercoupe and was fortunate to find an immediate purchaser, my friend Tex Anderson, who had a Bonanza for himself, but whose wife was having difficulty learning to fly with a tail dragger. (Tex's wife did get her private license in the Ercoupe.) As long as I stayed with his company, and even for a while after my retirement, Piper furnished me with everything from Tri-Pacers to Cherokees to twin Comanches to fly around in. This privilege ended only when the Pipers themselves were eliminated after reorganization as part of Bangor-Punta.

By the time I left Texas in 1957, the Piper Cubs had of course become quite famous. When one of our friends with a Texas drawl found that I was leaving to go with Piper, her reaction was, "I don't see why it is necessary to have an aeronautical engineer of Mr. Weick's standing to design a pay-puh cup." While this sounded very amusing to us, Pug Piper, like Queen Victoria, was not amused when he was told about it.

The Piper Aircraft Corporation was a family affair run by seventy-six-year-old patriarch William T. Piper, Sr. Bill, who was born in Knapps Creek, New York, in 1881, was the company president and chairman of the board; Bill Jr. (b. 1911) was executive vice-president; his middle son, Tony (whose real name was Thomas; b. 1914), was vice-president for production and operations; and his youngest son, Pug (whose name was Howard; b. 1917), was vice-president for research and development and the general manager of the Vero Beach plant.

I had known and admired Bill Piper ever since 1945, when we both served on the CAA's Non-Scheduled Flying Advisory Committee. We had called each other by our first names, but when I referred to him as Bill within the Piper organization, I was looked at as if I had taken an undue liberty. Within the company, everyone referred to him as "Mr. Piper." Out in the field, however, people usually called him "Bill," and I think he liked it. Piper was a forthright and honest man with an open countenance. His build was husky and he was of medium height. His tastes were simple, but he had an astute business sense. In sum, William T. Piper was a man of outstanding character.

Although Bill and I were quite different in many ways, our thoughts about aeronautical engineering, airplanes, and flying were very similar. He was conservative but willing to step forward in new directions when conditions appeared to be right. He was a great leader in general aviation and private flying.

Piper had graduated from Harvard in engineering, and in the 1920s, after working as a construction engineer for U.S. Steel and other companies before World War I, had gone into an oil business started by his father in Bradford, Pennsylvania. In 1928 Bill invested in a company started in Bradford by C. G. Taylor to manufacture a two-place airplane, known as the Taylor Chummy; this little plane sold for about $4,000. Eventually, when Taylor's company experienced financial difficulties, Piper was induced by the Taylor investors to become the company treasurer and a member of its ruling board.

At this point Piper asked Taylor to design a very low-cost airplane, and this request resulted in the Taylor Cub, Model E-2. This plane was powered with a Continental A-40 engine and sold originally for only $1,325. Unfortunately, however, the Great Depression was just starting. The company sold some Cubs, but the going was tough. In January 1933 Walter Jamouneau, a twenty-two-year-old engineer from Rutgers University, joined the company, first working in sales and later in engineering. At first he worked without salary, just to get into the airplane activity.

During those years the Taylor Cub airplane performed pretty well, even though the Continental A-40 engine was not reliable and gave a great deal of trouble. Several other engines were tried in the Cubs, including the three-cylinder radial Lenape engine. (A Taylor Cub with a Lenape engine was entered, incidentally, in the Detroit News Trophy Contest that I worked up and ran in the 1935 National Air Races.)

In the 1930s Piper and Taylor did not see eye to eye on many points, and there was considerable friction between them. Finally, Piper bought out Taylor's holdings in the company and made Walter Jamouneau the chief engineer. Taylor then moved down to Butler, Pennsylvania, where he started designing and constructing the first Taylorcraft. This was a two-place, high-wing airplane somewhat similar to the Cub, but with side-by-side seating and a bit cleaner aerodynamic design. Later Taylor set up a factory in Alliance, Ohio, and the Taylorcraft became one of the best known light planes of its era.

After taking over control of the Taylor activity in Bradford, Bill Piper expanded his operation to the point that by the end of 1936 he employed two shifts of workers that were putting out eighteen airplanes per week. In March 1937, however, the Bradford plant burned down, and the company was forced to move to an abandoned silk mill in Lock Haven, Pennsylvania. A Cub distributor by the name of Jake Miller, a Lock Haven native, had in fact been urging this move for some time; Miller later became Piper's sales manager.

At Lock Haven the business continued to increase, and when more money was needed for further expansion of the operation, the company went public and sold stock. At that time the name was changed to the Piper Aircraft Corporation. When a more reliable Continental engine became available, Piper put it into the Cub. This new engine improved the performance and safety of the Cub significantly. Walter Jamouneau continued to refine the Model E-2, and in recognition of his efforts the model with the more powerful engine was named the J-2.

Continued refinement led to the Cub J-3, which became the most widely used training airplane through World War II. During the war it was used also as a military liaison airplane called the L-4. During the early 1940s the Piper Aircraft Corporation flourished making Cubs.

Piper's three sons were all in school (all three graduated from

Harvard) when their father started the aircraft business in Bradford. Bill Jr. had gone with his father's company well before the war and stayed with it. Tony demonstrated Cubs to the military services, was instrumental in getting them to adopt the Cub, and became a pilot in the Army Air Service. Pug became a navy pilot and ended up as a lieutenant commander.

After the war the three boys all worked with the Piper Aircraft Corporation. As discussed in chapter 10, there was a great surge in civil aviation, both private flying and training, during this period. All of the light plane companies were putting out large numbers of airplanes. Piper developed several other models, some of which were offspring of the Cub and were put into production. In 1946 the company sold 7,773 airplanes, or an average of 30 a day. For 1947, it planned to build 10,000.

But then the postwar demand for light planes was suddenly filled, and the bottom dropped out of the sales picture. The dealer pipelines were filled up, and unsold airplanes flooded the factory fields throughout the entire industry. The factories had to lay off most of their employees and also had to cancel orders for materials and equipment, all at some cost. Piper had extremely rough going, and the banker-creditors took charge of the company, putting their own men on the board of directors and hiring a hatchet man named Shriver to run the company and cut expenses. Although Bill Piper was allowed to retain his nominal title as president, Shriver took over his office, relegating Bill to a small spare room in the hangar. But he took it in stride and did not complain.

The company struggled along as best it could. Bill Jr. was moved to the West Coast as a factory representative and salesman. (Bill Sr. was delivering Bill Jr.'s car to California when we happened to meet in Springfield, Missouri, as I mentioned in chapter 10.) Shriver wanted an even lower-cost airplane than the Cub, and Tony and Pug were given the job of working one out. With the help of chief designer Dave Long, they cut down the size of the Cub, using a shorter wing with simpler bracing. The result was a two-place side-by-side seater called the Vagabond, and it sold reasonably well starting in 1948.

Piper then enlarged the Vagabond design to make a four-place airplane first called the Piper Clipper. But because this name interfered with the Pan American Clipper airplanes, it was soon changed to the Pacer. This plane also sold fairly well.

In 1951 Piper gave the Pacer a tricycle gear and changed the plane's name to the Tri-Pacer. This new model soon outsold all other light airplanes, and it was not long before Cessna began to equip its light planes with tricycle gears. Shortly thereafter, the tricycle became the conventional rather than the unconventional gear, which naturally pleased me.

About half a year earlier, in 1950, Shriver was replaced by August Esenwein of the Aviation Maintenance Corporation in Van Nuys, California. Esenwein, who had worked for Curtiss-Wright before U.S. entry into World War II, was interested, as Bill Piper, Sr., was, in getting into the more expensive twin-engine market, and a start was made toward the design of one. In the meantime Norman J. Greene, a financial man from Philadelphia, became friendly with Bill and purchased a large amount of Piper stock at what was then a very low rate. With Greene's assistance, Bill finally regained control of his company. He put Greene on the board of directors, and in that position Greene helped to guide the company's financial affairs in a more sophisticated manner. Things were looking up again. By the skin of its teeth, Piper (along with Cessna and Beech) had survived the light plane depression.

In December 1953 Piper's twin-engine model was put into production as a four-place airplane with two 150-HP Lycoming engines. It was priced at $32,500 and represented Piper's first step into the manufacture of expensive airplanes, although it was still the least expensive twin available. Pug Piper named it the Apache, and Jake Miller, the company's sales manager, suggested that it be the first in a series of Piper airplanes named after American Indians. The Apache's model number was PA-23.

The next model, the Comanche PA-24, was a four-place 180-HP single-engine all-metal airplane that incorporated, just as the Apache did, a retractable landing gear and a controllable-pitch propeller; when I started with the company in April 1957, the Comanche was still under development. It was a relatively sleek airplane with a rearward-swept vertical tail like those of contemporary jets. The Comanche had an all-movable horizontal tail surface, which had been introduced by Johnny Thorp when he was working for Lockheed.[1] But the idea for this control surface had been originated by Langley's Robert T. Jones in his 1943 report, "Theory and Preliminary Flight Tests of an All-Moveable Tail Surface" (NACA Wartime Report L-496).

Howard "Pug" Piper, 1970, Piper Aircraft Corporation vice-president for research and development and one of my best friends.

Near the end of March 1957 I loaded all the books and technical information that our 1950 Buick could carry and drove to Vero Beach to begin work as director and chief engineer of the Piper Aircraft Development Center. In the beginning the entire operation involved just me and five other people. One of the five was George Roth, the fellow who had been in charge of the construction of the Ag-1 in College Station. In the interim George had been employed by Murryaire in Honolulu, Hawaii, but when he had heard of our venture in Vero Beach, he asked to join us, which we were glad to have him do. Another one of the men was Slim Revel, who had done much of our sheet-metal work in College Station and who had also asked to come along with me. The other three people came down from the Lock Haven plant. One was Clarence Monks, an experimental mechanic, and he eventually became our shop superintendent. The second was his wife, Ruth, who had worked in the financial-clerical section, and she became my secretary until I retired. The third was Tom Heffner, a pilot, who with my coaching later became our test pilot.

Our plant was to be on the Vero Beach airport. During the war the field had been used by the navy to train fighter pilots. The field, which originally had been a small one, had been created in the late 1920s by a group of Vero Beach men led by Bud Holman and John

Schumann. When the mail was being flown in little open-cockpit Pitcairn Mail Wing airplanes, Vero Beach was a fuel stop between Jacksonville and Miami. Beginning in the early 1930s, when Eastern Airlines was formed and started a passenger service, Vero Beach also became a passenger stop between these two coastal cities. Bud Holman, who was manager of the Vero Beach airport until the time of his death in the early 1970s, was a friend of Eddy Rickenbacker, the famous World War I military pilot who founded Eastern Airlines and was its president.

When the Vero Beach airfield became a naval air school in the early 1940s, it was enlarged immensely and provided with several paved runways, the longest of which was something over 7,000 feet. After the war the field was returned to the city of Vero Beach, and Eastern Airlines continued to use it as a stop. A large wooden hangar built by the navy became the terminal building, and later the CAA established a VOR Omnirange navigation aid nearby and installed a flight service station in the same building. This was one of the factors that influenced us to select Vero Beach for our Piper operation. By the time we started in 1957, Eastern Airlines was using some DC-3 airplanes but was starting to use the larger, twin-engine Martin 404 planes.

When I arrived in Vero Beach, the plans for our new plant were still up for bid, meaning that for several months we were going to have to use temporary quarters. The old wooden hangar had long lean-tos on each side that were two stories high, some of which had been used by the navy as classrooms during the war. Three of these rooms were made available to us for our office and drafting rooms, and part of a smaller metal hangar next door was made available for our shop work. The roof over our drafting room leaked, and some of our drawings got wet, and the metal roof in the hangar had so many holes in it that we had to be very careful not to locate our new milling and other machines under them. But by and large we got along reasonably well.

During the first week in April the bids for the building were won by a general contracting firm, H. J. Osborne. Soon thereafter construction began, but not until there was a little ceremony in which Vero Beach mayor Jim Young turned over the first spadeful of earth with other officials and spectators in attendance. The building was completed in October 1957, and we were happy to move into our new facility. By that time our team had grown to about twenty-five people.

As director and chief engineer of the Piper Aircraft Development Center, I reported to Pug Piper, who was vice-president of the corporation for research and development. During the twelve-year period that I served in this capacity, our center would get involved in four main airplane projects, as many as three going on at the same time. These projects were (1) the Pawnee series of agricultural airplanes; (2) the Cherokee series of light passenger airplanes and trainers; (3) the experimental Papoose training airplane, which was constructed of fiberglass and plastic; and (4) the prototype PA-35, an eighteen-passenger commuter and light-cargo airplane. Rather than mix these all up month by month in a chronological log, I will tell the story of each separately over the years required.

As explained previously, the Ag-3 airplane had the main characteristics of the Ag-1 in regard to the general arrangement and the protection of the pilot, but it had the steel tube fuselage and fabric-covered construction of the Piper PA-18A and PA-22. Because of the highly corrosive nature of many of the agricultural chemicals, we had made the hopper of the Ag-3 of stainless steel. Though the hopper was highly serviceable, the stainless steel was not only very expensive and hard to work with but also heavier than desirable. Composite structures of fiberglass and plastic were coming into use about that time, particularly in connection with small boats. These materials were highly resistant to corrosion. Some of the aluminum or plywood hoppers used in the converted training airplanes had been lined with fiberglass and plastic reinforcment in order to help prevent corrosion, but no one had yet made an entire hopper of fiberglass and plastic. We decided to try it, and one of the first things that we did was to study the information available on this subject and then to experiment with forms and lay-ups.

One of our first additions to the shop staff was a local man, Heber Lynn, who was not only an easy man to work with, but also one of the most ingenious persons I had run across. Lynn played a large part in the early development of the fiberglass and plastic hopper and later became our experimental shop foreman. Over the years Clarence Monks, the experimental shop superintendent, and Heber Lynn, the shop foreman, would have a very great influence on the design of the Piper airplanes that were developed at Vero Beach. This would be true particularly in connection with the power plant layouts—which are easier to lay out for satisfactory inspection, maintenance, and replacement of parts from full-scale mockups than from flat, two-dimensional drawings on top of a drawing board. The draftsman could then make the drawings from the full-scale mockup. Monks and Lynn were also very helpful in working out sound devices for difficult services, such as door locks and door stops, which someone always found a way to misuse or damage.

Eventually, the fiberglass and plastic hopper worked out very well. The translucent nature of the material permitted the pilot to see the fluid or solid matter in the hopper. We marked a scale on the back of the hopper, and the pilot could tell how full or empty it was merely by looking at the level of the material inside. It was not many years before the fiberglass and plastic hopper became used universally in agricultural airplanes.

By incorporating the fiberglass and plastic hopper, we were also able to simplify the airplane construction in one regard, by using the top of the hopper as the external surface of the fuselage. We then used the same form of fiberglass and polyester plastic construction for the fuel tank, which was in the bay ahead of the hopper.

The first engineers that I hired during the summer of 1957 were Sam Snyder, who came to us with a master's degree directly from the University of Illinois; and Glen Stephen and John McCreanor, both of whom had graduated from Embry-Riddle Aeronautical University, which at that time was located in Miami. I had gone to Miami on business about the time these two had graduated and had been roped into giving a commencement address. Snyder, Stephen, and McCreanor, plus a couple of draftsmen, got to work immediately on the engineering necessary to ready the PA-25 for production. In addition, Professor Ben Hamner of Texas A&M, who had helped me with the Ag-1 and Ag-3, began to do consulting service on structures for us. Glen Stephen became the project engineer for agricultural airplanes. Later Peter Peck joined our structures group, and he is the only early engineer still with Piper in 1987.

After being in operation for a year or so, we acquired a fiberglass and plastics specialist, Bob Drake, who had carried out a program of designing and constructing small fiberglass and plastic boats for the army, to be used for landing troops on beaches. Drake not only helped to perfect the designs, but after production of the PA-25 had started, he was in charge of the manufacture of the hoppers and the fuel tanks, all of which were made of fiberglass and plastic and

Ag-3 (above), which developed into the Piper Pawnee (below). The Pawnee is being fitted with a spray boom.

constructed in Vero Beach. These parts were then trucked up to Lock Haven where the Pawnee PA-25 was constructed.

Sometime in 1959 we completed the prototype airplane and got our flight test program under way. All of our structural, operational, and flight testing had to be approved by CAA personnel, but because Vero Beach was in the CAA's fourth region, whose headquarters were in Fort Worth, Texas, some distance away, there were some minor delays before we finally obtained the approved type certificate (ATC) that was necessary before production in Lock Haven could begin.

The first Pawnee had a number of special features. The airplane was powered with the 150-HP Lycoming O-320 engine. Its fiberglass and plastic hopper could carry 20 cubic feet of dust, fertilizer, or dry chemicals, or 150 gallons of chemical spray liquid. The hopper was located right on the airplane's center of gravity, and therefore no change in longitudinal trim was required by the pilot from full load to empty load. The adjustable gate at the bottom of the hopper was controlled by a lever at the pilot's left hand, and the flow of dry material could be regulated accurately. When liquid was being used, the closed gate sealed tightly, but if an emergency occurred and the pilot wanted to lighten his load quickly, he could open the gate fully and dump the entire load in a matter of a few seconds.

The Pawnee had as standard equipment the pleated-paper type of air filter tested with the Ag-3. This gave the engine much better protection from dusty and grimy air and extended the life of the engine substantially. We used a standard Fram filter like that then being used in a Chrysler automobile model. I believe that this was the first use of a pleated-paper type of air filter on a production airplane. For operation under unusually dusty conditions we also made available as optional equipment a full-flow oil filter for the engine oil.

At the time the Ag-1 had been developed in the early 1950s, most of the airplanes used in agriculture were open-cockpit biplanes that required the pilot to use helmet and goggles; originally, the Ag-1, though a monoplane, had an open cockpit also. But when we recognized how much pilots needed more protection in the wintertime, we then provided the plane with a portable enclosure.

For the Pawnee, however, we provided a full enclosure. Sometime later we even made provisions for providing the pilot with fresh filtered air in case he flew back and forth through some of the poisonous haze that he had dispersed. Today just about all agricultural airplanes provide enclosures for the pilot. They also provide as much comfort as possible to help the pilot keep in as good condition as possible throughout his long hours of meticulously accurate flying during the season when his work load is very high.

The general arrangement of the Pawnee PA-25, including the pilot's field of view and the provisions for his safety in a crash, were very similar to those of the original Ag-1. Because approximately half of the fatal cropdusting accidents had been the result of collisions with wires, trees, and so forth, it was obvious to me that the field of view both forward and downward was of extreme importance. To help in this regard, we used a flat engine and located the pilot high in the fuselage. In addition, by giving the plane a low-wing arrangement, we enabled the pilot to see where he was going in turns close to the ground. This provided, as well, an excellent view to the rear for those pilots who wanted to look back at the swathes they were laying. To help the airplane break through wires or tree branches, sharp leading edges were provided for the landing-gear struts and in the center of the windshield, as had also been done for the Ag-1 and the PA-18A. Also, as had been introduced in the Ag-1, a cable was strung from the top of the cockpit to the top of the rudder to prevent the vertical tail from being snagged, as had happened many times in the past.

As mentioned previously, I had kept in touch with the work of Hugh DeHaven and Howard Hasbrook of the Crash Injury Research Unit of the Cornell University Medical College ever since work on the Ag-1 had started in 1949. After looking carefully at the Ag-1, they had sent me a list of ten items that they recommended for improved crash-survival design. So far as I know, these items were never published by the Crash Injury Research Unit itself, but I listed them in a handbook for agricultural aviation, which was published later at Texas A&M, and in a paper on the design philosophy of agricultural airplanes that I presented in England. For the last several years I've been sorry that I listed them, because in the last few years they have been thrown back at me by attorneys in product liability court cases as absolute gospel that it would be sacrilegious not to follow exactly.

The Ag-1 and the Pawnee conformed reasonably well to all but one of the ten crash survival recommendations made by DeHaven and Hasbrook. We designed the forward fuselage to absorb energy by "progressive collapse"; by this, I mean that the first bay would fail first in a nose-on collision with the ground, followed by the second bay and the third bay. We hoped that the pilot's cockpit itself would be strong enough not to deform substantially in ordinary crashes. The upper longerons in the region of the cockpit were bent slightly outward so that in case of a head-on crash they would buckle outward rather than inward in such a way as to harm the pilot. The pilot's seat was located as far aft as feasible in the fuselage and behind all heavy loads.

In regard to the instrument panel we went even further. In the Ag-1, I had put the instrument panel so far ahead that, even with just a seat belt and no shoulder harness, in a crash the pilot's head would not stretch far enough to hit the instrument panel. This was all right for me, because I was six feet three inches tall and had long arms. The general run of pilots, however, could not reach the instrument panel to adjust the instruments or use controls. So the arrangement was not practical.

To solve this problem and to protect the pilot's head in case it tended to crash against the instrument panel, I devised what I called a "metal cushion." Fortunately, agricultural airplanes did not require a large number of instruments and navigation equipment, so in the PA-25 it was possible to put all of the instruments in one row across the bottom of the instrument panel. Just above the panel, where the pilot's head might normally strike in a crash, I put a half cylinder of ductile aluminum sheet metal about five inches in diameter. The pilot's head striking this rounded surface would deflect it inward, and it would have several inches to come to a stop, thus reducing the deceleration and the shock.

In 1965 tests on a couple of Piper instrument panels with the metal cushions were made by John J. Swearingen of the FAA Civil Aeromedical Research Institute in Oklahoma City. Instrumented dummy heads representing humans were crashed against the panels, both with and without the cushion. Swearingen found that the metal cushions were very effective in reducing the impact force on the human head. He concluded that such devices could be installed on present-day aircraft "with meagre weight and cost penalty and would save hundreds of lives in survivable crashes." The metal roll cushions are now used not only on Piper's agricultural airplanes but also on some of the competitors' planes as well.

Following a visit to Vero Beach by Howard Hasbrook during the early design period of the PA-25, and following his suggestions, we also put in a cushioning headrest to act against whiplash.

Additionally, for the first production PA-25s, we incorporated extra-strong seat belts and shoulder harnesses and anchored them directly to strong structural truss points in the fuselage. As in the case of the Ag-1, the shoulder harness straps were linked permanently to their respective sides of the seat belt. This made it unnecessary for the pilot to hunt up and put together four loose ends and made the harness easy to slip into and fasten with a single buckle.

The DeHaven-Hasbrook recommendation that the PA-25 and the Ag-1 did not conform to involved our location of the fuel tank. The

Cornell researchers objected to our locating the fuel tank in the fuselage between the fire wall and the instrument panel and preferred a location in or on the wings. For the first Pawnee we opted for the fuselage location, however, because it permitted the use of a single, short fuel line with simple gravity feed. Wing tanks, with the low-wing arrangement, would have required a fuel pump and a more complicated plumbing system, including a selector valve.

Statistics showed that many accidents and a fair number of fatal ones were caused by failure of the complicated plumbing system and misuse of the valves. They also showed that low-wing monoplanes having tanks in the wings had about the same percentage of fires following crashes as did airplanes having the fuel tanks in the fuselage located behind the engine. Statistically, it appeared to us then, and I believe that it still does today, that the overall safety would be greater by using the simple, direct fuel system than by the use of wing tanks with two fuel pumps, selector valve, and a more complicated plumbing system. A fire following a crash is a horrible thing, however. Fires put more fear into pilots than any other hazards. And it did appear to the pilots that there should be fewer fires following crashes if the fuel tanks were in the wings rather than in the fuselage behind the engine.

After the original Pawnee had been in service for a while, and some fires did of course occur following crashes, we realized that our fiberglass fuel tanks were somewhat more likely to split open than metal tanks and thus aggravate the fire difficulty. We therefore fitted the tanks with synthetic rubber liners or bladders, which helped to contain the fuel in the tank even if the fiberglass cracked. In addition, in 1967 we furnished, as optional equipment on the PA 25-235, a dry type of fire extinguisher that automatically went into action following a crash. This helped to put out fires in the engine compartment, where most postcrash fires started. The system could also be operated manually by the pilot if he desired. It consisted of a heat fuse mounted in the engine compartment on the forward base of the fire wall and a dry chemical fire extinguisher mounted just back of the fire wall. Although this looked like a worthwhile installation and was offered as optional equipment, very few of the purchasers asked for them.

For the first production PA-25 airplanes, Piper did not provide a dusting system, but it did make available a sprayer system with a boom just back of the trailing edge of the wing where the pilot

Above, a Pawnee laying a dust swath; below, Pawnee workers, left to right, yours truly, Bob Boob, Glenn Stephen, and Carl Heimer.

could watch all of the nozzles and see whether all of them (except for those directly under the fuselage) were operating satisfactorily. The list price of the airplane alone was $8,995, and the cost of the sprayer system was $675. The distributors received a 25 percent discount.

I wanted our Piper company to give excellent service, of course, to the people starting to use these rather unusual airplanes. So after the design was well along, I suggested to Jake Miller, the sales manager in Lock Haven, that he get hold of an agricultural pilot-mechanic who was thoroughly familiar with the problems that applicators had in dealing with the farmers and that he send him down to Vero Beach to get thoroughly familiar with our new aircraft before we put it into mass production.

Miller agreed that this was a good idea, but he did nothing about it. No one in the Lock Haven organization knew much about the use of airplanes in agriculture, and I was afraid that we would not be able to give good service. After months went by and it looked as if no action was forthcoming, I scouted around myself and found a man I thought would be suitable for the purpose. He was Carl Heimer, a local man who had worked for a number of agricultural airplane operators in the Vero Beach area and who was thoroughly experienced in agricultural piloting and taking care of the airplanes. I took the liberty of hiring Heimer as a mechanic with relatively meager salary, hoping that ultimately he could be transferred to the service department. He was willing to start under these conditions, because the prospects for the future looked bright. By the time the Pawnee was ready for production, Heimer had become familiar with every detail and had flown the prototype under all sorts of conditions, including simulated agricultural spray and dust runs. I had been willing to use engineering funds for this purpose, and Pug Piper had let me do it.

The first five production Piper Pawnees were delivered late in July 1959 to Wes-Tex Aircraft Sales, Lubbock, Texas. Wes-Tex president, Roy Neal, and four other pilots left Lock Haven in formation and flew them to Lubbock. The airplanes had been sold to aerial applicators in the western Texas area. Fortunately, Jake Miller, the sales manager, recognized the desirability of having a service man help the new owners get used to their unusual airplanes and asked that Carl Heimer be sent out for a couple of weeks to help.

Dorothy and I were about to take off for a family reunion on the north bank of the Grand Canyon in a 180-HP Piper Comanche. Carl Heimer went with us as far as Lubbock. We then stayed in Lubbock for a couple of days to see how things were coming along. Carl was a great aid in helping the new owners get the best possible performance from their new, unusual airplanes and they were all very appreciative of his help. From then on, he gave great service to Pawnee users throughout the United States and ultimately throughout the world. I carried him on the engineering payroll for another couple of years, but ultimately he was transferred to sales and service, where he belonged. Carl not only helped the users of the

Pawnees, but he also helped the various state and national aerial applicator organizations. Later, he became the worldwide sales and service representative for Piper's agricultural airplanes. (For further elaboration of Carl Heimer's talented work for Piper, see Mabry Anderson's *Low and Slow: An Insider's History of Agricultural Aviation* [San Francisco: California Farmer Publishing Co., 1986], pp. 67–69.)

Our trip to the Grand Canyon was especially adventurous because we were to land at the north rim of the canyon on a gravel strip only 3,800 feet long and at an elevation of 9,000 feet.

The main Grand Canyon airport at the south rim was only about 6,600 feet above sea level and had a long runway, but it required a drive of 140 miles to get to a bridge that would cross the Colorado River and back to the lodge where our family reunion was to be held on the north rim. I had mentioned this to Pug Piper some time before the trip, and he had told me about a Piper dealership in Tucson, Arizona, run by the Hudgin brothers, who had an operation during the summer months at the main Grand Canyon airport at the south rim. They took people for rides down in and around the canyon, and they also had a small strip at the north rim. I immediately wrote them a letter and included a small portion of the regular section chart for that area and asked about the practicality of landing there with our 180-HP Comanche. One of the brothers, Henry Hudgin, wrote me a friendly and encouraging letter and spotted their landing strip on our section chart, after which we decided to land there.

Still, considering the possible hazardous condition associated with the little strip on the north rim, I decided to land at the main airport at the south rim and talk things over with Henry Hudgin, who was operating there at that time. We landed at about one o'clock, almost a day ahead of schedule, for we had arranged for our son Dick to meet us at the little strip at about ten o'clock the next morning. It was (and still is) good practice, of course, especially in the hot summertime, to land and take off from a high-altitude field in the morning when the air is relatively cool and smooth and before the thermals and their resultant turbulence are in action and the density altitude is a couple of thousand feet higher. Henry Hudgin asked how long we expected to stay at the north rim with the airplane tied out in the open, and I said about four days. He then counseled that this was the season of severe hailstorms and that we were likely to get our airplane all dimpled up if we left it out there for four days. We therefore arranged for him to ride over there with us, fly the airplane back to the south rim, and put it in a hangar, and then four days later go back to the north rim field and pick us up. We would then drop him off at the south field on our way east.

The next morning I flew to the north rim strip under his guidance, and I was very happy that we had landed and talked to the people who knew how to operate under those conditions before dropping in to the strip by ourselves. I had received a number of pointers. The strip was noticeably lower in the center than it was at either end, and so whether one were landing or taking off one started downhill but ended uphill. This was probably an advantage in getting off the ground quickly in the beginning of the take-off run, but it did mean that you had to climb as soon as you got off the ground.

When our family reunion ended four days later, Henry flew the airplane back to the north rim strip, and when we were all loaded he asked me in which direction I intended to take off. The field was in a sort of hollow, and one had to climb a couple of hundred feet in a distance of about a mile and a half in either direction. There was about a five-MPH wind from the south, and I had thought that I would take off in that direction. He said that while it seemed that we had only about a mile and a half to clear the terrain in either direction, if we took off toward the north, we could make a slight bend and have another mile and a half before we had to clear the higher terrain. With only a five-MPH wind, it was better therefore to take off downwind and have double the distance in which to make the climb. If the airplane had been fully loaded at the density altitude available, it could have climbed only about 150 feet for each mile traveled forward, even with the air speed held exactly at that for the best angle of climb. The take-off into the wind would therefore have been very marginal. We had not added any fuel since leaving Albuquerque, New Mexico, however, and were about 180 pounds light in fuel. With only three people instead of four in the airplane, we were probably at least 300 pounds under the maximum gross weight and therefore had an additional bit of margin. We had still more margin with the downwind take-off, and I was very happy to have had the advice of a competent, local pilot who knew the conditions under which we were operating.

Starting in August 1959 the production of the PA-25 in Lock Haven was scheduled for one airplane per day. This rate was then increased as the demand required. Soon a spreader for dust, fertilizer, seeds, and other solid materials was made available as standard equipment. The dust and spray equipment were so arranged that a change could be made from one to the other in a relatively short time—a half hour or less if everything was in order.

As the airplane's designer, we could not have the foresight, of course, to anticipate all of the problems that might come along in service throughout all parts of the world and with all sorts of people and operating conditions. Our project engineer, Glen Stephen, kept a record of all difficulties reported to us, and as time went on we made such modifications as seemed desirable. One of these was quite a surprise to me, although I don't suppose it should have been.

I had arranged the aerodynamics of the Ag-3 and the original Pawnee by providing a buffeting as a warning to the pilot that he was approaching the stalling speed. This simple inherent warning system avoided the need for a stall warning instrument with a horn or light. To meet the civil air regulations, the warning had to come somewhere between five and ten MPH above the stalling speed, and it had to happen for all conditions of loading, center of gravity, and flap position, both with power on and off. I thought I had done a fine job.

When the airplane got out into service, however, the ag pilots were highly annoyed with my warning system. They could save time on their procedure turns at the end of each run by flying at the lowest possible speed, and many of them wanted to fly within a couple of miles per hour of the stall. With my warning system, they were thumping around all of their procedure turns, and they objected violently to it.

I solved the situation by adding skewed leading edges to the wing where it joined the fuselage. This smoothed out the flow near the stall, but then we had to add the mechanical stall warning indicator. We used a light only, however, because the pilots also objected to a horn squawking during their procedure turns. Most of the pilots did not feel the need of a stall warning system at all, and I believe that in the field most of the systems were not operating.

We considered the 150-HP Pawnee about as small and light a plane as would be generally useful in the agricultural aviation field, although smaller and lighter converted training planes were in use. If large fields were to be treated, however, we knew that efficiency would be improved if larger loads could be handled. Though the hopper of the original Pawnee could carry 150 gallons of fluid, it was approved for only 800 pounds, because with a load of light dust, the 800 pounds would fill the entire hopper. The pilot, therefore, had to use judgment in not overloading his airplane. With some types of spray fluid the load could go up to as high as about 1,200 pounds if he put in the entire 150 gallons. Then the performance with 150 HP would not be at all acceptable, however.

After a time, a number of operators asked that the airplane be provided with a more powerful engine so that the entire hopper capacity could be used with the heavier materials. The company responded by coming out with a new model that used a Lycoming O-540 engine rated at 235 horsepower. Basically the airplane structure was the same as that of the 150-HP Pawnee, except that the strength was increased wherever needed throughout the entire airplane. The same 20-cubic-foot hopper was used, but with the 235-HP engine it could be filled up to a load of 1,200 pounds instead of being limited to the former legal load of 800 pounds. With the 235-HP model, it was impossible to overload the hopper significantly beyond the permissible 1,200 pounds with the more commonly used spray fluids or fertilizers. This had the advantage of being a kind of enforced safety factor. As a duster, though, the 150-HP model would do just about as well and at less cost. The 235-HP Pawnee retained all of the safety features of the 150-HP model, including the flying and handling characteristics, the wide field of view in the needed areas, and the crash protection for the pilot. Moreover, we now made the nose cowl of the engine compartment out of fiberglass and plastic. Customarily this cowl had been made of aluminum alloy, as it was for the original Pawnee, and had been subject to cracking in service due to vibration. The fiberglass and plastic nose cowl was not only easier to mold into suitable shape, but was also much more durable.

Production of the 235-HP model started in 1962. The airplane was received remarkably well, and the orders for the 150-HP model dwindled to the point where it was soon discontinued.

Starting in 1967 we made a still more powerful model of the Pawnee available. This made use of the same six-cylinder Lycoming O-540 engine, but the compression ratio was increased from 7.20 to 8.50, and the RPM was increased from 2,575 to 2,700. The rated horsepower was increased from 235 to 260, and the airplane was available with either fixed-pitch or constant-speed propellers. But the simple 235-HP Pawnee, which burned 87-octane fuel and used a fixed-pitch propeller, seemed to have about the best overall proportions for a light agricultural plane and was by far the most popular of the Pawnee models. In the early to mid-1960s, when about 3,000 Pawnees had been produced, the PA25-235 represented about half of all of the agricultural airplanes that were helping farmers to produce food and fiber in America.

In order to save on tooling costs and the time required to get a new model into production, we gave the Pawnee a new configuration, but incorporated the same form of structure and as many details as feasible from the PA-18 and the PA-22 airplanes. On this account the PA-25's structure was somewhat obsolescent as first produced. This was especially true with regard to the ruggedness and the ability of the airplane to withstand the harsh treatment and the severe corrosion associated with agricultural aviation.

With these problems in mind I suggested, shortly after the first PA-25 was put into production, that we start on a new improved model. My idea was to rectify the severe operating conditions and make a Pawnee that would be as easy as possible to inspect, maintain, and repair. Piper management did not appear to be against the idea, but year after year they gave no approval to go ahead.

Texas A&M had continued to hold an annual agricultural aviation conference, and each year after I had left I would fly to College Station, usually with Glen Stephen, the Pawnee project engineer, and my wife, Dorothy. Returning from the conference in 1965, we got weathered in at Mobile and knew that we would have to stay there for at least a day or two. I had been trying for some time to get together with Glen to lay out a set of specifications for the new airplane, but our daily activities had kept us from finding the time. In Mobile, I took advantage of the situation.

We settled in a motel with Dorothy and me in one room and Glen in the adjacent room with a door in between. We started right in on the specifications in Glen's room: I, pacing back and forth in my usual manner, and Glen putting the ideas down on paper.

We worked through the early morning hours of the first night, all the next day and night, and part of the following morning. Then we were able to fly our Cherokee 6 back home to Vero Beach. We came home with a fairly comprehensive set of specifications, had them typed up, and then I submitted them to Pug Piper, who in turn showed them to the rest of management, including the sales department.

Pug was all for going ahead with the project, and had been for some time. But the rest of management gave no go-ahead. Finally I talked Pug into letting me put one man, Tony Morley, a designer from England, on the preliminary design, even without formal approval from the rest of management. On a couple of my trips to the west, I had stopped off to see Chuck Diefendorf, an aerial applicator in Casa Grande, Arizona, with regard to his possible employment with Piper in Vero Beach. Diefendorf had a degree in mechanical engineering, had been a navy pilot during World War II, and since then had been an aerial applicator with a partner. They flew mostly converted navy N3N trainers and constructed their own dusting and spraying equipment. I knew that Chuck would therefore make a valuable addition to our staff. In September 1966 he did in fact start working with us in Vero Beach; his job was to help me with the preliminary design of the new ag plane, which I called the Pawnee II.

Within a few months our idea of a new ag design got around to some of the dusting and spraying operators, and they expressed enthusiasm for it. Their interest in it grew to the point where the Piper sales department even wanted top management to approve the project, and of course they wanted it the day before yesterday.

Finally, in January 1967, the design project got going full blast. Carl Heimer and the sales department sent questionnaires to the operators and got their ideas before the design was completed. The Pawnee II, or PA-36 as it was designated, was to replace the Pawnee but was eventually to have a larger hopper capacity plus provision for larger powers. Originally it was to be fitted with the same 235-HP Lycoming engine, as was most popular for the Pawnee and had given excellent service. Before long the sales department had named the new plane the Pawnee Brave.

The Pawnee Brave, or PA-36, had the same general configuration

Piper Pawnee II, Model PA-36, later called the Pawnee Brave and then just Brave. This was designed from scratch as an agricultural airplane suitable for easy and proper maintenance under the corrosive conditions of agricultural chemicals. Up to this time the Pawnees had been made partly with parts from other Piper airplanes and were thus not as well designed for agricultural use as was, in particular, the Pawnee Brave.

and pilot protection features as the original Pawnee but with a number of improvements and differences. It was slightly larger and the structure, besides being simpler, was much more rugged and corrosion resistant. The span was increased from a little over 36 feet to 39 feet, and the wing area was increased from 183 square feet to 225 square feet. As standard equipment, the hopper volume was increased from 20 cubic feet, or 150 gallons, to 30 cubic feet, or 225 gallons. A 38-cubic-foot, or 275-gallon, hopper was available as optional equipment.

The wing of the Pawnee Brave was a simple aluminum-alloy cantilever structure with the NACA 63_3-618 airfoil section. Because the leading edges of applicator airplane wings could easily be damaged by contact with trucks and other ground equipment, we made the leading edges of the PA-36 out of easily removable and identical fiberglass and plastic structures. Damaged sections could either be repaired or replaced with spare sections kept on hand for the purpose. With regard to the fuel system of the PA-36, we decided to follow the pilots' desires and put the tanks in the wings. This complicated the system substantially, requiring more fuel lines, an engine-driven fuel pump, an electric fuel pump, check valves, and an extra header tank at the bottom of the fuselage.

A new fuel system arrangement had come into use during the last couple of years, and we adopted it. This permitted the pilot to operate the system as simply as that of our original Pawnee, with its one shutoff valve with no selections to be made from different tanks. The fuel flowed by gravity from the wing tanks to a small header tank of less than one gallon capacity that was located in the bottom of the fuselage. From there the fuel went through the single shutoff valve, the fuel strainers, and the two fuel pumps to the engine. From the standpoint of pilot operation and the likelihood of mishandling, the system was just as safe as that of the original Pawnee. With the extra complications, however, mechanical failure was much more likely, even with great attention paid to high quality. (In the early 1970s the Pawnee's fuel system was modified to be substantially like that of the PA-36, that is, with the main fuel in two wing tanks and a header tank at the bottom of the fuselage, with only one shutoff valve for the pilot to operate.)

A 45-gallon bladder-type fuel cell was mounted in each wing root. Each tank was filled with reticulated polyurethane safety foam, which acted as a baffle and provided maximum slosh suppression. In a crash that ruptured the tanks, the fuel would thus tend to stay in the same location, rather than be splashed over the rest of the airplane. Incidentally, by moving the fuel tanks from the fuselage to the wings, we provided extra room in the fuselage for the enlargement of the hopper. All of the safety features of the regular Pawnee were retained; in addition some extras were included.

The instrument panel included my metal cushion, or "crash roll," as it had been termed. But at the suggestion of a number of pilots, the main instruments—the ones that the pilots looked at the most (i.e., the air-speed indicator, spray pressure gauge, tachometer, and manifold pressure gauge)—were placed above the crash roll, closer to their line of sight over the nose of the airplane. These instruments were also set farther forward, away from the pilot so that his head could not contact them in a crash.

We sealed the cockpit area off from the rest of the fuselage and pressurized it to minimize the inflow of toxic chemicals. Even the outside air taken in by the overhead ram air scoop was filtered and diffused through two adjustable outlets, one below the headrest to cool the pilot's neck and back, and the other above the windshield to cool his face and front. A wide comfortable seat was adjustable up and down, and the rudder pedals were adjusted fore and aft so that most any size pilot could be seated very comfortably and still have a good view outside of the airplane.

The fuselage was a truss structure made of steel tubing that was well protected, both outside and inside, against corrosion. We covered the top and the bottom of the fuselage with noncorrosive fiberglass and plastic molded panels, and both sides of the fuselage were covered with quickly removable panels so that the inside could be inspected and cleaned very easily.

According to our original concept, the airplane was to use the 235-HP Lycoming engine that had given such excellent service in the PA-25-235, with provision for going to a more powerful engine if it was needed. As the design work progressed, however, the hopper size and load increased, and it became apparent to us that we were going to have to start with a somewhat more powerful engine.

During the same years that the design of the PA-36 had gone on, Continental Motors Corporation had been developing a new engine that looked very promising. This new engine came out in four-cylinder, six-cylinder, and eight-cylinder models, and the six-cylinder model, named the Tiara, which was rated at 285 HP, seemed to fit into our picture very well.

Toward the end of 1968 Continental had these engines flying in Piper, Cessna, and Beech airplanes, and in early 1969 the company started merchandising them. The Tiara was a relatively radical design with some outstandingly favorable features. It got a high power from a small displacement by running at a high RPM (as did automobile engines), but its propeller was mounted on an extension of a large camshaft that ran at just half the engine speed; this arrangement gave a high propeller efficiency. The power plant system included a unique method of vibratory torque control that incorporated a long, flexible torque-shaft for normal engine operation, but a rigid drive for idling speeds. This eliminated the necessity for the usual torsion dampeners and helped to keep the engine weight low. With the Tiara, therefore, there was a substantial saving in engine weight, which gave just that much more useful load.

In March 1969 Pug Piper and I stopped off at the Continental plant in Muskegon, Michigan, on the way to a business aircraft meeting in Wichita. In Muskegon we got a complete briefing about the engines and had an opportunity to fly with them in the Piper, Cessna, and Beech airplanes in which they were installed. We were very well impressed by the whole situation, for the engine appeared to suit our requirements very well indeed and would improve the performance of our airplane. The engine was also a neat, compact package that would be easy to service and maintain because all of the items that needed to be worked on appeared to be very accessible.

After we got home and had a chance to digest the matter, Pug was all for putting the Tiara into our new PA-36. It was against my principles to put a new engine into a new airframe, but the Tiara appeared to have been so well worked out and to have so many advantages that I caved in and went along with it. The Tiara was then incorporated in the design, and the PA-36 first flew with the new engine a month or so after I retired from Piper on September 15, 1969. The performance with the large, slow-turning propeller was excellent and, in addition, the noise level was very low. As it turned out, the airplane in dusting and spraying did not disturb neighbors as much as it would have done if it had had the regular engine and propeller combination.

Production started in 1970, and the airplane was very well received. One item that bothered me, however, was that I had counted on other airplane companies using the Tiara engine before our first PA-36s were produced, giving us some information about its performance. The other companies were more conservative, however, and this did not occur, so that we found ourselves to be the first company using the new engine in a production airplane.

After the airplane had been in service for some time, a crankshaft failure did occur in one of the engines. Not long thereafter, another failure occurred, prompting Continental to do some redesigning that beefed up the crankshaft. The company appeared to have solved the problem, but people remained afraid of the engines. Because so few of the Tiara engines were being sold, their manufacture was discontinued.

This of course gave the PA-36 a real setback. Ultimately Piper put it out with the old Lycoming engines rated at 300 and 375 HP. These engines were substantially heavier than the Tiara, and did not give the same satisfactory performance. Finally, however, the new Pawnee was received reasonably well, and a fair number of them were produced by Piper.

According to a brochure put out by Piper in the early 1970s, more than 5,500 aerial applicator planes had been manufactured by the company since 1959. About 1982, however, Piper decided to discontinue the sale of agricultural airplanes, and the worldwide distribution was turned over to Roy Neal, the Piper distributor in Lubbock who had received the first five Pawnees that had been produced back in 1959. Up until very recently, Neal still ordered batches of 50 or so Pawnees or Braves from Lock Haven. This stopped in 1984, I believe, when Piper abandoned the Pennsylvania plant and moved all activity to Florida.

In 1959 when the 150-HP Pawnee was first produced, there were only a couple of other new agricultural airplane designs that took advantage of what had been learned from the Ag-1. These were the Grumman Ag-Cat and Leland Snow's S-1 and S-2 airplanes.

Although designed by a couple of Grumman engineers, the Ag-Cat was manufactured by the Schweizer brothers who made sailplanes in Elmira, New York, and who had made parts for the Grumman Company during World War II. It was a biplane, unlike the Ag-1, but the designers had made use of the information available both from the Ag-1 and even from the Texas A&M measuring station in developing satisfactory distribution patterns for their spray and dust systems.

Leland Snow had built his S-1 and S-2 model airplanes in Harlingen, Texas, which is at the southern tip of the state, near Mexico. In the late 1950s he moved his operation to Olney, Texas, about 80 miles northwest of Fort Worth, where he received backing from the local businessmen. In a small hangar on the Olney airport, Snow started building a new design with the pilot in back of the load—which, of course, was to my satisfaction. After a bit he also built a small factory next to the hangar. At that time he had no car but was known around the town as the businessman who rode a motorcycle for transportation.

By 1962 Snow's factory was putting out one airplane every four to seven days.[2] In 1965 his company became a part of North American Rockwell, and the Snow airplane became known as the Thrush. Two models of the Thrush were available, one with a 450-HP engine and another with a 600-HP engine. In 1968 Snow moved his operation from Olney, Texas, to Albany, Georgia, where he stayed for only two years before returning to Olney. In the early 1970s Dorothy and I visited him during an auto trip, and he was working on a new design that he called the Air Tractor. If I remember correctly, he was thinking in terms of a turbo-prop installation.

Both the Snow and Ag-Cat airplanes were somewhat larger than the Pawnee and filled a slightly different need. Both are still in production and over the years have contributed very substantially to the use of airplanes in agriculture.

While I was still at Texas A&M, I had suggested to the people at Cessna who had helped by furnishing the landing gear for the Ag-1 that Cessna was in an ideal position to go ahead with the design and manufacture of an agricultural airplane. I had also said that I thought there would be a reasonable market for it. The Cessna people had replied that they had been considering it, but that the market appeared too small for the kind of production that Cessna wanted to engage in.

In 1963, when the Pawnee was dominating the market for the relatively small agricultural airplanes, Tom Salter, Cessna's chief engineer, who happened to see me at a meeting, told me that he wanted me to know that they had decided to do what I had suggested previously—and what Piper had done with the Pawnee—that is, produce a small agricultural airplane that used as many existing Cessna airplane parts as would fit in reasonably well.

Salter wanted me to know that Cessna would be going into direct competition with our Pawnee and that they were going to go full blast on the project. Cessna's first cropduster, called the Ag-Wagon, flew in February 1965, and the company has been at it ever since in a much more serious manner than has Piper. Cessna has upgraded its ag airplanes continually and merchandised them aggressively. It has added two models called the Ag-Husky and the Ag-Truck and has even turbo-charged the Ag-Husky for better high-altitude and high-temperature performance. By 1983 Cessna dominated the market for the relatively small agricultural planes to such an extent that it was to claim, as it did in full-page advertisements, that "We're the leader in the field." In the mid-1980s, however, production was discontinued.

Today there are a number of fine agricultural airplanes available, many with turbo-prop power plants. And I am happy to see they all incorporate to a large extent the features pioneered in the Ag-1.

14.

The Cherokee

The seed for the Cherokee was planted during a dinner conversation that Bill Piper, Sr., his son Bill Jr., and I had at the third annual agricultural aviation conference of the National Flying Farmers Organization in Memphis, Tennessee, in 1951. (As readers might remember from chapter 12, the Pipers were there to present a Piper Tri-Pacer to the Flying Farmers, and I was there to tell about the Ag-1, which was being demonstrated.) Among other things, we had discussed the cost of building light planes, and I had made the statement that I thought that the time had come when a light airplane covered with metal could be built for as low a cost as one covered with fabric.

Because my remark was such a heresy to the Pipers, they kept mulling it over back in Lock Haven. Finally, in 1953, I received a phone call from Pug Piper asking me to work out an academic treatise that would prove it. I told him that I couldn't prove it that way with any assurance but that I had done a cost-reduction project for Cessna on their 170 model and had the cost, labor, and weight data for all of the parts. If Piper would furnish me the same information for the Tri-Pacer, and if Cessna would let me use their data (and I thought they might if they could get a copy of the results), then I could compare the two types of construction on a cost-per-pound and a cost-per-square-foot basis. Piper did want me to do this, and when I called up Cessna, its people were not only willing to have the comparison made, but they also furnished me with up-to-date cost material. This meant that I would not be bothered by the inflation problem, which even then amounted to 10 or 12 percent for the time that had elapsed between the two projects.

The comparison was revealing. Considering the complete wing surfaces as a group (wings, ailerons, and flaps), the materials and purchased parts of the completed fabric-covered surfaces of the PA-22 cost 27 percent more per square foot than the metal-covered ones of the 170. Also, the labor hours required for the PA-22 fabric-covered surfaces, with their wing stitching and many coats of dope, were 33 percent greater per square foot of area than for the metal-covered surfaces of the 170. The average labor cost was about $1.90 per hour in Wichita, as compared with only $1.54 per hour in Lock Haven. Assuming the same labor rate in both cases, the total cost per pound for the entire airplanes would be, I reported, about 8 percent *greater* for the fabric-covered PA-22 than for the metal-covered 170.

Three years later these results moved Piper to seek a low-cost all-metal replacement for the Tri-Pacer PA-22. It was this job in particular that brought me to leave Texas A&M for Piper's Aircraft Development Center in 1957.

During December 1956 and early January 1957, I worked out in some detail, with Pug Piper's help, the specifications for the new design. The designation of the new model was PA-28, or the twenty-eighth Piper Aircraft model. It was to be a four-place airplane powered with a four-cylinder, 150-HP Lycoming engine. The plane was to be relatively small overall, with a low wing of about 30-foot span that could support a wide 10-foot tread tricycle landing gear with 600-by-6-inch wheels and tires. The wheelbase was to be as long as feasible, and the nose wheel—which was the critical wheel in soft field operation with a tricycle gear—was also to have a full-size 600-by-6-inch tire. (In a soft field, with the wheels dragging down below and the propeller thrust above, the nose can sometimes carry more load than either of the rear wheels.) With the wide-spread tricycle gear and with the low wing and the correspondingly low center of gravity, the airplane should handle very well on the ground in strong winds, we thought, even if they were crosswinds.

The construction of the airplane was to be of all metal, but as simple as possible, with a straight wing. All ribs were to have the same shape, and the structure was to be made up of as few large pieces as possible. The control surfaces were to have beaded skins and to be free from internal ribs or stiffeners.

The cabin of the Tri-Pacer was only 35 inches wide inside of the steel tubes, and I wanted the inside width of the new airplane to be 44 inches to give ample comfort. Piper, however, was preparing for production a new, more expensive, single-engine four-place model, the Comanche, and it had an inside width of 44 inches. The management insisted that the comfort of the new low-cost airplane not be in direct competition with the Comanche and therefore insisted that we limit the overall inside width to 42 inches. And so many of the details of the airplane were worked out in the original specifications, but I certainly did not have time to go on with the design work during that period when I was finishing up my business at Texas A&M.

Not wanting to wait, Piper hired Johnny Thorp of California to do a preliminary design study for us. About the middle of January 1957 there was a meeting at my house in College Station about the new plane, with Pug Piper coming west from Lock Haven and Thorp coming east from California. After a couple of days of discussions Johnny went back to California and started on the preliminary design study.

Thorp finished his report in the late spring of 1957, but it lay dormant for about four months until Karl Bergey, an aeronautical engineer with North American Aviation in Los Angeles, came to work with us. After hearing about the start of Piper's Aircraft Development Center, Karl had gotten in touch with Pug immediately, and in the summer of 1957, he flew to Vero Beach in his Vagabond for a visit. He started working with us in September of that year, and I immediately put him on the Cherokee project. He soon became my assistant chief engineer, and in that regard was associated to a certain extent with the Pawnee project in the latter portion of its history. Karl had gone to college at Penn State and had done some graduate work in aeronautical engineering at MIT, and he was an exceptionally competent designer and an easy person with whom to work; naturally, he became a very important element in our work at Vero Beach. In fact, I was counting on him to take over my job when I retired.

Karl and I went right to work to whip out quickly an experimental airplane with which we could prove the main features of the new airplane. Johnny Thorp had done an excellent job on the preliminary design report, and his layout fit in very well with our detailed desires. I thought we made excellent progress from that time on, designing a prototype of the production model, making production drawings, and doing everything else needed to get an approved type certificate from the CAA, but of course the business management naturally wanted the whole enterprise wrapped up in half the feasible time.

In our detailed design we naturally kept in mind first what the airplane was supposed to do, that is, the performance and the flight and handling characteristics. We wanted the structure to have ample strength, but we also wanted it to be as light as possible so as to allow a large useful load to be carried. And we wanted the structure to be simple, with as few parts as possible and with parts that were easy to make. In addition, we wanted the airplane to be rugged and easy to inspect, maintain, and repair, and flying in it to be comfortable and pleasant, as well as safe.

A good example of our drive for a simple structure was the floor of the airplane, which was also the outside skin of the bottom of the airplane. To accomplish this required outside longitudinal stiffeners that increased very slightly the drag of the airplane but that also allowed for a low overall height of the cabin but still with ample inside height for the comfort of the passengers. Substantially all of the sheet metal covering the airplane required no special forming other than bending. The parts that required double-curvature forming, such as the nose cowl, wing tips, stabilator, fin, and rudder tips, were formed of fiberglass and plastic in molds.

An extreme example of the saving in the number of pieces showed up in the aileron construction. The Cherokee aileron had ten parts compared with thirty-six parts for the Comanche aileron. Overall, the structure of the Cherokee had less than half the number of parts of the Comanche's structure. The Cherokee also had less than half the number of rivets: 1,785 as compared with 3,714 for the Comanche.

Those were the end results, but in 1957 we were just getting nicely started. As the staff increased, we soon had designer Bob Lipinsky in charge of the fuselage work and Henry Hoeltje in charge of the wing details.

Ordinarily Hoeltje did a reasonably fine job, but he soon made a name for himself that he couldn't live down as long as he was with Piper. He designed the aileron control system so that the ailerons worked backwards. On numerous occasions in the past, mechanics had hooked up the aileron wires so that they worked backwards, and some flights had ended in catastrophe on that account.

When our system was redesigned, we attempted to arrange it so that it could not be hooked up backwards. It is surprising what mechanics and operators can do, however. For example, on our old Ercoupe, which had fuel tanks in the wings, the fuel tanks had vent holes that were supposed to point forward, and the mechanism was arranged so that no one, we thought, could put the cap on backwards. If the vent on one wing tank pointed forward and the other one pointed backward, the fuel would flow from one tank to the other. Occasionally, however, someone found a way of forcing it on backwards, even though it would partially ruin the mechanism.

One unusual feature in the development of the Cherokee had to do with the main wing beam or spar. In our original specifications I had decided to use the NACA laminar-flow-type airfoil that had been developed under the direction of my old friend at Langley Field, Eastman Jacobs. I made this selection partly on the basis of the airfoil characteristics, but also because it was a relatively thick airfoil section with its maximum thickness back near the middle of it. This type of thickness would enable us to use a single main spar that was deep enough for a reasonably lightweight construction yet placed far enough back as it ran through the fuselage that it was under the front of the rear seat. This arrangement would give us a clear floor for the entire cabin.

The particular airfoil that Karl Bergey and I selected after considerable study was the NACA 65_2-415. We wanted to be able to remove the wings quickly and easily in order to expedite the crating and shipping for overseas delivery. We could have used the Piper Comanche arrangement, which butted the wings up against the fuselage, for this purpose, but this arrangement had the spar extending clear into the center of the fuselage. This had two disadvantages that we wanted to avoid. One was the need for extra long crates. The other was that the fuselage without the wing spar in place was rather flimsy for handling on the ground.

In principle, my idea was to use the Comanche arrangement but to move the joint from the center to the sides of the fuselage. The Comanche's spar was a built-up I-beam with an extruded cap strip at the top and one at the bottom connected by a web of aluminum alloy. This gave an I-shaped cross-section. We bolted a plate of aluminum alloy over the top flange of the I-beam and another similar one under the bottom of the I-beam. This tied the two portions of the wing together. Completing the beam structure was a plate that connected to the webs.

My plan was to extend the top and bottom connecting plates to the sides of the fuselage and to provide at the edge of the fuselage the same kind of bolted joint for each half of the wing. Within the fuselage area we put webs of sheet metal stiffened on each side. This made a box beam rather than an I-beam. Then the I-beams of the right and left halves of the wing were slipped inside the box beam, and the joint was made at the edge of the fuselage. Inasmuch as the bending moment load on the beam inside the fuselage was substantially constant from one side of the fuselage to the other, we were able to use the same size and strength of joint.

After trying a number of variations in detailed dimensions of the joints, Bergey and I finally arrived at what appeared to be an optimum arrangement for the first experimental Cherokee and for the second one, which was the prototype on the basis of which we obtained the type certificate.

We were happy with the arrangement, but the CAA was not. When we submitted it to the CAA for approval, Clark Biesemeier, the structures man from the CAA's Fort Worth office, was not satisfied that the joints would operate satisfactorily and with integrity for an extended period of time under repeated loads in gusty air. And, unfortunately, our structures consultant, Ben Hamner from Texas A&M, agreed with him. Biesemeier and Hamner, incidentally, were old friends who had worked together years before on the structural design of the Swift airplane.

In my opinion, the integrity of the type of joint we were using had already been proven by the experience of the Comanche airplanes, which had been in service for a couple of years without difficulty. The Comanche had been designed in Lock Haven and had been approved by the regional office of the CAA in New York. However, in our case, the Fort Worth office and Ben Hamner were adamant in their views. Both sides finally agreed to an extensive series of fatigue tests with oscillating loads to prove the integrity of the joints. The tests were made on a combined fuselage and wing structure that had been constructed for static tests and on which the regular static tests had been completed up through the limit load values, that is, the loads that the airplane would be expected to withstand in regular and maneuvering flight without permanent deflection or set.

When the joints were checked at a load of 1 *g* (representing level flight in smooth air) plus and minus .75 *g* (representing gusts), no visible evidence was found of any type of failure in over 7,000 cycles. Witnessing these tests for the FAA (which had changed in the interim from the CAA) was Cal L. Stoner of the Fort Worth region. After Stoner returned to Fort Worth, we continued the tests with the same loading, however, until over 300,000 cycles had been applied, with still no evidence of any sort of failure in the joint. The cycling load was then increased to approximately 1 *g* plus and minus 1.25 *g* and the tests continued. In all, over 480,000 cycles were applied, and considering the up-loads and the down-loads separately, nearly a million individual loads were brought to bear on the joint.

Precise detailed measurements of the bolts and the holes showed no measurable differences between the conditions after the tests and the conditions before the tests were started. The joints were then approved, but we were very careful in production to specify very close tolerances on both the bolts and the holes so they would always have a snug fit. The joints gave excellent trouble-free service and were strong enough so that they could be used without modification on later Cherokee models that were much heavier than the original. All this, of course, required a substantial amount of engineering time and expense, but in the end we had by far the most fatigue-tested light airplane in existence. Since that time, everyone has paid more attention to taking care of gust loads in all kinds of airplanes.

The fuel tanks of the original experimental version of the Cherokee were, as in the Ercoupe, in the portion of the wing ahead of the spar and near the fuselage. The tanks were bolted with machine screws to flanges on the spar that could be easily removed for repair or replacement. Each tank held 25 gallons, making a total of 50 gallons.

The details of the landing gear were worked out by Johnny Thorp, who in his machine shop in California also built and furnished the first few gears for the production airplanes. After a time, and I don't remember the exact date, the experimental airplane was ready for its first flight tests, and the performance and the handling characteristics came out to be about as expected. Then over a period of months, slight modifications were made as appeared desirable. By about the end of 1959 we thought we were ready to start the production drawings for the second, or prototype, airplane and go after government approval. The Piper plan was to produce the Cherokees at the new production plant in Vero Beach, a large portion of which was now operational.

In early January 1960 Pug Piper came up with a scheme to get the design approved and ready for production in the shortest possible time, and after going over the pros and cons, we adopted it. His idea was to secure the type certificate by no later than February 1, 1961. For every day that we beat that date, each Development Center employee would get a bonus consisting of a certain small percentage of his salary. If we beat it by a large amount, the bonus would be substantial. In addition, according to Pug's incentive plan, we could work as much overtime as was feasible, and I could hire as much extra help as would actually be a help.

After going over the situation with the various department heads in the Development Center, we decided to work one hundred twenty hours every two-week period instead of the usual eighty. Starting on a Monday we would work ten hours a day for twelve days, going right through the next Saturday and Sunday. The succeeding weekend would then be free. This schedule gave us two free days every two-week period. And whenever possible, we took those free weekends at a time that would include a holiday, such as the Fourth of July or Labor Day, thereby giving us a three-day vacation.

Though a few people were enthusiastic about the accelerated schedule, most were not; and some objected to it rather strenuously. One of the men who objected most strongly was Slim Revel, who was by now the experimental shop foreman under Clarence Monks. (George Roth resigned from this post only a few months after taking it in 1957, largely because he had not been able to find satisfactory housing for his family, and because his family wanted to move back to Hawaii, which they did.) Revel didn't think that it was possible to get the approved type certificate by February 1, 1961, and thought that it was unfair for management to hold this bait out in front of its employees just to get them to work exceptionally hard for a long period of time and then get little if anything for it. He thought that when his fellow workers woke up to this fact they would grow disgruntled and be worse off than before. I honestly felt, however, that there was a good possibility that we could beat the target date by a full three months and that everyone would get a substantial reward.

I made up and posted on the wall of the shop a large milestone chart showing the dates by which the main portions of the new airplane would have to be completed in order that the approved type certificate be obtained three months ahead of schedule, or on October 31, 1960. The steps I included were the design and the structure analysis, the production drawings, the construction of parts for the prototype airplane, the structural testing itself, the assembly of parts on the prototype airplane, the flight testing of the airplane, the official flight tests for FAA approval, the submittal of all data to the FAA, and, finally, obtaining the approved type certificate.

As the program went along and the men saw that we were actually meeting the dates scheduled for the various parts, their enthusiasm grew; it seemed to me that in general they were giving the project all they had. As a result, we managed to get the plane built on schedule, the flight testing completed on schedule, and all of the data necessary for approval ready for the FAA one week before October 31, 1960.

Karl Bergey and I delivered the data personally to the Fort Worth office of the FAA. Fortunately, the officers there had a complete set of the production drawing prints, and we took along some drawing change slips and some drafting equipment. On the spot, we modified the drawings officially wherever the FAA said it was necessary. We had surprisingly little difficulty with the main items. However, we were pestered to death by secondary items, such as the plumbing fixtures and electrical equipment, that their specialists had not taken much time to consider. We kept after the FAA people, however, and even worked at nights on some of the drawing changes. At 4:00 P.M. on October 31, Herb Slaughter, the administrator for the FAA's fourth region, called us into his office and presented us officially with approved type certificate no. 2A12 for the 160-HP Piper Cherokee PA-28.[1]

A couple of months later, on Sunday, January 8, 1961, the company dedicated its Vero Beach production plant, making use of Bill Piper, Sr.'s eightieth birthday as the kick-off point. By then, the

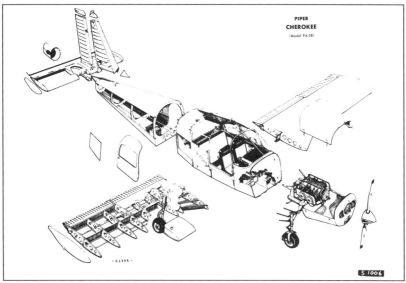

Above, the first Cherokee, November 1960, just after being certificated. Surrounding it are just about all of the people who had worked on it. I am standing to the far right. Below, a breakdown sketch of the Piper Cherokee PA-28.

Dedication of Piper production plant at Vero Beach, January 8, 1961, Bill Piper, Sr.'s eightieth birthday.

Piper Cherokee 180, 1971. The 180 was one of the best arrangements in the Cherokee series for general all-around use.

plant had grown to about five times its original size and included a new office building for the general management. The dedication was quite an event, with a crowd estimated by the press of more than five thousand people. Mr. Piper's friends had come to honor him from all over the country, many in some 250 private or business airplanes. Besides a number of local dignitaries, the visitors included Florida governor Farris Bryant, who had taken office just a week before; radio and television star Arthur Godfrey, who arrived in his private Convair; famed long-distance pilot Max Conrad, who had broken a number of records in Piper airplanes; and the Reverend Billy Graham, who pronounced the dedication. The new factory had constructed the first production Cherokee by this time, and it was exhibited in the center of the activity.

Production of the Cherokees started very slowly, but by the end of the summer of 1960 we were up to about five a day. The new airplane was well received by the flying public, and the rate of production continued to increase. As time went on, we added a number of new Cherokee models. In August 1962, a 180-HP model was approved and started into production. This model differed from the original chiefly in that it used a four-cylinder Lycoming O-360 engine in place of the original four-cylinder O-320. This change permitted a slightly higher gross weight and a higher useful load. It also improved the airplane's performance at high altitude and provided an excellent combination of power, size, and weight for the general run of light plane flying.

In the spring of 1963, both the 160- and 180-HP models were approved as seaplanes with Edo floats. Incidentally (as I mentioned in an earlier chapter), Edo stands for Earl Dodge Osborn, a notable man (born in Garrison, New York, in 1893) whom I have known for many years and who I believe is still alive. He and Casey Jones, whom I first met sixty-five years ago at the 1923 National Air Races in St. Louis, together with three others whom I did not know, founded the organization called the Quiet Birdmen, of which I happen to be a member. It was founded just after World War I and now has chapters, or "hangars," as they are called, throughout the entire country. I still get a great deal of pleasure "hangar-flying" with pilots from all around.

The Cherokee did not make a very good seaplane, however, largely because it had a single door on the right-hand side only. When beaching or docking, a seaplane pilot often wanted to get down on either the right-hand float or the left-hand float in order to facilitate the operation. But with the Cherokee, getting to the left-hand float required an impractical acrobatic maneuver. Very few Cherokees were purchased with floats, and after a time the model was dropped.

From the early 1930s until sometime after World War II, most of the primary training for civilian pilots was done in first Taylor and then Piper Cubs. This experience helped to influence the pilots trained in Cubs, of course, to buy the more advanced Piper aircraft as they became available. As the use of the tricycle gear became almost universal, however, and as larger instrument panels were needed to support radios and other navigation equipment as well as gyroscopic instruments for instrument flying, the tail-dragging Cubs with their narrow tandem fuselages became obsolete. Also, side-by-side seating was found to be a better arrangement for training.

Shortly after World War II Cessna came out with Model 120, a small high-wing trainer with side-by-side seating and an all sheet-metal fuselage; as I remember it, it was powered with a 65-HP Continental engine. Sometime later an improved model called the Cessna 140, with a somewhat more powerful engine, was produced. These models still had fabric-covered wings and tail-wheel-type landing gears. In fact, all of Cessna's single engine models at that time were tail-draggers, although their twin-engine models were fitted with tricycle gears.

As mentioned previously, Piper put a tricycle gear on its Pacer model in 1951 and called it the Tri-Pacer. This airplane was accepted immediately by the flying public and far outsold the Cessna 170 tail-dragger. Cessna then put a tricycle gear on its 170 model and called it the 172. Cessna then gradually fitted all of its models with tricycle gears except one, the 180, which was particularly suitable for bush work. By about the mid-1950s the company had also put a tricycle gear on the 140 model and called it the Cessna 150. This model and its successor, the 152, have dominated the training field ever since.

In the mid-1950s Piper was in dire need of a modern training plane so that more people would learn to fly in Pipers and then continue with the Piper line. The company even considered taking over the Ercoupe and making a training plane of it, but Bill Piper,

We left most of the fiberglass and plastic portion of the Papoose unpainted so that we could look through for possible defects that might develop.

Sr., wanted quicker action. His designers decided to strip the four-place Tri-Pacer down to a two-place trainer and call it the Colt. Though this airplane was to be fitted with a new 115-HP Lycoming O-235 engine, it could be produced with the same tooling and methods as the Tri-Pacer, which was already in production. The Colt sold fairly well for a couple of years, but it could not compete with the lower-powered, all-metal Cessna 152, and the model was dropped about 1964.

Shortly after the Aircraft Development Center in Vero Beach was started in 1957, and we were using fiberglass and plastic in the Pawnee hoppers and other nonstructural parts, Pug Piper and I started thinking in terms of a possible trainer made of fiberglass and plastic composite construction. When we had our Pawnee and Cherokee projects well enough along so that we could take on another project, we started in earnest on the design of the composite trainer, which we called the Papoose. For the Papoose project engineer we used Sam Snyder, an aeronautical engineer from the University of Illinois, my alma mater. Bob Drake, our plastics specialist, was put in charge of working out construction methods suitable for production.

Our hope for the Papoose was to get a savings in cost and possibly a savings in weight also. To facilitate getting a low cost with high quality, we decided to make the airplane small, with a span of only 25 feet and a wing area of only 110 square feet. This would give a relatively high wing loading for a trainer, but by using full span flaps we felt that we could achieve acceptable minimum speeds. According to our design, these flaps were to be deflected to a maximum of only 30 degrees and then operated differentially as ailerons.

We decided to use a low-wing monoplane arrangement with side-by-side seating and a wide-tread tricycle gear. This gave us a general configuration somewhat like that of the Ercoupe. The wing of the Papoose was moderately tapered, however, which helped in obtaining lower weight and which, with a simple molded type of construction, would not increase the cost. Also, the wing was one piece from tip to tip, with the fuselage resting on top of it. Inside the fuselage the wing became the bottom of the seats for the occupants.

In construction the wing was molded in two halves: a top half and a bottom half that were cemented together. The fuselage was molded in right and left halves including the fin, and then they were cemented together. By using female molds, the outer surfaces of the wing and fuselage were smooth and needed no additional finishing. In fact, by using a suitable colored gelatinous coating against the mold, the final finish could be obtained with any color desired, and no additional painting was required. We carried out a great deal of research so as to make use of the best materials available at the time and the best details in construction.

The wing skins were one-half inch thick and comprised a paper honeycomb with outer and inner surfaces of fiberglass layers in polyester plastic. The curing was done at about 240 degrees Fahrenheit. Polyester plastic was used partly because we knew how to handle it and partly because epoxy was just coming into the picture and we were uncertain how to handle it properly—particularly in view of its highly toxic effects on the workers, which no one had yet learned to overcome.

The first Papoose airplane, which was really a prototype because it was made from molds suitable for production, first flew in April 1962. During the next six months of exposure, which included some eighty hours of flight testing, we experienced no trouble with the plastic structure. When the external wing and fuselage surfaces came out of the molds, they had been very smooth, and we had anticipated getting aerodynamically smooth surfaces and substantial laminar flow if the wings were kept clean and polished.

As time went on, however, it became apparent that the curing had not been absolutely completed in the molding operation. The honeycomb pattern was showing through on the surface to a slight extent, spoiling the aerodynamically smooth surface. This detail would have to be taken care of, we knew, by improving the curing process.

As the work progressed we made aging and weathering tests. This was done by placing samples on the roof of our Vero Beach plant for maximum exposure to the sun and humidity conditions. Before long, we realized that the unprotected polyester plastic was losing a lot of strength. To remedy this problem due to exposure to the environment, we gave the plastic a solid coating of black paint along with a dark undercoating next to the polyester itself.

The paper honeycomb of the airplane structure, which had been treated with phenol formaldehyde, had a sort of Bakelite composition that was resistant to water but was not entirely waterproof. This condition needed to be improved, we knew, because if a leak in the surface occurred and water got inside, the strength would be lost.

Though this problem could have been solved without too much difficulty, two factors, the weight and the cost of the new airplane, were major barriers preventing further development. The weight turned out to be greater than that of a comparable aluminum-alloy structure. This was partly due to making the first design somewhat over strength because of the unknown quantities of the material, particularly with regard to aging. It was obvious that with the materials that we were using, there was no likelihood of any savings in weight.

As I remember it, the material costs of the fiberglass and plastic Papoose would not have been greatly different from those for a metal airplane. The labor hours, however, would have been greater. Inasmuch as the molds that we used were suitable for production, we were in a position to make a fair estimate of the labor hours required. It would seem, offhand, that molding only four large pieces and bonding them together would take much less time than cutting, fitting, riveting, and forming all of the different parts for the wing and fuselage of a metal airplane. But in order to take care of the weight and strength requirements, it was going to be necessary to cut to size and lay up in the molds a very large number of pieces of fiberglass cloth of different kinds. Thus, although only four large pieces would have to come out of the molds, a large number of smaller pieces would have to go into them, and they would have to be cut and placed in position very carefully. A rather large amount of hand labor would be required, and it appeared certain that there would be no savings in cost.

The project was then dropped, at least until some future time when improved materials became available. They have been available for the last few years, and there are now several aircraft projects that are going ahead with them—but none in the light low-cost trainer airplane field, because the materials are still quite expensive. The Papoose was, I believe, the first airplane in which the major structure, including the wing, the fuselage, and even the main landing-gear legs were made of composite fiberglass and plastic construction.

It was painful to see the project dropped, but the Papoose is now displayed in the museum of the Experimental Aircraft Association at Oshkosh, Wisconsin.

With the demise of the Papoose, Piper was still in dire need of a training airplane. The company decided to repeat the Tri-Pacer–Colt experience by stripping a four-place Cherokee 150 down to a two-place trainer. The rear seats were removed, and the baggage area and close-out panel were moved up to that area. The same Lycoming O-320 engine was used as in the 150, and although the engine was still rated at 150 HP, a higher pitch propeller was used with it that held the RPM and power down a bit. We called this airplane the Cherokee PA-28-140. We obtained the approved type certificate for the PA-28-140 in February 1964 and immediately put the airplane into production.

The Cherokee PA-28-140 had gentle flying and stalling characteristics and served well as a trainer. With its low-wing arrangement, it had a low center of gravity and a low center of drag, as well as support for a wide-tread landing gear that gave good stable support when the airplane was on the ground. Students were able to operate the airplane safely under substantially higher wind conditions than with the narrow-tread high-wing trainers. Numerous reports came in to us that in many cases of high and gusty wind conditions, after training in Cessna 150s and 152s had been forced to cease, training in the Cherokee 140 had gone right on without difficulty.

Also, with a nose wheel tire that is the same large size as those of the rear wheels, the airplane could be operated from relatively soft grass fields. As was brought out by my tricycle ski experiences in Minneapolis in 1945, under high drag conditions such as snow or soft ground the nose ski or wheel may get at least as large a load as that taken by either of the rear wheels. Under those conditions the tire should be at least as large as those of the rear wheels. Also, the nose wheel is the first to go over rough terrain. In general it takes more punishment than the rear wheels.

Although the Cherokee 140 appeared to make a good training airplane, with its larger engine and increased fuel consumption, it cost more to purchase and operate than the Cessna 152. Therefore, it was not used nearly so widely as the Cessna 152. In the 1970s Piper replaced it with a smaller and lower-powered design called the Tomahawk.

We made the next Cherokee model change by fitting the regular four-passenger model with a six-cylinder, 235-HP Lycoming O-540 engine. To increase the fuel capacity with the larger engine, we extended the wings by one foot on each side, so that the span was increased from the original 30 to 32 feet, and formed the wing tips into fuel tanks. Each wing-tip tank held 17 gallons, which increased the total fuel capacity from the original 50 to 84 gallons. The 235-HP model was available with the same type of fixed-pitch aluminum-alloy propeller as was used on all of the other Cherokee models up to that time. The maximum speed of the airplane was 166 MPH, however, which meant that the propeller pitch was too high for best take-off and climb performance. It was when airplanes such as the Lockheed Vega had reached that speed level in the early 1930s that the manufacture of controllable-pitch propellers had commenced.

Because it was available with either the fixed-pitch propeller or a controllable constant-speed propeller, the 235-HP Cherokee did well in short field operations, particularly fields at high elevations in the high plains and mountain areas. The approved type certificate for the Piper Cherokee PA-28-235 was received in July 1963, and the model was immediately put into production. The new model was well received by the flying public, and modern versions of the model are still being produced in moderate quantities. Modern versions of the 150- and 180-HP models are also still in production over twenty-five years later.

The user of an airplane is always, of course, the final judge. As reports about the new Cherokee came in from the field, our engineering department kept a record of them. We then made minor improvements where it seemed that they would help. Maintenance improvements were made as soon as it appeared that they were needed, and new items involving comfort, performance, and appearance were brought out in the yearly model changes. An example of the latter was changing from the old push-pull type of controls for the throttle, the mixture controls, and the propeller pitch control to a quadrant-type of control in which all were grouped together in a single cluster, as has been the practice in larger military and commercial airplanes with piston engines.

I had done the same thing twenty years before with the Ercoupe in order to avoid misuse of the throttle control by automobile drivers, for the automobiles at that time had push-pull throttles that operated on the dashboard in the opposite direction.

The next Cherokee model to come out was given the 180-HP Lycoming engine and fitted with a retractable landing gear; we called it the Arrow. The approved type certificate for the Piper Cherokee Arrow PA-28R-180 was obtained in June 1967. Except for the retractable gear and a change in the 180-HP engine fuel system, the airplane was essentially the same as the fixed-gear Cherokee 180. The latter had a Lycoming O-360 engine with a carburetor that hung below the engine. For the retractable version, we changed to a Lycoming IO-360 engine, which had a fuel-injection system and gave room under the engine for retraction of the nose gear within the cowling. Even with this extra room, though, it was necessary for us to reduce the nose wheel size from the regular 600 by 6 inches to 500 by 5. This limited soft field operation to some extent, and I did not like to have to do that, but by that time almost all operations were from paved fields or well-prepared and firm grass fields.

By that time, moreover, the use of the 500-by-5 nose wheel had been established by the experience of the Beech Bonanza, which had been using it for many years. Incidentally, the 180-HP Cherokee Arrow had about the same size, weight, and performance as the original Beech Bonanza, which was first manufactured about

Top, Cherokee Arrow; middle, Cherokee 6-260; bottom, Seneca PA-34.

1947. I have always admired the Bonanza design and like to think of it and the North American Navion as the first four-place light airplanes to follow the general arrangement of the Ercoupe with its tricycle gear and low wing.

By the late 1960s the Bonanza and Cessna 210 four-place, retractable-gear airplanes had become heavier and more powerful and therefore more costly. It did not take long before the Cherokee Arrow outsold all of the others in that field. With its retractable gear, the 180-HP Cherokee Arrow was slightly faster than the 235-HP fixed-gear Cherokee. The Arrow was therefore fitted with a constant-speed propeller as standard equipment. The Arrow gave a more economical performance from a fuel standpoint, but the 235-HP fixed-gear Cherokee was more of a workhorse in that it could carry heavier loads and operate better at high-altitude fields.

The most unusual feature of the Cherokee Arrow was the way the retractable landing gear was controlled. In the period before the Arrow came out, every year several hundred retractable-geared light airplanes would be emergency landed with the gear in the up position. Besides being dangerous, this was quite expensive, because it usually meant replacing or repairing an expensive controllable-pitch propeller and repairing the bottom of the airplane (and possibly the flaps, which may have been down). These gear-up landings were usually made even though the pilot had a great deal of warning, when the throttle was back and power off in preparation for a landing, by flashing red lights and squawking horns to tell him that the gear was still up. It happened that Pug Piper had had two of those experiences himself, and he asked me if we couldn't devise a system that would take care of that situation by putting the landing gear down automatically, even if the pilot forgot to.

I recognized that such an automatic back-up system would have to sense both the air speed and the engine power. With our Cherokee Arrow, which had a landing speed with flaps down in the low 60-MPH range, this meant that if the pilot was coming in approaching a landing in a power-off glide, the gear should come down automatically and lock when the air speed got down to about 100 MPH. On the other hand, during a take-off run with full power, the maximum angle of climb would occur at about 85 MPH, and the landing gear would have to be retracted and remain retracted throughout the climbing range—that is, at air speeds of 85 MPH and above. Previously the Beech Bonanza had been fitted for a short time with a device that could accomplish this purpose by sensing both the air speed and the engine manifold pressure, but its use had been discontinued.

It occurred to me that the propeller slipstream velocity would be increased by applying power, and that if I could find a spot within the slipstream area that with the airplane flying in full throttle climb at 85 MPH would give a local air-speed reading of slightly over 100 MPH, I could get the effective power with a single Pitot-static air-speed sensor alone and have a very simple arrangement.

The Arrow was still in the design stage, with Englishman Graham Gates doing an excellent job on the retractable landing gear and Gill Trimmer on the details of the gear's automatic extension mechanism. So I took a Cherokee 180 and, with the aid of Clarence Monks, flew a number of tests exploring suitable locations for an air speed sensor in the slipstream. We were looking for a place that would give the same air-speed reading on a separate indicator with the airplane flying at 85 MPH and full throttle as with the airplane flying in a glide with the propeller completely throttled and a reading of 105 MPH. We found a couple of suitable locations on the Cherokee for the instrument, but selected one that was well protected by being just outside the left-hand side of the fuselage and a couple of feet above the middle portion of the wing.

For the Arrow I located a Pitot-static sensor at that point with a design similar to the one used for the indicated air-speed instrument for the Cherokee. I made this sensor larger, however, so that a greater amount of air could be used to move a diaphragm that opened or closed a hydraulic valve. When this valve was open, the gear fell down by the pull of gravity and locked in the down position suitable for landing.

The usual retraction and extension of the gear by the pilot was done by hydraulic actuators; these were operated by an electric motor driving a gear pump, which could be run in either direction. An electric switch on the instrument panel (the handle of which was in the usual form of a wheel and tire) was moved to an up position to force the gear to retract and to a down position to force the gear to extend. The entire operation was carried on in the standard way with blinking light and squawking horn if the throttle was moved back to the landing position without the switch calling for gear down. Also, the usual squat switches were attached to each of the wheels in order to prevent the gear from being retracted while the airplane was on the ground with its weight on the wheels.

Thus, in ordinary operation, the pilot operated the gear just as he would any ordinary retractable gear. In case of a malfunction where the gear would not go down, there was an emergency control lever by which the pilot could open the hydraulic valve manually, releasing the gear of its own accord and locking it in place. If the pilot was making an ordinary landing and forgot to put the gear down, however, the automatic feature opened that valve and the gear came down and locked by itself.

There were two conditions under which it was desirable to override the automatic gear-release feature. The emergency extension lever, which was located between the forward portion of the two front seats, also functioned as an override lever that eliminated the automatic extension function. When placed in the downward position, as mentioned previously, this lever caused the gear to extend and lock. When held in the upward position, it eliminated the automatic feature and placed the gear under electrical control just as in the case of all ordinary retractable landing gears. With the lever in the up position, stalls and slow flight could be practiced with the gear retracted. The up position to hold the gear retracted was also used in full-power climbs at high altitudes, where the indicated air speed was lower than the true air speed. With the automatic feature, the gear tended to come down within the climbing range and reduced the climb performance.

As the Arrow was first produced, its pilot had to hold the lever up to keep the gear retracted under these conditions or get a copilot or passenger to hold it up for him. This was done so that when the maneuvers were finished, the lever would return to its neutral position and the automatic feature would be ready in case it was needed for a landing in which the pilot forgot to lower the gear. Piper produced the airplane with this arrangement for several years and, as mentioned previously, it soon became the best-selling retractable-geared airplane in the world. (Insurance companies allowed a reduced premium for retractable-geared airplanes fitted with the automatic back-up system.)

After a time a number of instructor pilots expressed a desire to be able to lock the gear in the up position for the practice of slow flight and stalls. Also, after a pilot, who apparently did not know enough about the system to hold the override lever up and keep the gear retracted during a climb at high altitude, crashed at the 9,000-foot elevation at the north rim of the Grand Canyon, the National Transportation Safety Board demanded that Piper supply a means of locking the override lever in the up position. This was accomplished within a year or two after I retired in 1969.

All in all, the system has worked well over a period of many years. I know of only three cases in which gear-up landings were made. In one case, the pilot forgot to lower the gear and landed at a high air speed well in excess of 105 MPH; naturally, the gear did not come down automatically. In the other two cases, the pilots had left the override lever in the locked up condition and the airplanes had acted like ordinary retractable-gear airplanes.

The best measure of the success of the system is that it is still in use on the Arrows, which are still in production, and, in addition, was incorporated into a retractable-geared model of the Cherokee 6 that has higher horsepower and improved performance. This model will be discussed a little later.

After the Arrow had been in production a few months and the automatic landing gear back-up system had been well received, the Piper sales department thought that the company should have a patent on it, if possible. Up to that time Piper had no patents whatsoever. It happened that I had anticipated this possibility and had prepared a description of the system, had mailed it to myself, and had then filed it away unopened so that the original date could be verified as stamped on the sealed envelope. A year or more later I ran across the letter unopened in my files and, in my usual absent-minded manner, did not recognize it. I opened it, breaking the seal and spoiling the record. Fortunately this did not matter, however, because in its search the U.S. patent office found no significant prior art. On May 12, 1970, a very good patent (no. 3511455) was obtained in my name and assigned to Piper.

During my last year at Piper we did some preliminary investigation toward improving the climb of the Cherokee by increasing the span without requiring a substantial strengthening of the inner portion of the wing. This could be done, we thought, by tapering the outer half of the wing (the portion beyond the flaps) so that the tip chord was smaller than the root chord, thus reducing the load at the tip.

In 1973 this change was finally made, to the 150-HP model, and Piper designated the new version of the Arrow the PA-28-151. To give the plane better climb and flatter glide characteristics, the span was increased to about 35 feet. This change was well received, and by 1978 all of the Cherokee models still in production were fitted with the tapered outer wing panels.

A few PA-28 models are still in production but have been given names such as Warrior, Archer, and Arrow. The smallest PA-28 still in production is the PA-28-161, which is called the Warrior II. In 1983 its suggested list price was just under $40,000, as compared with just under $10,000 when it first came out in 1961. The model has been spruced up a bit, but most of the difference in the sales price represents inflation. This same model, fitted with the usual amount of avionics, sells for anywhere between $50,000 and $70,000. Under these conditions, the production rate has dwindled to a small proportion of its former amount.

The 235-HP model, the PA-28-236, is now called the Dakota; and the retractable Arrow, the PA-28-R-201, is now called the Turbo-Arrow IV.

Early in the 1960s Pug Piper had the idea of expanding the Cherokee series to include a six-place multiengine model. He thought that we might fit it with three 115-HP Lycoming O-235 (the "O" is for "opposed") engines and that, like the original Ford and Fokker trimotors, we could get by with a fixed landing gear and fixed-pitch propellers and have a relatively low-cost multiengine airplane that would carry six people. I doubted whether engines of that power would be sufficient when operating with one engine out.

By the time we were ready to start the project, we already had the four-place 235-HP Cherokee in production. I suggested that in our first experimental multiengine model we put the 235-HP installation in the nose of the fuselage and install the smaller 115-HP engines in the wings. In the flight tests we could then throttle the center engine down to 115 HP and see what the airplane would do under those conditions. If the performance with only the two wing engines operating was not satisfactory, we could then use as much extra power from the center engine as was necessary to give the desirable performance. And from that, we could tell what the size of each of the three engines should be.

With the six-place seating arrangement, we wanted to have a narrow aisle so that people could get from the front to the rear seats easily. The cabin portion of the fuselage, therefore, had to be both wider and longer. To accomplish this and still use as much of the original Cherokee fuselage structure as possible, we sliced the cabin portion of the fuselage in half longitudinally and moved the halves out so that the width was increased by 7 inches. We kept the portion of the fuselage back of the cabin essentially intact, but extended it by 30 inches and fitted a new tapered section into the 30-inch gap. To balance the two additional rear passengers, we moved the center engine forward and placed an additional baggage compartment between the fire wall and the cabin. (The Cherokee 235 wing structure, with its fuel tanks at the tips, was used just about as it was except that we strengthened it slightly where needed. The tail surfaces were also essentially the same as those of the 235.)

Not long after the design and construction of the experimental model had started, I had the idea that this structure would make a good six-place, single-engine airplane if it only had a more powerful engine. It happened that the 235-HP, six-cylinder Lycoming O-540, which had been rated very conservatively, was also available with a high compression ratio and higher RPM rated at 260 HP. Fortunately, it fit right into the same place in the power plant installation as the 235-HP model. Pug Piper agreed to test the experimental multiengine plane first as a single-engine plane with the 260-HP engine in the nose and then later to install the 115-HP wing engines for multiengine tests.

This was done, and the performance as a single-engine airplane turned out to be excellent. We put an extra door at the back of the cabin on the left-hand side so that the rear passengers could get in and out easily without going through the front door and down the aisle. With all but the front seats removed, a large cargo space was available, and an extension was made to the opening for the rear door so that large pieces of cargo, even coffins, could be put in and out with ease. The airplane could then be used as a general-purpose workhorse as well as a six-place passenger plane. An approved type certificate was obtained for the Cherokee 6, and the Piper PA-32-260 was put in production about 1965.

In 1966, a 300-HP version of the same engine was available from Lycoming, and manufacture of the PA-32-300 was started. The extra power was appreciated, particularly in mountain flying. There was a good demand for the Cherokee 6, particularly for carrying the whole family, moving executives, and hauling cargo, and its production was continued at least up through the end of 1983. Sometime in the 1970s, a semitapered wing was incorporated, adding about three feet to the span of the airplane and improving its climb characteristics. It was then called the Saratoga. Later, the airplane also became available with a turbo-charged engine, which increased its cruising speed at optimum altitude from 173 to 190 MPH.

During the late 1970s, what was originally the Cherokee 6 was fitted with a retractable gear and became known as the Saratoga-SP (for special performance). In 1983 it was still available, with either a turbo-charged or a naturally aspirated engine. With the turbo-charged engine the cruising speed at 75 percent power and optimum altitude was listed as 204 MPH, while with the naturally aspirated engine, the listed speed was 183 MPH. It pleases me that the automatic landing-gear back-up system, which puts the gear down for landing even if the pilot forgets, was used on this model just as it was still being used recently on the retractable-geared Cherokee Arrow.

As soon as the tests were completed with the prototype of the single-engine Cherokee 6 with a 260-HP engine in the nose, we added the two 115-HP wing engines and commenced testing our trimotor. With the center engine throttled back so that it gave the same horsepower as the wing engines, making a nominal total of 345 HP, the performance was acceptable. With the center engine shut off, however, the performance with the two 115-HP wing engines alone was not. So we installed two 150-HP models of the Lycoming engine, which was the next model up in terms of power, in place of the 115-HP ones. With a total of 450 HP, the speed was so high and the required propeller pitch so high that we needed to have controllable-pitch propellers.

But with the extra cost and complication of three controllable-pitch propellers, and the two more powerful wingboard engines, our original concept of a simple, low-cost trimotor was destroyed. Our only option was to change the concept to a conventional twin-engine arrangement with controllable-pitch propellers and a re-tractable landing gear.

We eventually developed this model as the Cherokee Twin-6, known officially as the Piper PA-34. Originally this airplane possessed two 180-HP Lycoming O-360 engines and a wing span of 36 feet 7 inches. After getting the prototype flying, which was just about when I retired in September 1969, we considered increasing the power to 200 HP. Production started a couple of years later, with the name changed by the marketing department to Seneca, after an Indian tribe in the Seneca Mountains. The demand for the airplane was good, and since 1973 it has outsold every other twin on the market. The 1984 model was available as the Seneca III.

This concludes my story of the Cherokee series. Piper no longer calls them Cherokees, but many of the original Cherokee design parts are still in use, and tower operators still refer to all of the single-engine models as Cherokees. In all, up to the end of 1983, 41,666 Cherokees were produced. This included 34,672 of the PA-28 series and 6,994 of the PA-32 or Cherokee 6 series. Of the Seneca twin-engine series, 4,162 have been manufactured, making a total of 45,828 airplanes. All of these airplanes include at least some parts that are the same as those of the original Cherokee produced in 1961 as a low-cost all-metal low-wing airplane replacing the obsolete fabric-covered Tri-Pacer.

One other sizable project was undertaken at Vero Beach before I retired in 1969, but it was never completed. This was the design and production of an eighteen-passenger commuter and light cargo airplane known as the Pocono.

In early 1965, Bill Piper, Sr., suggested that there might soon be a sizable market for a large bush-type plane for South America, Africa, and other unsettled areas. If that market alone was not enough to justify development, Mr. Piper thought that the design could be sold to the small commuter airlines. Pug Piper agreed with his father. In a memorandum written March 23, 1965, Pug wrote:

> The idea I have is this: we have a breakthrough in a low-cost high-utility six-place airplane in the PA-32. This same concept could be extended again to a model twice, or even four times, the size of the PA-32. This plane could carry 12 to 20 passengers and two pilots. The PA-32 concept of easy flight characteristics, simplified and light-weight structure, simplified and safe flight features, low landing speeds, short field characteristics, etc., would be incorporated. The new plane might or might not have retractable gears.

After mulling over the possibilities for several months, Karl Bergey and I prepared preliminary specifications calling for an airplane driven by two 400-HP Lycoming IO-720 engines and hav-

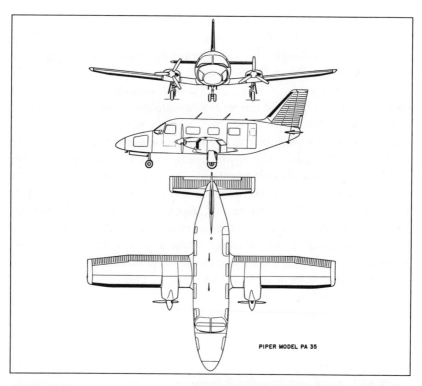

Piper Pocono, Model PA-35, a proposed commuter liner, in 1967.

ing a gross weight of 8,700 lbs. Its cruising speed was to be about 210 MPH. The main part of the fuselage was to be a circular cylinder large enough that three people could be seated side by side, two on one side and with an aisle between the single seat on the other side. The circular cross-section would be suitable for pressurization if that were required later. With a full fuel load of 200 gallons, fifteen occupants were to be accommodated comfortably. For short runs with less fuel, nineteen people could be crowded in. The estimated list price in 1965 was $80,000 to $90,000.

We wanted the plane to have a retractable tricycle landing gear with a double nose wheel arrangement. I was particularly in favor of this arrangement; I had hoped to use it on a design for some time but knew that it required an airplane large enough to justify the use of the two wheels. Instead of involving a fork carrying a single wheel that was supported at the lower end of a shock-absorber strut, the strut itself would simply support an axle at its lower end that had a smaller wheel on each side of it. The two wheels were to be fixed rigidly to a single axle that turned in a bearing at the lower end of the shock-absorber structure. The usual tendency of a castering wheel to shimmy (which usually requires hydraulic damping of some kind) did not exist with this arrangement, I recognized, because when the combination started to make a turn to the right or left with the wheels fixed together but turning at different radii, a scrubbing action occurred that damped out any tendency to oscillate. I had had this in mind since we first started studying various aspects of the tricycle gear arrangement at the NACA back in the 1930s, and it had since been used on numerous large airplanes, but this was the first opportunity that I had to use it on an airplane that I was associated with.

In order for work on the Pawnee, Cherokee, Seneca, and Pocono (or PA-35) to go on without interruption, the company assigned Karl Bergey as head of a new section in charge of the Pocono project. During the spring of 1966, Bergey hired a number of new engineers and designers and some draftsmen to staff his new separate group. The engineers included Landis Ketner, an air frame designer; Eugene Dearing, a structures and aerodynamics expert; Robert Laber, a systems designer; Ed Jackson, an electrical engineer; Elwin Davis, a materials and process engineer; and stress engineers Roger Aderman and Marion Shin. Shin was a tiny Chinese lady from Hong Kong, and she was an excellent stress engineer. After retiring from Piper, she went into business for herself as a building contractor.

We recognized in the very early stages that if satisfactory airline-type performance was to be obtained carrying eighteen to twenty passengers, the airplane would have to have more than two 400-HP engines. At that time, however, that was all that the Lycoming IO-720 engine was approved for. But the Lycoming engineers were working on means to increase the power and expected to get an approval of 520 HP for each engine in the near future. As I remember it, however, they were willing to guarantee only 470 HP.

In October 1967 Piper issued pamphlets that stated that the company expected to fly its new eighteen-place commuter airline, the PA-35, in early 1968. The airplane was to have two 470-HP engines, and its gross weight was to be 9,000 pounds (a slight increase from the original specification). In addition, the engines were to be turbocharged. This would provide excellent high-altitude performance.

About that time we were fortunate to add another significant member to our staff, Herbert M. Toomey. I had known Herb since the 1940s, when the Ercoupe was being manufactured in Riverdale, Maryland, and I was reporting to FAA headquarters in New York City, where Herb was in charge of the engineering. Later he was transferred to Washington, and he was thoroughly familiar with all of the FAA procedures. He took an early retirement from his government service and came with us as FAA engineering coordinator. For a number of years before retiring from Piper, he helped immensely with relations with the FAA.

As the production of the various Cherokee models had increased, new bays had been added to our Vero Beach plant until all of the available space for that building had been used up. It was obvious that more manufacturing space and more people would be required if we were going to take on the production of the PA-35. The problem of space was considered by the company administration in Lock Haven, and on February 9, 1968, Bill Piper, Jr., wrote a memorandum to Luke Blume, our production plant manager, and to me. (Bill Jr. had been the executive vice-president when I started working with Piper in 1957, but by 1968 he had replaced his father as the company president.) Bill Sr. had relinquished the presidency and retained only the chairmanship of the board. This memo called for a new semi-independent manufacturing plant somewhere away from Vero Beach. Ultimately this satellite facility was built in Lakeland, Florida, which is about 100 miles west of Vero Beach.

In February 1968 the PA-35 project received a severe blow: Karl Bergey, the project's leader, left to go with North American Aviation. He was offered the vice-presidency of the light airplane division at double the salary he was receiving at Piper, and he felt that he could not refuse the opportunity. I was greatly disappointed, not only because we were losing an outstanding designer, but also because I was to retire in about a year and a half and was counting on Karl to take my place and then continuing to work with him part-time on a consulting basis. Our thoughts ran along somewhat similar lines, and we worked very easily and well together.

As stated earlier, when I was sixty-three years old, I had told Piper management that I would be willing to retire at age seventy, in 1969. This was now only a year and a half away, and for the time being I had the full load of the PA-35 program as well as the others. Pug Piper and the rest of the management in Lock Haven immediately began looking for a replacement for me to train so that by the time I retired he would be in step with things. I was in favor of building from within our group and suggested Bill Barnhouse, who was not only a competent designer, but an excellent pilot. At that time Barnhouse was in charge of our experimental flight testing. I also suggested Glen Stephen, who had been the project engineer on the Pawnee agricultural planes almost from the beginning and who was an excellent organizer.

Piper management, however, wanted to bring in someone from outside who had made a name for himself. After much interviewing, including psychological testing at the local college in Lock Haven, the company selected Robert C. Scott, who was then chief engineer of Mooney Aircraft, Inc., at Schreiner Field in Kerrville, Texas. Apparently he had passed the tests with flying colors. Bob Scott then started with us in Vero Beach about June 1968.

Scott had completed a course in aeronautical engineering and had a bachelor's degree also in business administration. He overflowed with formal methods and systems involving a great deal of paperwork. This was a far cry from my method of operation, which was relatively informal and involved as little paperwork as was feasible. Inasmuch as Scott's training involved the latest thing, however, and because he would be in complete charge of the Aircraft Development Center within a year or so, I let him work his methods into our general procedures insofar as they did not appear to hinder our activities noticeably.

The prototype PA-35 with its 400-HP engines was ready to fly about the time that Karl Bergey left in February 1968. By June the plane had survived over fifty hours of preliminary flight testing by Bill Barnhouse and his crew. The tests were made with the airplane at a gross weight of 9,000 pounds, but during the course of its construction, the airplane's empty weight had increased several hundred pounds above the original estimate. Some of this could have been worked out, but it was apparent that if the original payload was to be obtained, the gross weight would have to be increased to 9,500 pounds or more.

In general, the flight tests showed that after a few readily made refinements, the airplane would serve its purpose as a commuter airliner and cargo plane very well if it had sufficient power. It appeared, however, that the 520 HP hoped for from each engine would be the very minimum.

Studies regarding the use of turbine engines for the PA-35 had been made as early as February 1968. Ample power could have been obtained with well-proven turbine engines that were already on the market, such as the United Aircraft PT-6 series. But the cost of the turbine engines was several times that of the piston engines, and Pug Piper wanted very strongly to use the piston engines if possible in order to keep the price down.

It took over a year to conclude flight testing of the PA-35. We improved the airplane's longitudinal stability by lengthening the fuselage and increasing the size of the horizontal tail surface. Also we managed to reduce the aileron control forces, which were rather high, to a satisfactory value. The pilot for much of the flight testing was Lew Mason, an excellent man who had been with us since the early days in Vero Beach. Occasionally, though, Pug Piper himself checked out the plane.

In November 1968 evaluation flights were made by Herb Toomey, who had come to us from the FAA, and by Ward Evans, one of our design engineers. Evans had fifteen years as a professional pilot with airline experience flying airplanes from 5,200 to 13,500 pounds, thereby covering the range of the PA-35. We made further improvements following suggestions by Evans and Toomey, and in the spring of 1969 Piper came out with a beautifully illustrated brochure describing the Piper Pocono/PA-35, its new commuter/cargo plane, which, the brochure said, would be available in the near future.

Considering that the main portion of the fuselage was, as was the case with most airliners, a rather large diameter cylinder (although shorter than usual for its diameter), the long tapering nose and the tapering tail made a rather sleek-looking airplane out of it. The gross weight had been upped to 9,750 pounds and the power plants were still to be fuel-injected TIO-720-B1A turbo-charged Lycoming engines rated at 520 HP each. The wide cabin and large easy entrance were ideal for the type of service required, and it appeared that the airplane would be a winner if the engines came out as specified and the plane was available at the time expected, sometime in 1970.

In the meantime we explored other possibilities. These included the possible use of Pratt and Whitney R-1340 radial air-cooled engines and the use of four smaller flat air-cooled engines. Neither of these two options was entirely satisfactory to us, however, and we continued to study the use of turbine engines as a more likely possibility.

In the latter part of 1968, Pug and the Piper management decided that we would have two versions of the PA-35. First there would be the piston-engine version and next there would be a turbine-engine version that would come out at a somewhat later time.

In the interim, Beech was already in production with a third-level airliner called the Beech 99. This had a gross weight of 10,400 pounds and would carry about fifteen paying passengers plus a pilot. It was driven by two PT-6 turbine engines. The airplane accommodated only two rows of passengers with a narrow aisle in between, and the fuselage had to be unusually long.

We rented one of the Beech 99s from a local airline and put it through some trials. We found it to be a fine airplane with good performance and handling characteristics. The seating arrangement was very cramped, however, and the interior configuration was nowhere near so well suited to both passenger and cargo hauling as was our PA-35. The Beech 99 was already on the market, however, and was gradually filling up the demand for that type of airplane.

In mid-July of 1969 we received a devastating shock. The Lycoming people advised us that it was not possible for them to develop and approve the TIO-720 engine with a rating of 520 HP. They could get the power up to only 470 HP, and even this would require substantial redesign of the engine and would take considerable time. This eliminated the low-cost piston engine version of the PA-35.

Like the case of the new Continental Tiara engine used in the Pawnee Brave, which appeared to be an ideal design but which failed in service, this case also reinforced my favored practice of always using a tried, true, and well-proven engine in a new airplane design. In the real world, however, it is not always possible to follow one's favored practices.

We had continued to study the potential of a PA-35 with turbo-prop power plants, and two arrangements appeared promising. One, which involved a gross airplane weight of 11,000 pounds, made use of the PT-6A-27 turbo engines rated at 680 HP. The other, which involved a gross airplane weight of 12,500 pounds, made use of the PT-6A-30 turbo engines rated at 800 HP. The latter arrangement also involved stretching the fuselage a bit so that it could carry a couple more passengers.

The design effort on these two possibilities was carried on for some time. Before it was finished, however, I turned seventy (in July 1969) and retired (on September 15, 1969).

By the time of my retirement, preparations for the manufacture of the PA-35 had been going on for several months. The satellite plant in Lakeland, where the airplane was to be constructed, was nearing completion. But during the summer of 1970, management decided not to carry on the project further. It just did not appear that it would be at all profitable to do so. In October 1970 Bill Barnhouse ferried the PA-35 to Lakeland accompanied by Bob Holmes, the Vero Beach plant superintendent who had been in charge of the construction of the Lakeland plant. They left the plane in the bare, new unoccupied factory structure on the Lakeland airport, and so far as I know, that was the end of the PA-35.

This concludes the story of the airplane designs that I was associated with at the Piper Aircraft Corporation Development Center at Vero Beach. In the final part of my memoir I will tell about my aeronautical activities and associations since retiring from Piper in 1969.

6.

Retirement?

(1969 to the Present)

*At my retirement party at the Aircraft Development Center hangar on
September 15, 1969, I was given a large cake decorated like a runway, with
models of some of the airplanes I had helped to design during my career.*

15.

Trials of a Light Plane Designer

At the end of the day (September 15, 1969) on which I retired from Piper, the Aircraft Development Center employees at Vero Beach threw a party for me in our experimental hangar. They had a big, flat cake decorated like a landing field with three beautiful models supported as if flying just above it. The models represented some of the designs for which I had been responsible. One was the agricultural Pawnee, complete with spraying equipment. Another was the retractable-geared Cherokee Arrow. The third, in deference to my pre-Piper days, was a model of the Ercoupe. For nearly twenty years now these models have been supported, one behind the other, on the wall of our living room, as if they were flying down to a landing on our long mantelpiece above the fireplace.

The models were made by Earl Brown, who at that time was a draftsman in our engineering department and made models on the side as a hobby. He did such an excellent job with the models that a great demand developed for them, and now he is spending full time with his own modelmaking business, making models of a more sophisticated nature in many cases, for wind-tunnel tests and such uses, as well as just to look at and admire.

365

That night a dinner was held for me, presided over by Pug Piper and attended by his lovely wife, Helen, and attractive daughter, Patricia. Pug could not resist carrying on a bit of horseplay. Removing his daughter's fashionable wig from her head, he placed it upon his own, which needed a little more hair. Then he fit it upon my head, which needed even more hair. This antic made an enormous difference in our appearances and brought out a lot of laughter and good humor. One of our loyal employees in charge of the blueprint operation, Bette Stockho, was offended, however, and thought that I should have been treated with greater respect. But after the monkeyshines, the customary accolades did come.

After a short vacation to visit our children and grandchildren in Maryland, South Carolina, and California, I met with Pug Piper and my successor, Bob Scott, to go over the consulting work that I was to do with Piper in retirement. Pug and I had had an understanding for some time that I would continue to be active on consulting jobs, possibly up to half a day much of the time. The meeting turned out to be a very short one. Before we got into any details, Bob Scott said that he wanted no part of me connected with the Aircraft Development Center.

As mentioned previously, Scott's methods were quite different from mine. I was inclined to let the people build up their strong points and then form the organization around the people. He had a modern business method of designing a rigid organization and then fitting the people into the holes, whether they were square or round. After a couple of years Bob was fired.

The consulting work that I did after retiring was done directly for Pug Piper himself. My main project involved studying the cost and weight of various forms of light airplane structures. From the cost-savings standpoint, I considered items, such as wings, tail surfaces, and fuselage, that made up only about 32 percent of the total cost of, say, a PA-28-140 airplane without special equipment. In other words, if the cost of the fuselage, wings, and tail surfaces could be cut in half, the total airplane cost would be reduced by about 16 percent.

To obtain all of the information that I needed in addition to that which was available from Piper, I visited a number of airplane plants that used different methods of construction. One of these plants was Windecker Research, Inc., of Midland, Texas, which had constructed and obtained complete approval for the first time on an all-composite airplane, the Windecker Eagle. Another was the

American Aviation Corporation in Cleveland, Ohio, which manufactured the American Yankee, an all-aluminum airplane held together by bonding rather than with rivets. Still another was Bryan Aircraft, Inc., in Bryan, Ohio, where a man by the name of Dick Schreder was manufacturing a highly refined sailplane involving both composite fiberglass and plastic for the fuselage and sheet-aluminum wing surfaces bonded to polyvinyl chloride foam ribs. In addition, I visited the Messerschmitt company in Munich, Germany, where I studied two types of construction. One was fairly standard aluminum sheet-metal construction in the Messerschmitt VO-209 Monsun sport and trainer airplane. The other was the LFU-205 fiberglass-reinforced plastic airplane, which in size and power was comparable to our Cherokee Arrow.

The information I collected permitted me to make comparisons among three airplanes incorporating fiberglass-reinforced plastic main structure and various airplanes with aluminum-alloy structure, both riveted and bonded. I found that the construction with the lowest cost was the bonded aluminum sheet construction used in the American Yankee; this beat the others by a good margin. Some of the advantage, however, was due to the simplified and squared-off form of construction used in that particular model. The labor cost of the fiberglass-reinforced plastic construction in 1972 (the year my project was completed) was higher than that of even the riveted aluminum-alloy construction. This demonstrated for me that there had been no progress in the reduction of cost of riveted aluminum-alloy construction since the early 1950s. I concluded that with the stronger fibers and improved resins that were then being developed, reinforced plastic structure for light airplane wings and fuselages might in the future be lighter than riveted aluminum-alloy structure. But at the stage of development in 1972, the fiberglass-reinforced plastic was definitely heavier. It was also more expensive.

Today, with strong, light reinforcing materials such as carbon filaments and Dupont's Kevlar-Aramid fiber, and with improved epoxy plastics, it is likely that the weight can be reduced to less than that of the aluminum-alloy construction. The prices of these new materials are still quite high, however.

In 1969 I got an instrument rating from Flight Safety International in Vero Beach, a prestigious organization with several centers that mainly trained airline pilots, many from other countries. I did not really expect to do much instrument flying in my seventies, but I did plan to make some experiments involving control in an attempt to reduce the pilot's workload, particularly under critical conditions. I wanted to know first-hand what the pilot's duties were in instrument flying, and since I was now retired, I would have time to carry on such investigations.

After taking the ground-school course and passing the FAA written examination, my flight training started under Douglas Bachelor, who was fortunately a very understanding and considerate person. I was not only old and, I suppose, rather fixed in my ways, but in trying to follow the instruments only, I had forty-six years of seat-of-the-pants flying to overcome. I probably set a record in the flying time required to get an instrument rating, but ultimately I did it at the age of seventy.

Two incidents from this experience stand out. During the first portion of my training, we flew in a retractable-geared Cherokee Arrow, but after a time we switched, fortunately, to the Cherokee 6, which had four fuel tanks. On one occasion we were returning home after practicing holding patterns, and I was making a standard VOR instrument approach with, of course, my outside vision blanked out by a hood. I had just passed the VOR at about 1,500 feet outbound and had made a 45-degree turn to the left when the engine stopped. We had been flying the entire time on the left main tank, and realizing that the left tank was now empty, I reached down instantly to the fuel valve that was ahead of and between us and switched to the right main tank. The instructor took a little longer to figure things out, but then he reached down and unknowingly shifted tanks back to the empty one.

A long and rather heated discussion ensued, with neither of us giving in, and all the time the airplane losing altitude. Finally we agreed to shift to a tip tank. We were over relatively open country, but it was fine to have the engine start up again when we were at about 500 feet above the ground and to go back and make another instrument landing without difficulty.

The other incident occurred during my final flight test for the instrument rating, which was made by an FAA designee, Bush Narigan, who has since become a good friend and fellow QB (Quiet Birdman). Among other things, Narigan had me file an instrument flight plan to Melbourne, Florida, only about 35 miles north of Vero

Beach. As soon as we were off and up to about 1,000 feet, I immediately contacted approach control, which instead of letting me go ahead with my flight plan, informed me that due to traffic conditions I had to take a certain course that went out over the ocean. The approach control changed my course a couple of times and then finally headed me right to the VOR at Melbourne, which was right at the airport.

Up to here, everything was all right, but just after I had passed the VOR and had turned west on the outbound portion of my standard instrument landing procedure, approach control immediately ordered me to make a holding pattern on the 180-degree radial— that is, to the south—with two-minute legs. The FAA recommended three standard methods of entering a holding pattern, all to occur when approaching the place where the pattern was to be held. This, however, caught me going away, and none of the three methods seemed to apply. Confused, I wallowed around for some time before finally establishing the holding pattern. The two-minute-leg feature did not bother me, although I had done all my practicing with one-minute legs with a one-minute turn at each end. But all of this was happening while I was under the hood, of course, and could not see out, while the check pilot was sitting next to me enjoying the situation. Shortly I was directed to go back to the landing approach procedure, and the landing turned out to be all right.

Later, after the whole check procedure had been completed and we were sitting in Bush Narigan's office, he asked me whether considering my performance I thought he should give me the rating. We agreed that I had not done very well in approaching the holding pattern and I agreed to take some more dual instruction in that regard. This turned out to be a good thing for me, for my instructor, Doug Bachelor, showed me a new, simple way, not indicated by the FAA, in which I could always enter a holding pattern from any position.

My second check for the instrument rating turned out to be an easy and successful one and included an instrument landing system (ILS) approach at West Palm Beach.

In the last few months of my employment with Piper in 1969, and for a few years thereafter, the Piper Aircraft Corporation experienced some very tough times, organizationally speaking. In the following pages, I would like to explain some of this Piper history, a lot of which distressed me greatly.

But first some more background about the company. During the 1950s Tony Piper had done the main managing of his father's company. In May 1960, however, he told Bill Piper, Sr., that he was through. Tony retained the vice-presidency as well as his position on the board of directors, but he no longer took part in the daily decisions and activities. During the 1960s it appeared to me that Pug Piper, with his initiative and drive, was the main influence in running the company. Bill Jr. acted as a sort of flywheel, keeping things running smoothly.

Piper employees, particularly in the sales area, were carrying on in a rather lavish manner, and I was concerned that the old, frugal atmosphere instilled by Bill Piper, Sr., was being abandoned. I realized by that time that business cycles had their ups as well as their downs, and that if one were going to sell airplanes that cost many thousands of dollars, it would be worthwhile to have appearances commensurate with the product. But it bothered me to see the money flowing out more loosely than before.

Trouble began for Piper on January 23, 1969, when Herbert J. Siegel, president of the Chris-Craft conglomerate, phoned Bill Piper, Jr., our president, and told him that Chris-Craft had purchased 200,500 shares of Piper stock. The Chris-Craft plan, Siegel said, was to continue purchasing shares and to take over the company. He hoped that Piper would cooperate.

The Pipers wanted to control their own company, and a struggle began. Chris-Craft needed to possess 51 percent of the 1,638,350 shares to take over, and at this point it had just less than 200,000, or about 12 percent. Chris-Craft put out a tender offer at $65 per share for up to 300,000 more shares. The Piper stock had been selling on the market for about $50 a share. By February 4, Chris-Craft had 545,000 shares. The conglomerate needed about 300,000 shares more to take over, so it put out another tender offer. In the meantime, Piper had negotiated with Grumman, U.S. Concrete Pipe Company, and Southply Incorporated in an effort to arrive at some deal by which the family would not lose control of its company.

At the Piper annual meeting on March 25, 1969, Chris-Craft, while it did not have enough stock for control, had enough of the shares to get two men on the board of directors. A new board, con-

One of aviation's great men, William T. Piper, Sr., about 1945. Behind him at his plant in Lock Haven, Pennsylvania, is a Cub Trainer, the plane in which roughly 75 percent of U.S. civilian pilots had learned to fly.

sisting of Bill Piper, Sr.; Bill Piper, Jr.; Tony Piper; Pug Piper; Charlie Poole; and Walter Jamouneau from Piper, and two men by the names of Gordon and Rochlis from Chris-Craft, was formed. Dropped from the board were R. K. Griffin and Norman Greene; Greene was the fellow who had helped save the company in 1950. According to aeronautical writer Devon Francis, author of *Mr. Piper and his Cubs*:

> The inclusion of W. T. Piper, Sr., was a courtesy to the founder of the company and patriarch of the clan. He promptly resigned as a director and chairman and was named to those posts emeritus. Both Mr. Piper and Jamouneau, the company secretary, bawled without shame as the resignation was offered and approved. They had worked together for 35 years. Bill, Jr., assumed the chair pro tem.

The fighting between the Pipers and Chris-Craft continued unabated for the next few weeks, with the Pipers still in control. (At the board meeting Pug had been made executive vice-president and chief operating officer.) But Chris-Craft would not give up and put out another tender offer to get more stock.

On May 8, 1969, Piper finally arranged to become part of the Bangor-Punta Corporation, a holding company whose factories turned out sailboats, houseboats, campers, motor homes, life-saving resuscitators, traffic-control devices, and law-enforcement equipment, including firearms and emergency power units, among others. It also produced cottonseed oil from land it owned and leased in California. Bangor-Punta was attractive to the Pipers because of its long-standing policy of maintaining autonomy in the management of its operating companies, and so the family would presumably remain in control of its own unit, but it did not work out that way.

Again, a new board was formed, this time with four men from Bangor-Punta, three from Chris-Craft, and only one, Bill Jr., from Piper. Pug remained as part of the administration, but Tony divorced himself completely from the company, moving to Texas to manage some of the family properties. Walter Jamouneau became the vice-president. Because he was such a competent person, all of the different managements appeared to respect him and be able to work with him.

Still, both Bangor-Punta and Chris-Craft campaigned for more Piper shares and, together with the Piper family shares, Bangor-Punta finally obtained 51 percent of them and gained control. The in-fighting continued, however, with Chris-Craft maintaining that some of the Piper family shares should not be eligible to vote. After that, the management of the company deteriorated somewhat.

During the next few months after losing his company, Bill Piper, Sr., kept going to his office nearly every morning. One morning when Pug and I were driving around the airport at Lock Haven, we saw him on his way from his home, which was on one side of the field, to the plant at the other side. He would shuffle-jog for possibly 50 feet and then walk for another 50 feet and kept repeating this, like the old Boy Scout practice. Bill was trying to keep his health so that he would one day be able to lead the Harvard parade as the oldest living alumnus. But, sadly, he did not quite make it. In November 1969 he went to the hospital with a circulatory ailment and, on January 15, 1970, a week after his 89th birthday, he died.

William T. Piper, Sr., had received many honors which were richly deserved, for he was a great man who had an important influence on general flying.

Sometime in 1970 the engineering department of the Aircraft Development Center in Vero Beach had to quit reporting to Pug Piper and instead report directly to the local management in Vero Beach. The in-fighting continued between Chris-Craft, Bangor-Punta, and the Piper family. In early 1973, Bill Jr. and Pug were thrown out of the corporation. Pug and his wife, Helen, moved shortly thereafter to Wichita, where he became a consultant to Beech. (In 1980 Pug founded Piper Advanced Technology, Inc., and started the development of a modern four-place canard airplane of composite construction. In 1981 he died of cancer, which he had been fighting for years. His death was a great loss to me as well as to the light airplane industry.) Chris-Craft had sued Bangor-Punta because of the manner in which the Piper family stock had been taken over by Bangor-Punta. Chris-Craft lost the first case in the Pennsylvania courts, but won the appeal, after which Bangor-Punta appealed. The case went to the Pennsylvania Supreme Court, which also favored Chris-Craft. The case then went to the Supreme Court of the United States, which reverted to the original decision in favor of Bangor-Punta.

After the U.S. Supreme Court decision in its favor, Bangor-Punta was in full charge of the Piper operation, and it immediately eliminated the Chris-Craft members from the board of directors. In addition, it relocated much of the engineering work that used to be done in Vero Beach to Lakeland. A number of the former Vero Beach engineers also moved to Lakeland.

By 1984 the entire Bangor-Punta conglomerate, including Piper, had been absorbed into a still larger conglomerate, Lear-Siegler Corporation of Santa Monica, California, a diversified manufacturer of aerospace electronic and electromagnetic equipment. This resulted in some drastic organizational changes within Piper, including the abandonment of both the Lock Haven and the Lakeland plants and the shift of the entire Piper operation to Vero Beach. In 1987 Lear-Siegler was acquired by Forstman Little, which sold the entire company to an individual businessman and experienced pilot, Stuart Millar. This is good news, as Millar is taking steps to get Piper back to a thriving business again.

The entire light aircraft industry has had a terrible slump during the last few years, one of the worst that has been experienced to date. In 1979 the industry produced 17,048 aircraft. By 1983 this number came down to a miserable 2,691. Each of the main companies, especially Piper, had to lay off a large proportion of its work force.

During all the years that I had been responsible for designing airplanes, from the Ercoupe in the 1930s to the Pawnee and Cherokee series in the 1960s, and for several years after I had retired, I had never been required to defend any of the designs in court. A few years ago, however, the subject of product liability came to the fore, and now the airplane manufacturers have to spend a substantial amount of effort and money in court cases following accidents. Because the practice is very lucrative to attorneys, it grew very rapidly. After every airplane accident there is now always the possibility of trying to find a way of blaming the design for the accident, and a plaintiff attorney can offer to take on a case for a person who may have been injured directly or indirectly by the accident.

In the early days of aviation there were law suits of this nature, of course, but all the engineers were requested to do was furnish occasionally, possibly once a year, some technical data for the attorneys. Now Piper has several legal officers in the Vero Beach plant whose entire time is spent furnishing information to the attorneys retained by the insurance company to protect Piper in these cases.

I have been told that 17 percent of the cost of the Cessna airplanes is due to court cases. The practice of suing the airplane designer has grown to an absurd state and in some ways is threatening the light plane industry. For example, Piper is putting most of its design effort on the large, expensive business airplanes, which cost over $1 million each, not only because the company makes a larger percentage profit from the more expensive airplanes, but also because the chances for being sued are much less. For every million-dollar-plus airplane Piper builds, the company could build many low-cost light planes. But then there would be many times the likelihood of a court case, and often even the light plane suits involve funds in the millions of dollars. Although occasionally these cases have merit, most of them appear to me to be pretty farfetched.

Between 1977, after I had been retired for nine years, and 1984, I was involved in about fifteen different court cases against Piper.

Piper Airplane Prices, 1961–1986

The prices of the Piper airplanes have increased immensely over the past few years due to inflation, liability insurance, and some product improvement. The present Warrior II, which is the modern version of the original Cherokee 160 and is fitted with the same engine, in July 1986 had a base list price of $69,860 as compared with the original Cherokee 160 at $8,500 in 1961. During the same period of time, consumer prices have increased about 3.5 times; so the airplane price has increased well over twice as much as inflation.

The following list gives the base list price of the Piper airplanes in production as of July 1986.* All, except the Cheyenne and Malibu models, have grown from the original Cherokee 160 and incorporate some of the same parts.

PA-42-1000	Chenenne 400LS	$2,731,000
PA-42-720	Cheyenne IIIA	2,294,000
PA-46-310P	Malibu	363,000
PA-34-220T	Seneca III	231,120
PA-32R-301T	Turbo Saratoga-SP	179,820
PA-32R-301	Saratoga-SP	163,730
PA-32-301	Saratoga	137,160
PA-28RT-201T	Turbo Arrow IV	124,400
PA-28-236	Dakota	106,920
PA-28-181	Archer II	75,450
PA-28-161	Warrior II	69,860

For the past few years the large manufacturers of light airplanes have concentrated on the most expensive models; thus, the number of airplanes produced per year by the entire industry is now but a very small part, possibly less than one-tenth, of what was produced in the 1960s and 1970s. Cessna has recently stopped production of all its piston-engine models and is continuing with only its jets and turbo-props. Piper had stopped production of all but its top three models, but has recently started the small ones again in a small way. The above list was given to me by Piper as models available in July 1986, but actual assembly of the "low"-priced ones appears to be minimal, if any.

Though the interest in private flying, sport aviation, and light aviation appears in general to be continuing with some vigor, the regularly manufactured small airplanes available at low enough cost for ordinary people may be a thing of the past unless some major changes are made pertaining to the laws of product liability and the resulting excessive insurance rates.

---

* The list price does not include all the navigation equipment usually purchased.

Age seventy-six, in 1975.

Because cases usually do not get to court until some years after the accident, by the time they are tried the airplanes involved may be several years older than at the time of the accident, and they might easily have been old at the time of the accident, and the basic design may have been completed several years before the airplane was constructed. I got into the picture at this late time because the attorneys for the plaintiffs wanted to get an admission of a design defect from the man who had been in charge of the design.

The main difficulty for me, or any other engineer, in these cases is this: that every design feature or change is decided upon and made because it has some important advantages. But that is not to say that the same design feature or change does not also have, from certain points of view, important disadvantages. For example, if an airplane is designed to carry a greater useful load, then the gross weight is increased and the airplane has to take off and land at higher speed. Everything about designing an airplane is a trade off.

Many times during this time period, I opened our front door to a caller, only to be handed a subpoena commanding me to appear at a certain time and place for a deposition to be conducted by the plaintiff's attorney. Sometimes the arrangements have been made by the plaintiff's attorneys through the Piper insurance company's attorneys, and in some cases the Piper insurance company or its attorneys have wanted me there on their own account. In all cases in which I have been retained it has been through the insurance company and its attorneys, not by the Piper Aircraft Corporation itself. I have a couple of file cabinet drawers full of information on these cases; it may be of some interest to touch briefly on a few of them.

The first case had to do with a fatal accident in central Georgia involving a 235-HP Pawnee agricultural plane. The airplane had been constructed in 1968 while I was still with Piper. The accident occurred in 1973. The actual trial was in Americus, Georgia, in January 1978.

There were several witnesses to the accident, but they were very close-mouthed about what happened leading up to it. The pilot was returning to his landing strip after having sprayed a field of peanuts, and it appears that he went up to a fairly high altitude and put on a demonstration of aerobatics for some of his friends on the ground, although the witnesses would not confirm this exactly.

One witness, another agricultural pilot, did state that he first heard the engine because it sounded like a very high RPM. He also stated that when he observed the aircraft, it was in a nose-down attitude at a higher-than-normal altitude. He stated that he saw the left wing come off and the aircraft continue temporarily in straight flight before it began to spin. The plane struck the ground in approximately vertical position, and its engine was buried in the ground.

The Pawnee was a strut-braced low-wing monoplane with the struts going from the upper surface of the wing to the upper portion of the fuselage. The struts were therefore in compression in all normal flight conditions with the airplane right-side up. Examination of the struts (and this was confirmed by the examination of the National Transportation Safety Board) showed that they failed very definitely in tension. The failing force on the wing was therefore opposite to the usual lifting force and had tended to push the

wing downward with respect to the airplane. This must have occurred in some kind of aerobatic maneuver for which the airplane,
an agricultural workhorse, was not designed.

The NTSB report concluded that the airplane was subjected to
maneuver airloads well in excess of design values. The plaintiff's
attorney tried to maintain that the wing structure was defective
and that it had come off in the normal course of flying.

At the trial, as was the custom, the plaintiffs pled their case first.
When they were finally finished, the judge ruled that they had not
made a case for themselves and gave the victory to Piper, without
the defendants having to say a word. None of the other cases in
which I was involved resulted in such a quick and easy decision.

The next trial that I will tell about took the longest, a total of ten
weeks in two separate sessions nearly a year apart. On January 25,
1974, a thirty-one-year-old private pilot, with 135 hours of piloting
experience, including the dual instruction while learning to fly,
flew another man and two women from Las Vegas, Nevada, their
home town, to Phoenix, Arizona, about 250 miles away. All four
worked for a heart specialist in Las Vegas, the two men as technicians and the two women as nurses. In Phoenix the foursome attended a symposium sponsored by the Arizona Heart Institute.
That evening the pilot was tired and wanted to stay overnight in
Phoenix and fly back the next day. Some of the others wanted
badly to return that night, however, and they convinced the pilot
to do it.

The weather was clear and the flight should have taken only
about an hour and three-quarters. (For some technical reason the
information about the arrangements was not allowed to be presented in court, possibly because it had merely been heard by
others.) The airplane involved was a four-place 235-HP Cherokee,
the PA-28-235. At 9:05 P.M. the pilot had opened a flight plan with
the Phoenix flight service station to go to the North Las Vegas airport via Prescott and Boulder, with a cruising altitude of 10,500
feet. Following take-off he contacted the Phoenix departure control, and after a bit was told that he was on radar about four miles
north of Sky Harbor, the Phoenix airport. A couple of minutes later,
departure control informed him that there was northbound traffic
two miles away at eleven o'clock, but he replied "no visual sight at
this time." At about fifteen minutes into the flight, departure control told him "radar service terminated 25 miles north of Sky Har-

bor." When the pilot did not reply, the control tower asked again if he had received the information, but again he did not reply. Nothing more was heard from him, and the plane did not arrive at Las Vegas.

The next morning the wreckage of the plane was found about 37 miles north of Sky Harbor airport and 8 miles northwest of the little town of Carefree. It had come down in an uninhabited, rather rough desert area at an elevation of something over 4,000 feet above sea level. Parts of the airplane were scattered over a 3,000-foot path in the opposite direction from that of the flight toward Las Vegas. This indicated that there had been a structural failure while the airplane was still in the air. All four occupants had been killed.

There were three lawsuits filed against the Piper Aircraft Corporation in this case, but the main one was filed by the husband of one of the nurses who was killed. The plaintiff's attorneys were part of a Los Angeles firm, and the attorney handling the case was a presentable young man in his early thirties. After the trial, he indicated to me that he was on a sort of crusade on the side of pilots who were always being blamed for crashes as pilot error. I think he had talked himself into believing this, but to me it was a rather neat rationalization.

The defendants, Piper and its insurance company, were represented by a Phoenix firm of attorneys, with Roger C. Mitten handling this particular case. Before the trial, depositions had been taken of the proposed witnesses on both sides, and a great deal of computing and testing had been done by expert witnesses for both sides.

Roger Mitten had me sit next to him throughout the trial to sort of represent Piper, even though I had been retired for some time, and to give him suggestions for cross-examination of the opposing witnesses. The trial was held in the Superior Court of the State of Arizona, and I was put up in the Adams Hotel, which was very close to both the courthouse and to the attorneys' offices in downtown Phoenix.

The court sessions started on June 5, 1978, and the opening statements of the two attorneys made clear what each side aimed to prove. Both sides agreed that the left wing had been torn off in flight and that it had probably been swept back and carried away part of the tail surfaces also. The wing was attached to the fuselage in three places, the main one being the large spar attachment that I have described in connection with the development of the first Cherokee. There was also a single bolt attachment at the front and another at the rear of the main wing panel.

The fitting on the fuselage and the fitting on the wing that the rear bolt held together were still intact, and the holes were still in relatively good shape, but slightly elongated. The bolt, however, was never found. This was not surprising to me, for in my opinion, it sheared in half and the two little pieces would be very hard to find over a rugged desert area covering two-thirds of a mile or so. The plaintiffs claimed that this bolt was not in place at the time of the accident and that the structure was therefore not complete, but was defective. As a result, they said, a flutter had developed at a cruising altitude of 10,500 feet that had torn the wing off. The bolt had been fitted with a self-locking nut, which during assembly was torqued, or tightened, to a certain specified value. The plaintiffs maintained that the torquing had not been done completely and that the nut had vibrated off in flight. This had allowed the bolt to work its way out of the joint.

Piper's defense was that the bolt had been in place and operating satisfactorily at the time that the wing was torn off. In the company's opinion, the accident had been caused by the low-time non-instrument-rated pilot flying into what amounted to a black hole over an unpopulated desert area on a dark, moonless night with no visible horizon. The pilot became so disoriented, Piper's lawyer argued, that he allowed the airplane to attain an excessive speed, probably in a spiral dive—which is not unusual in such circumstances. In trying to recover, the pilot overstressed the airplane to the point of destruction.

Previous to the trial, Piper had rented a Cherokee 235 similar to the one of the accident and had simulated the accident flight as closely as possible. Piloting the plane was Larry Young, a well-known and respected instructor pilot in the Phoenix area, and three of us from Piper went along with him. We flew on a clear black night a couple of hours after the moon had set, which was about the same time as the accident flight. When we got up past the Carefree area at an altitude of about 10,500 feet, the view ahead was almost black. Stars were visible overhead, but for about 20 degrees above the horizon, judging by the instruments, there was a slight haze and we could see no stars. There were a very few widely scattered dim lights on the ground, probably at ranchhouses, and when the airplane was put in a bank for a turn, we sometimes confused these with stars.

The whole view ahead from one side to the other gave no indication of the horizon or of a level attitude. If the airplane was turned and one looked back, the lights of Phoenix were quite apparent, but if we were in a 30- or 40-degree bank, it was still hard to tell which way was up without referring to the instruments and forgetting about the outside horizon.

Our testimony in regard to these matters never got into this part of the trial, however, nor did any of the defendants' testimony. The plaintiffs' attorney put one witness after another on the stand for a period of two weeks. These included a pilot who was flying at the time of the accident, to tell about the weather conditions; the pilot's flight instructor; a metallurgist; a specialist in fine measurements who had measured the deformations in the holes of the fittings; an accident reconstruction specialist; the plaintiff and his three children; and an economist who had figured out the loss in income and support that plaintiff's wife would have provided as a nurse over a normal lifetime, with adjustment for inflation.

During the cross-examination of the economist, a matter came up that permitted the plaintiff's attorney to object and to throw the entire case out of court on a technicality, which he did. His case did not appear to be going over very well with the jury, and I believe that he was glad to get a fresh start. At any rate, the judge stopped the entire proceeding, and a new start on the case was to be made the following November, five months later.

The new trial in Phoenix did not get started, however, until February 18, 1979, and then it had a different judge and a different jury, an entirely new affair. As before, the trial involved a number of specialists, but this time the plaintiff's testimony extended to over a month. The testimony was built entirely around the assumption that the bolt in the rear fitting attaching the wing to the fuselage was not in place at the time that the wing came off. They maintained that the nut had worked off and the bolt had come out of the fitting some time before the flight of the accident, possibly several weeks. The metallurgist testified that after the rear fitting bolt had come out, the front fitting bolt had gradually deteriorated due to impulse loads from gusts and landing and so forth, until it failed. Then, with only the single main spar fitting holding, the wing was so flexibly supported that it developed a flutter while simply flying along. At about 10,500 feet the flutter amplitude had suddenly increased, he said, to the point where the wing was torn off. All this was based on the fact that the bolt for the rear fitting was not found.

I don't believe that the bolt was even missed until after the wreckage had been moved to another area. Apparently no one even looked for it at the crash site where the wing fell and landed a great distance away from the fuselage. To me, the story represented a practically impossible dream, with no real foundation. It was presented to the jury in a very impressive manner, however, with results of many tests on exemplars, or specimens, representing parts of the fittings showing strengths and deflections, and many, many other details.

The jury of eight was made up of five women, three men, and two alternates in case of sickness or necessary absence. None of them had any special knowledge of aeronautics. They appeared to be a good group, however, comprising housewives, stenographers, an electrician, and one man who was a retired high-school principal and who, like me, required a hearing aid, which fortunately for me made everyone speak up.

One expert plaintiff witness, an accident reconstructionist, worked out backwards, from the scattering of the parts on the ground, and from an examination of the parts themselves and their deformations, the path that the airplane must have taken from the time it was cruising at 10,500 feet and the wing allegedly came off to where it contacted the ground over 6,000 feet below. I disagreed entirely with his findings, as I testified later, because I believed, and had shown by means of a model test at home, that with the wing off more than a mile above the ground, the rest of the airplane would have to have spun down vertically in a straight line until it hit the ground. It could not have left a string of parts along a path the best part of a mile long. The man who made fine measurements with an electronic microscope that was ten times as accurate as was meaningful in this particular case, and also a metallurgist, went on and on in exceedingly great detail based on doubtful premises. I wondered whether the jury detected it for what it was, or whether it made the intended impression.

It is apparent to me from this and other trials that the expert witnesses, although honest men and women usually, can in many cases be hired to present the matter in such a way as to give whatever information the attorney desires, and I think that the attorneys themselves often work themselves into believing such testimony and can make their presentations in a very dramatic manner, without entailing the disadvantage of knowing that they are fabricating.

During the trial, incidentally, our attorney Roger Mitten, and his paralegal assistant, Curtis Bay, worked every night until about midnight and most of every weekend, making sure that every detail would be carried out as well as possible. I thought that they would do better to get more sleep and recreation so that they would be fresh and clear-headed during the trial itself, but at 45 and 25 years old, respectively, they were young enough and had energy enough to last it out.

During the entire month in which the plaintiffs had been injecting their ideas into the minds of the jurors, the defendants could present no ideas except through the cross-questioning of the witnesses by Roger Mitten. It was obvious, however, that they had no case at all if we could prove that the critical bolt was in place and functioning when the wing came off of the airplane.

At the end of the testimony by the plaintiff's experts, the plaintiff himself took the stand, as did each of his three children. It was then five years after the accident and the oldest child was now a young lady of twenty, followed by a girl of fifteen, and a boy of fourteen. Their attorney drew out their legitimate heartfelt stories, and the girls sobbed and shed tears, drawing sympathy naturally from the jury.

When it was his turn, Piper's attorney, Roger Mitten, put on his own succession of expert witnesses, some of which had also performed exemplar tests to prove point by point, if possible, that the plaintiff's witnesses had been wrong. One of our expert witnesses for the defense was Howard Hasbrook, who in the 1940s and 1950s had worked at Cornell University Medical College with Hugh De-Haven on crash injury research and who had helped me in the design of our Ag-1 and Pawnee agricultural airplanes. For some years Hasbrook had been living in Prescott, Arizona, where he worked as a consultant and as an expert witness. He was a very experienced pilot, and he brought out the extreme difficulty that a non-instrument pilot would have in flying the airplane satisfactorily when that pilot could not see the horizon or know when he was in a level position.[1] Howard mentioned that he had lost a son in such a situation.

The next specialist put on the stand as part of Piper's defense was Larry Young, the instructor pilot who took us up in June 1978 on a night flight simulating the accident flight. (We had made another such flight in March 1979 to refresh ourselves on the subject.) Among other things, Young mentioned that we had arrived at the accident site some eight minutes or so before the accident plane had, which indicated that the pilot of the accident plane had had quite a long time to wander around, possibly in some confusion. Also, the accident site was some miles off the direct course between Phoenix and Prescott, which the flight plan indicated that he would follow.

Young's firm opinion was that the spatial disorientation of the pilot had caused the crash. Young was obviously a sound and reliable person, and I believe that his testimony had great weight with the jury.

I was the last witness put on the stand for the defense. After having sat through the whole trial next to Roger Mitten and occasionally feeding him suggestions on technical matters, I was able to address many of the matters that had been brought up during the trial. I was on the stand a full day.

If I made a significant contribution, I think it was that I was able to prove that the left rear wing attachment bolt was in place and functioning when the wing came off. I did this by using the plaintiff's own test data as well as the defendant's, both of which showed the same results when viewed in the same manner.

The fitting was made up of two strong steel plates, one on the fuselage and one on the wing, which overlapped when the wing was in the proper position. The two plates were held together by a snug-fitting strong steel aircraft-type bolt with a self-locking nut. When the wing came off the airplane, the two plates had slid with respect to each other and had sheared the bolt in two. The high pressure of the bolt on the hole surfaces in the plates had caused the holes to deform and elongate slightly. The deformation of the hole in the wing portion of the fitting was less than that in the fuselage portion of the fitting, but both were within reason as shown by the exemplar tests, which had been made by both parties.

The exemplar tests were made by taking similar fittings bolted together in the same way and pulling them apart in a test machine. The strengths of the joints were noted, and later the dimensions of the deformed holes were measured accurately. A number of the exemplar tests were made by the specialists of each party, and, in general, the results agreed very well. Individually, however, the dimensions of the deformed holes varied to a certain extent because of the slight variations in dimensions and material composition that existed within the usual acceptable tolerances.

The plaintiffs had claimed that the bolt was not in place at the time of the wing separation and had based this claim on the fact that the deformation in the hole of the wing fitting plate was substantially less than that in the hole of one of the exemplars that had a larger deformation than average. The attorney claimed that the deformation that was apparent in the wing portion of the fitting was due to ordinary wear and tear, particularly since, as he claimed, "the bolt was loose without the nut being tight for some period before the failure occurred." The deformation was similar to that of the exemplar tests, however, and must have been made by the bolt shearing off completely.

But, as I pointed out, the deformations of the holes of both the wing and fuselage fittings of the actual airplane were well within the limits shown by the numerous exemplar tests. This convinced me, and I believe I was able to convince the jury also, that the bolt was definitely in firmly and functioning properly when the wing came off the airplane.

Roger Mitten made his final statement for the case and was followed by the plaintiff's attorney. (The plaintiff gets both first and last crack at it.) Then the case was turned over to the jury. This was at about six o'clock in the evening of April 20, 1979—a full two months after the retrial had started. Later that evening a number of us had dinner together, including the judge, Melvin McDonald, and the opposing attorneys.

The judge and the two attorneys carried on an animated conversation, talking about the tactics used by a certain attorney in a certain case, the scheme to influence the jury by another attorney in a different case, etc., etc. On more than one occasion during the trial, the plaintiff had brought out that it was a very serious affair, which of course it actually was, and that it was not "just a game." After a time, I mentioned to all three of them that they reminded me of three football coaches going over their tactics and game plans.

The judge then responded, "Well, there is a certain amount of gamesmanship involved." Later on, I asked Judge McDonald whether he didn't think it would be better in a case as technical as this one to have it held before a judge who had some technical knowledge, rather than a jury of people in general who knew nothing about the subject. I was thinking of the Reed propeller case in which I had taken part in the 1930s before a competent technical examiner representing the U.S. Court of Claims. He gave it a moment's thought and then replied that he thought no, it was better in general to have a jury rather than a single judge. The next day with the jury still in session, I flew the airlines back home to Vero Beach.

After I had been home a while, a joyous phone call from Roger Mitten in Phoenix told me that the jury had decided in our favor and that the Piper Cherokee design was absolved of blame for the crash.

The airplane did crash, however, and four people were killed because the pilot could not see a horizon and had lost his spatial orientation—which was very easy to do if the airplane started turning either purposefully or inadvertently and the pilot lost control of the airplane.

I would like to see an airplane that would always inherently fly straight unless it was deliberately overcontrolled by the pilot. The airplane in this case was equipped with an auto-pilot that would have done that if the pilot had merely turned it on and adjusted it properly. It was found switched off, however, and there is no evidence that the pilot tried to use it at all. Possibly he was unfamiliar with it. Some airplanes have been equipped with so-called wing levelers that keep the airplane flying straight but do not hold it on a given course the way an auto-pilot does. The Mooney airplane was equipped with such a wing-leveler device for a period of time, and I believe it was effective in reducing that kind of accident, but it was eliminated after a time because the pilots did not like it. Perhaps an improved version can be worked out with controls that are acceptable to pilots. I hope so, for accidents of this nature continue to occur. Of course, instrument pilots with suitable equipment— which this airplane had—should be free from that type of difficulty.

Before closing out my historical reminiscences with a short discussion of my participation in the activities of various aeronautical organizations, particularly the Experimental Aircraft Association's annual fly-in at Oshkosh, Wisconsin, I want to address one area of flight operation that has bothered me for nearly fifty years; occasionally I have tried to do something about it, but up to now it has been to no avail. The area involved is the low-speed range of an airplane from the stall up to the speed for maximum angle of climb, which is also approximately the speed at which minimum power is required to maintain level flight.

Within this low-speed area near the stall, the longitudinal controls work backward from the way they do in the range of ordinary flight. Throughout the ordinarily used range of air speeds with cruising power or more on, pulling the longitudinal control back a bit and holding it will make the nose of the airplane go up and the flight path go up also. At speeds below that for the minimum power required for level flight and the maximum angle of climb, however, pulling the longitudinal control back a bit and holding it will make the nose go up momentarily, but the flight path will actually be less steep than before, which is the opposite of what is desired.

It is natural for a pilot after he has taken off and is trying to clear an obstacle or a hillside with very little margin to try to steepen his flight path by pulling back on the longitudinal control. This will work satisfactorily down to the critical speed, but he has no definite signal as to just when he reaches that speed. To avoid going below it, he must know what it is for the particular airplane and loading and atmospheric conditions in which he is flying, and he must be watching the air-speed indicator also.

Sufficiently competent pilots can do this, but it appears that many, many pilots have pulled back a bit too far on the controls and have hit obstacles or hillsides, and many are no longer with us. If they have pulled back far enough to make the airplane stall, they have cinched the deal. Those pilots and their passengers would have continued to live if they had resisted the inclination to pull back too far and had maintained the speed for the best angle of climb, the steepest climb. This assumes, of course, that their judgment that they could clear the obstacle had been correct in the first place.

This reminds me of a dangerous incident from my own private flying. In July 1951 Dorothy and I started in our little Ercoupe on a five-week vacation trip to Yellowstone Park, Seattle, San Francisco, Los Angeles, Phoenix, and back home to Texas. On the way to Yellowstone we stopped in Denver at an airfield where Ercoupe parts and services were available, and the field's proprietor, a Mr. Vest, gave me quite a lecture on the hazards of mountain flying. He thought that flying in the mountains should be done with more powerful airplanes, and he cautioned me against taking off from a high-altitude airport and trying to climb out in the heat of the midday in summertime.

The next morning we took off from Vest Field about six o'clock in clear, cool, smooth air. We were having a beautiful flight, sailing along at 10,000 feet above sea level but only 2,000 to 3,000 feet above the ground. That height above the ground was Dorothy's favorite, for it was high enough to recognize landmarks and make piloting reasonably easy, and yet low enough so that she could see the cattle, the cars, and some details of the landscape.

We stopped at Laramie, with a field elevation of nearly 7,300 feet and a density altitude in midday of about 11,000 feet, and spent most of the hot day there. In the evening, after it had cooled off a bit, I decided to try a take-off and just go to Rawlins, about 110 miles away, which we could make comfortably by dark. There was about a five-MPH wind from the west, and I determined that if we were not airborne by the time we reached a spot I had in mind about 2,000 feet westward down the 6,000-foot runway, I would close the throttle, taxi back, and leave in the cool of the next morning.

In the take-off run we had no difficulty getting off the ground within the 2,000 feet, but then we climbed up to 30 or 40 feet above the ground and just stayed at that height. I held the plane at about 60 MPH indicated, which was close to the air speed for the steepest climb and also that requiring minimum power, but we just barely stayed at the same height above the ground to the end of the airport and beyond.

At this point in my story I want to emphasize that *it was very hard for me to hold the air speed at 60 MPH and not pull the nose up higher* to clear the ground more, even though I was aware that at the lower air speed the power required would increase and the climb would be *reduced* instead of *increased*, making contact with the rocky ground likely. If the control were pulled back far enough, hard contact would be certain, and many pilots have not lived through such a situation.

It took me at least a couple of miles before I was able to gain a height of 60 or 70 feet above the terrain, where I was willing to bank very slightly and make a gentle turn to the north. Once I had turned enough, the ground fell away fairly rapidly. I then held the plane at approximately the best rate-of-climb speed halfway to Rawlins until we reached a pressure altitude of 13,000 feet, which showed that the plane was giving its full rated performance.

What I had not taken into account at the beginning of my take-off run was that although the airport itself appeared to be substantially level, the ground to the west of the airport kept getting higher at a very gradual rate—which was hardly perceptible until it reached the mountains in the distance. I should have taken off in the opposite (eastern) direction in spite of the five-MPH tail wind, where the almost imperceptible downward slope would have helped instead of hindered. This was a close call and a lesson I have always remembered. A close call is about the most effective teacher one can have.

How, then, can the airplane designer make it easier for the pilot to overcome natural human reactions and solve this problem of low-speed stalls? The stall portion can be taken care of by arranging the aerodynamics so that the airplane cannot be maintained in a stall, as has been done in the Ercoupe and some other planes (particularly Burt Rutan's canards), and which has no doubt helped in many cases, but this is not enough to solve the whole problem by any means. For one thing, if the pilot pulls back the controls suddenly at the last moment, he can get a slight whipstall with the nose then lowering and the flight path going down until he picks up enough speed to come out of it.

One way of minimizing the general problem is for the designer to reduce the range of speeds between that for the stall and that for the maximum angle of climb. I understand that Burt Rutan has accomplished this in some of his canard designs in which the speed for the steepest climb is not as far as usual above the stall speed, and in which the stall cannot be maintained in flight. This does not solve the problem completely, but it appears to me that it minimizes it to the greatest extent that has been accomplished so far.

Another way of minimizing the problem to some extent is to provide a surplus of power and climb ability. A good example of this is the improvement that came with the old Piper Cub when the power was increased from 40 HP, with which the plane usually staggered over wires and obstacles with a small margin, to 65 HP, with which it cleared ordinary obstacles easily. The safety record improved substantially.

This was fine in a two-place airplane that carried very little baggage or fuel. With modern light airplanes carrying four people or more, however, where substantial baggage and fuel for a good range are desired, it is customary to load the airplanes up to the point where with full load gross weight, the minimum climb performance required by the FAA is just barely attained. In fact, as most such airplanes are delivered to the customer today, they cannot be fully loaded with passengers, fuel, and baggage without exceeding the nominal gross weight permissible, and the pilot has to use care in loading his airplane to see that he does not overload it.

Although the climb ability is better than that of the old 40-HP Cubs, the present airplanes are ordinarily not overpowered at gross weight, and the only way to provide excess climb ability is to fly them with partial load.

Nearly fifty years ago, while I was still at ERCO and working with the Ercoupe, I had the thought that a different approach to the control of the air speed might help to solve our problem. A customary method of controlling the air speed was, and still is except for some of the most sophisticated airplanes, to move the longitudinal control so as to get the desired reading on the air-speed indicator and then adjust it slightly if necessary to maintain that speed. Then, if a force is required on the control to maintain that condition, the longitudinal trim is adjusted until the force is reduced to zero and the control tends to stay in the proper position to hold the air speed desired. A properly stable airplane will then remain at that air speed with the controls free in perfectly smooth air, but if the air is turbulent the pilot will have to keep making adjustments in order to maintain the air-speed reading that he desires within reasonably close limits.

The pilot is now consciously using the longitudinal control to control the flight path as well as the air speed and of course with the help of the throttle or power also. Thus when he gets in a tight situation trying to clear an obstacle, he is already using the longitudinal control, and it is extremely difficult not to pull it back too far when he desires to clear the obstacle rather than to maintain the speed for the maximum angle of climb, which would give him the best result.

Would it not be better in helping to solve this problem to change from one air speed to another by using the trim control alone and not leading with the elevator at all? The trim control would then be the primary control for air speed, and in ordinary flight away from the ground the trim control would be the only means of controlling the air speed. A trim indicator could be provided, preferably on the instrument panel, which, among other things, would have a mark on it to show the condition for the maximum angle of climb, the steepest climb. To get the steepest continuing climb-out from take-off, then, the pilot would set the trim to the correct indicated position before starting the take-off run. The elevator would be used to rotate the airplane as it left the ground, after which the pilot would gradually release all force on it, and with an ideal arrangement, the airplane would go right to the angle of attack and air speed giving the maximum angle of climb and would maintain that condition steadily, even in turbulent air. Other marks on the trim indicator could represent the best rate of climb and the flattest glide, that is the glide giving the greatest distance from a certain altitude, which could be useful in case of engine failure.

With an arrangement such as this, once the pilot had set the trim for the air speed or condition that he wanted, the airplane would go to that air speed and maintain it indefinitely, and the pilot would be free to put his main attention on other necessary items. I have called an arrangement such as this a "firm-trim control." I prefer having the main longitudinal control wheel or stick tend to stay definitely in the correct position for each speed for which the trim setting has been made and to require a small break-out force, say of four or five pounds, to move it from the correct position. This enables the pilot to rest his hand on the control wheel without accidentally moving it.

This is a questionable item that some pilots no doubt would object to, but inasmuch as the air force permits a break-out force of up to four pounds due to friction for airplanes not greatly heavier than most of our light ones, it appears to me to be something that most pilots could get used to and eventually like.

With this arrangement, all air-speed control in ordinary flight away from the ground would be done by means of the trim control, and the pilot would not be in the habit of moving the elevator control forth and back for this purpose. Ideally the trim control would be arranged so that it could not set the speed below that for the maximum angle of climb. Then, with the pilot being in the habit of controlling his air speed by means of the trim only and setting the trim to give maximum performance for the condition desired, he would always be flying at or above the speed for the maximum angle of climb, and if he understood the situation, as he should, he would not be so likely to pull the control back beyond the trimmed-for position and get into the region of poor performance on the backside of the power-required curve.

The pilot would not only stay out of the low-speed, poor performance, and reverse control area, but he would fly at the speed giving the maximum performance that the airplane was capable of in the steepest climb, with the maximum rate of climb and the best glide. This would be better than most of us pilots can do under present conditions.

In all ordinary flight, including the pattern around an airport and the final approach to the landing, the air speed would be controlled by the trim device alone. The elevator control would be used to override it only for rotation in the take-off and in the final flaring off of the flight path in touching the ground while landing. This assumes that all turns in the air would be made gently at about the rate for instrument turns. For steeper turns without noticeable loss of altitude, it would be necessary to add a bit of power or to come back some on the control. The latter could be dangerous at low speeds. The pilot would always have the full control available in order to avoid a collision or to accomplish aerobatic maneuvers, if he desired.

Ideally, in my mind at least, such a firm-trim arrangement should eliminate most all accidents in the stall-spin or failure to maintain flying speed category—a category that has been reduced from about two-thirds of all the accidents in the early days of private flying to less than one-quarter of them now. But it is still a large element worth reducing further, if possible.

In 1973, four years after I had retired from Piper and twenty-six years after I had first experimented with a firm-trim control system on my Ercoupe, an opportunity presented itself to continue with the experimental work on the firm-trim control. Dr. Richard A. Kroeger, who had worked in the Vero Beach Piper engineering department after I retired, but who was then in charge of aeronautical graduate work at the University of Michigan, invited me to work with his department, advising and initiating research projects.

We arranged to get NASA support for a project involving further work on the firm-trim control, the first part to be carried out by me in Vero Beach, with tests to be made later at the Ann Arbor campus. With this research in mind I purchased a 1968 Cherokee 140, which was suitable for the purpose. I kept it tied down in the Piper Aircraft Corporation flight line in Vero Beach, and although I did much of the work on it myself, I got the help of a couple of my old Piper mechanic friends in their spare time, outside of working hours.

We fitted the airplane with a firm-trim control arrangement that was an interconnection between the longitudinal trim control and the main longitudinal control. The modification consisted of two main portions. The first was a connection between the regular longitudinal trim control and the main longitudinal control. The second portion was a replacement of the usual trim indicator by one that is mounted on the instrument panel and that included a scale of indicated air speeds with markings showing the settings for the optimum performances. The linkage was so designed that for any trim position set, the main longitudinal control was held in the correct position matching the trim, that is, the position giving zero control force on the main longitudinal control wheel for the air speed that was selected.

The main longitudinal control wheel was held in the trimmed position by a preloaded spring arrangement. The control wheel could be moved back or forth, however, by overcoming the preload or break-out force, and the entire original movement of the control wheel was still available. With the initial setting, a force of 12 pounds was required to move the control wheel from its trimmed position. After many trials with a number of pilots, break-out force of approximately 5 pounds was determined as the probable optimum, although some pilots preferred a higher one and some preferred none at all.

Ideally, the airplane would fly at any speed that the trim was set for, regardless of the power being used, from wide-open throttle to fully closed. Fortunately, I had designed the Cherokee 140, so that like the Ercoupe, it came reasonably close to this, and although it was not perfect, it was acceptable at that stage of development, even with the flap either up or down.

Markings on the trim indicator enabled the pilot to select the optimum indicated air speed for the particular performance (i.e., maximum rate of climb, maximum angle of climb, climb-out following take-off, flattest glide, and normal landing approach speed) he desired at the loading that he happened to have.

After adjusting it to the point where I was reasonably well satisfied with it, I flew it to Ann Arbor with one of their pilots, where five instrument instructor pilots connected with the university gave it flight trials of at least five hours each. It was then more thoroughly tested with quantitative control force measurements by Col. Raymond L. Jones, an experienced test pilot and instructor of test pilots at Edwards Air Force Base in California. Jones then flew it back to Vero Beach—a good part of the way under instrument conditions. After getting a supplementary type certificate, or STC, for the modification, Dorothy and I flew it out to the West Coast and back again, getting some more cross-country experience under various conditions.

During that trip and some earlier ones, I had a number of experienced pilots try out the system, including Seth Anderson of NASA Ames; Bill Barnhouse, Lew Mason, and F. B. O'Donnell of Piper; Karl H. Bergey of the University of Oklahoma; Leighton Collins at Hendersonville, North Carolina; H. C. Hansen of Flight Safety, Inc., of Vero Beach; and Howard Hasbrook in Oklahoma.

I also had Pug Piper, who had moved on to work as a consultant for Beech in Wichita, Kansas, try it out. In an approach to a landing, instead of letting the airplane fly itself while trimmed at the approach speed desirable for a landing, Pug jockeyed the longitudinal control back and forth, getting the feel of it all the way down to the final flare-off before contact. As an old navy pilot, he was following, I guess, the standard slow-landing procedure. Thus he got no help from the firm-trim control at all, which was to fly the entire approach at an air speed having enough reserve to give a good flare-off for contacting the ground gently.

Burt Rutan of Mojave, California, also tested my firm-trim control arrangement on the Cherokee 140. He got along with it all right and seemed to agree with my reasoning behind it, but I doubt that he thought it was necessary for the future of aviation. More about the incredibly talented Rutan in the next chapter.

The trim indicator showing the optimum air speeds for the various climb and glide performances was well received. It was generally agreed that being able to trim directly to the particular air speed for the performance desired was a definite help in obtaining the optimum performance, particularly if the pilot flew a variety of airplanes. It was agreed that the arrangement should enable most pilots to obtain essentially the same optimum performance from the airplane that would be attained by a highly skilled professional pilot who was thoroughly familiar with the particular performance requirements of his airplane.

It appeared that all of the pilots who had tried out the firm-trim control agreed that a reduction of workload had been accomplished in smooth air and in light turbulence. The Cherokee, like the Ercoupe, however, depended on the longitudinal stability of the airplane to damp out any oscillations, and in severe turbulence the natural longitudinal stability of the airplane, with its fugoid oscillations, did not prevent undesirably large excursions of the air speed from the value trimmed for. This condition was not acceptable.

A better system for damping out the oscillations due to turbulent air will have to be devised before the firm-trim system could become generally usable. Further exploration in this area was considered desirable.

I completed the report on this work in 1977 and immediately started on an arrangement in which the trimmed air speed was controlled directly by the indicated air speed itself. It consisted of a large Pitot-static tube, or other similar dynamic pressure sensor that operated a spring-loaded bellows, which itself was connected directly to a tab on the horizontal tail surface.

Full-scale wind-tunnel-type tests of a partial span tail surface projecting out from the side of our Volkswagon camper, with Dorothy driving and me observing, showed that such a system was feasible. Large bellows were required, however, and the forces required to adjust the spring tension were too great to be satisfactory as a trim control. Supplementary power to operate the trim controlled by smaller bellows would operate satisfactorily, but I desired not to have an extra power supply if possible.

In June 1980, while I was resting in the back seat of our car while Dorothy was driving on a trip north, I got the idea for an arrangement for longitudinal trim that would possibly hold the airplane firmly at the angle of attack and indicated air speed that it was trimmed for, hopefully even in rough air. It would consist of a vane floating with the airstream out of the propeller slipstream, connected by linkage to a tab on the elevator. Following "wind tunnel" tests with the VW, the system looked promising.

16.

The Octogenarian of Oshkosh

Although I have never thought of myself as a joiner, I find that over a period of more than seventy years, I have belonged to quite a number of organizations having to do with aeronautics. After becoming a member of the Illinois Model Aero Club as a boy, the first one I joined as an adult was the National Aeronautic Association (NAA), which was chartered in 1922 as the successor to the Aero Club of America, which in turn was founded in 1905, just two years after the first powered flight at Kitty Hawk. During the 1930s, as has also been mentioned in an earlier chapter, I was on the NAA's contest board and even served as its chairman. Following World War II, I was also on the NAA board that determined the winner of the prestigious Robert J. Collier Trophy.

In 1928, while I was working on the NACA cowling program, I joined the Society of Automotive Engineers (SAE). Although it started as an automobile engineering society, it soon included other means of self-propelled transportation, such as aircraft and watercraft. I took part in many of the SAE activities during its early years, presenting papers at meetings and serving on various committees which, among other things, established standards for propeller parts. In 1936 I became the SAE's vice-president for aircraft. In 1979 I was fortunate enough to be elected an SAE fellow, the highest honor presented by the society.

During the 1920s, the only other engineering society dealing with aeronautical technology besides the SAE was the American Society of Mechanical Engineers (ASME). I became a member of it, too, and was relatively active, particularly in the 1930s when I served on the council representing aeronautical activities.

The next organization that I joined, and which provided an outstanding professional forum for aeronautical scientists and engineers, was the Institute of the Aeronautical Sciences (IAS), of which I was a founding member in 1932. Among the notable men who participated in the founders' day meeting on January 26, 1933, were Jerome C. Hunsaker of MIT and the NACA, the first IAS president; Lester Gardner, editor of *Aviation* magazine and the first IAS secretary; William F. Durand of Stanford University; George W. Lewis of the NACA; Eastman N. Jacobs of NACA Langley; Ludwig Prandtl of the University of Göttingen; and Theodore von Kármán of the California Institute of Technology. Other founding members included Giuseppe Bellanca, Claude Dornier, Leroy R. Grumman, Sir Frederick Handley Page, James H. Kindelberger, Charles Lindbergh, Grover B. Loening, Glenn L. Martin, John K. Northrop, Igor I. Sikorsky, and Elmer A. Sperry, Jr. At the time of its foundation in 1932, the IAS had only one honorary fellow, Orville Wright. The organization kept growing as the industry advanced, and I kept fairly active in it, serving on the council and arranging for national and local meetings.

In the meantime the American Rocket Society (ARS) came to life. Its disciplines overlapped with those of the IAS, and many people were members of both. In 1963 the two societies merged to form the American Institute of Aeronautics and Astronautics. I attended many AIAA meetings, particularly those sponsored by the Cape Canaveral chapter, which was of course near my home in Vero Beach. The AIAA celebrated its fiftieth anniversary at Long Beach, California, in 1981. At that meeting I was made an honorary fellow "for a long career filled with major contributions to safety and efficiency of aircraft, including the development of the NACA low-drag engine cowl, the tricycle landing gear, and non-spinning and agricultural aircraft; and for the design of widely used general

With Dorothy at an Ercoupe Owners Club national fly-in at Minden, Nebraska, in 1983.

aviation aircraft." It had been a long time since I had done any of these things, however, and with the drift toward rockets and astronautics, I was hardly known to the then present AIAA officials. My recognition was generated on this occasion by my old friend Harold Hoekstra, who dug up my old history and presented it to them.

At the AIAA honors dinner in Long Beach, I sat at the table with both of the other people receiving honorary fellowships. One was Christopher C. Kraft, Jr., who was about to retire from the directorship of NASA's Johnson Space Center in Houston. Kraft, by the way, had received his original experimental flight test training at NACA Langley in the 1930s under my old friend, Langley's chief test pilot Melvin Gough. On my right sat Ed Aldrin, the astronaut, who with Neil Armstrong made the first lunar landing in 1969; Aldrin was the second man to put foot on the moon.

Another organization that I have been a member of for a large number of years is the Air Mail Pioneers, "an organization of, by, and for the former employees of the U.S. Airmail Service Post

Caricature presented to me by the Arizona 'coupe group in July 1981.

Office Department between May 15, 1918, and August 31, 1927." It was over sixty-five years ago that I worked for the Air Mail Service in Maywood, Illinois, and the membership of the pioneer club is dwindling rapidly to nothing.

One of the aeronautical organizations that Dorothy and I have been most active in recently is the Ercoupe Owners Club, started in 1969 by Norman F. ("Skip") Carden of Durham, North Carolina. Over the years ERCO and Sanders produced a total of slightly more than 5,000 Ercoupes; 500 or so more were eventually produced as Aircoupes by Forney Aircraft of Fort Collins, Colorado; by Air Products, Inc., of Carlsbad, New Mexico; and by Alon, Inc., of McPherson, Kansas. Also, Mooney Aircraft, Inc., of Kerrville, Texas, produced the Ercoupe in a completely modified form for standard training, called the Mooney Cadet. All of these follow-up versions were included under the Ercoupe Owners Club, which holds fly-ins with meetings so its twelve hundred or so members can exchange ideas on operation and maintenance and can get together socially. The club's first national fly-in was held in Talle-quah, Oklahoma, in May 1976. There were 142 'coupes from forty-two states.

"Arkansas Picnic," a fly-in of Ercoupe owners held annually at a chicken farm near Belleville, Arkansas.

Some of the most rewarding experiences that I have had in the last several years have been in my association with the owners of Ercoupes, who are still enjoying the airplanes nearly half a century after the first ones were produced. Many of the old planes have been spruced up so that they look better than when they came from the factory. Most of them are about forty years old, however, and I sincerely hope that the owners see that the structure is inspected very carefully and in detail and is kept in fully airworthy condition.

Other aviation organizations to which I have belonged are the Quiet Birdmen (which I discussed in an earlier chapter), the Flying Engineers International, the Florida Aero Club, and the OX-5 Aviation Pioneers, which is for those who have flown aircraft powered by the OX-5 engine or have been mechanics on the engines. I am also a member of the Aircraft Owners and Pilots Association (AOPA), which since before World War II has represented the general aviation community in the Washington, D.C., area, particularly in Congress and with regard to the FAA; and the Silver Wings Fraternity, which requires that a member be a solo pilot for at least twenty-five years—my solo date, 1923, is now sixty-five years old. Finally, for the last several years I have been a member of the United Flying Octagenarians (or UFOs), whose members must be at least eighty years old and have a valid pilot's license. I am now a sort of member emeritus of the UFOs, at least until my eyes improve enough for my vision to meet the requirements for a medical certificate again. Cataracts have been growing in my eyes for several years, so my piloting has had to stop. (The last flight that I piloted was to an Ercoupe fly-in near Belleville, Arkansas, and back to Vero Beach in 1983—I was eighty-four years old. Dorothy and I made the trip in a rented Piper Archer, the updated Cherokee 180.) I have recently had a lens implant, however, and may possibly be able to pass the physical exam again.

Fortunately, my vocation blended into a pleasant avocation. It has been our great satisfaction and joy to fly ourselves to all parts of the United States, much of Mexico, and a bit of Canada. Much of this has been at about 2,000 feet above the ground so that Dorothy could comfortably note the interesting details of the terrain and follow section charts.

Along with the Ercoupe Owners Club, the one aeronautical organization that I have been most active in during the last two decades is the Experimental Aircraft Association (EAA). I joined the EAA in the mid-1950s, a couple of years after it was formed. The idea of the organization's founding father, Paul H. Poberezny, was to create a means by which people who were building or designing airplanes in their homes could get together to share information and experiences. The EAA has grown into a popular national organization which puts out a monthly journal called *Sport Aviation*. It also holds an annual fly-in, for the last several years in Oshkosh, Wisconsin, where home builders can come and discuss their problems.

Because I have enjoyed the EAA's activities so much, and because its annual fly-ins have become such a wonderful national aviation event, I would like to devote the rest of this chapter to my EAA experiences and associations, particularly at Oshkosh.

My first real contact with the EAA was at a fly-in at Rockford, Illinois, in 1959, where I gave an illustrated talk about the development of the W-1. Attending the fly-in was a pleasant experience, for it was a relatively small affair, attended largely by home builders who were designing and/or building their own airplanes. Airplane designers like Johnny Thorp were there; he had just developed the T-18, had been selling plans, and was providing instructions to people on how to construct the airplane for themselves.

At that time the fly-in was small enough so that one could meet nearly everyone there. I got acquainted for the first time with Paul Poberezny, president and founder of the EAA, and with George Hardy, who was associated with *Sport Aviation*, the EAA's magazine. Hardy later asked me if his magazine could reproduce my old NACA technical note of 1925 entitled "Simplified Propeller Design for Low-Powered Airplanes," which was then reprinted in the magazine in 1960. The data were just as good then as they had been originally.

The EAA organization started in a small and relatively unimpressive way, its office for the first ten years being in a corner of the Poberezny basement. There was great interest in it, however, by people who wanted to build or at least assemble their own airplanes, and it grew rapidly. The annual fly-in and convention got too big for the facilities at Rockford and were moved to Oshkosh, where Steve Wittman was the airport manager. Wittman was a famous racing pilot of the 1930s who had designed, built, and flown his own airplanes in many races, and he is still at it. Steve is an ardent EAA enthusiast, and he has designed efficient airplanes such as the Wittman Tailwind, for which he has furnished plans for other builders.

The entire airport area at Oshkosh is two miles long north and south and one mile wide, and with Wittman as manager, it has been an ideal place for EAA activity to grow. It has grown immensely and is now the largest week-long aerial activity in the world. In 1983, three-quarters of a million people attended. If I remember correctly, there were over 10,000 airplanes there, including the manufactured light planes flown in by visitors. The air traffic problem was handled very well, with over twice as many landings and take-offs per hour as in the busiest airport in the world, Chicago O'Hare, and this with mostly low-time private pilots.

After ten years of operation, the EAA moved its office to more adequate quarters in Hales Corners, a suburb of Milwaukee, and after a bit, a museum was added where examples of antique and in some cases unusual airplanes, including Piper's experimental fiberglass and plastic PA-29 plane, were exhibited. The activity has been expanded to include most all of sport flying. For several years now, divisions have included not only the home builders, but antique and classic aircraft, war birds of World War II, aerobatic flying, and most recently the ultra-light activity.

Today the EAA is a large, multifaced business activity. Its office has been moved to a magnificent new headquarters and museum building on the airport at Oshkosh, and all of its activities are carried on from there. Although the administration and publishing have become a business, Paul Poberezny has collected around him a group of ardent enthusiasts, and most of the work is carried on by volunteers without compensation. Paul's son, Tom Poberezny, who among other things is one of the country's top aerobatic pilots and takes part in the daily air show at the annual fly-in, has taken on many of the administrative duties.

At the 1983 fly-in and convention there were eight large tents in which forums and similar activities were held throughout each day. Technical forums involving airplane design, construction, and use are held in the two main tents.

For the past twelve years, starting in 1974, I have held one or more forums in one of these tents each year. The first one, entitled "Thoughts on Mush-Stall-Spin Accidents and How to Avoid Them," introduced my work on the firm-trim control problem. This paper appeared in *Sport Aviation* in January 1975. My other forums have had to do with performance, control, or safety, with titles such as "Flaps for Improved Take-Off," "Spoilers for Lateral Control," "Design for Crash Protection," and "On Airspeed Control." The last mentioned paper was published in the September 1982 issue of *Sport Aviation*.

In the other tents, forums are sometimes held for enthusiasts using a certain type of antique or classic airplane, or certain homebuilder's type. Kelly Viets, a civil engineer from Kansas and an Ercoupe owner and antique airplane enthusiast, has carried on forums on the Ercoupe since 1972. He has been one of the most active EAA volunteers, particularly in regard to antique airplanes and the museums. For many years Kelly and his lovely wife, Edna, have run a mini-museum in a tent on the field at the annual fly-ins, and sometimes Dorothy has helped them. They have shown a number of artifacts, including a replica of the Wright brothers original 12-HP engine, which they would operate for a moment or two every hour or so. They have different items every year, and in 1979 they had a rebuilt Travelair Mystery Ship, the original of which won the Open Race at the 1929 National Air Races at Cleveland. This plane, as I have mentioned, was the first to use the NACA cowling in races; it gave me a big kick back then when it beat the water-cooled racers for the first time, also.

Another plane exhibited one year was a replica of the Laird Supersolution that was constructed by an EAA chapter in Florida under the supervision of Matty Laird himself. I had an indirect interest in the plane because I had talked with Matty regarding the cowling design of his previous airplane, the Solution, when he was making it at Ashburn Field south of Chicago. The Solution won the Thompson Trophy Race at Chicago in 1930, with Speed Holman flying it, as I have also mentioned before.

In Oshkosh, a city of fifty to sixty thousand, the hotel and motel accommodations are nowhere near adequate to house the tremendous influx of people during the week of the fly-in and convention. Reservations have to be made at least a year in advance to get accommodations within the city itself or within a radius of about 25 miles. A large camping area is available, however, on the west edge of the airport, and we have found it more convenient all around to take our little VW camper and live there on the edge of the airport, within walking distance—long walking distance, that is—of most of the activities. This gives us a home base from which Dorothy and I can go our separate ways, and it provides a spot where we can rest and take it easy if we wish. I have made an awning cover that extends from one side of the camper, and with a card table and chairs under it, it is comfortable and satisfactory for entertaining visitors.

After we had attended two or three fly-ins, a number of Ercoupe enthusiasts started camping together in a group, and this continued until 1984. We camped with them in a very congenial atmosphere. Recently, one of the long-time Ercoupe owners, but who no longer flew, Jim Jackson from Iowa, drove over early, a week or so early, in his van and established a camping area in a beautiful, shaded spot in the center of an area called Paul's Woods, with preliminary deposits from a number of us. We got there two days early to help him hold the area, and more than seven thousand campers had already registered ahead of us. Jim spent almost the whole time giving service to others, carrying them when transportation was needed, getting groceries, getting laundry done, and so forth. We grieve that he has died recently, in 1986.

One of the regulars at the camp site has been Father Tom Row-

These photos show various festivities that I was a part of associated with Father Tom Rowland's donation of his Ercoupe to the EAA museum at Oshkosh in 1983. I was a passenger as Father Tom took his Ercoupe around the field for his last flight in it.

land, a Catholic priest from El Paso, Texas, who flies his Ercoupe in every year and spends most of the time doing EAA work, such as parking airplanes. Last year he was stationed at the entrance to the brand-new museum to welcome visitors and tell them about it. He brings along a little pup tent and camps in it in our area. Father Tom's Ercoupe, by the way, was built in 1941 and was the fifty-sixth off the production line. He has kept it in as original shape as possible, with its shiny aluminum finish. In 1983 Father Tom presented it to the new EAA museum at Oshkosh. In the donation ceremony, he and Dorothy and I were interviewed over the speaker system covering the entire area by Tom Poberezny, Paul's son. Then Father Tom, with me as a passenger, made his last flight in it in a fly-by around the field.

One feature that has impressed me very greatly is the commendable cleanliness with which the whole area is kept during the meet. Trash containers are located at convenient spots throughout the entire area, and the administration has made a strong play for keeping the ground entirely free from loose papers, containers, empty bottles, and other trash. It is very pleasant to see myriads of Americans enjoying a holiday in such a clean environment.

I recall one incident on the field with both pleasure and amusement. I was walking along and passed Paul Poberezny in *Red-1*, a stripped-down, completely open VW bug painted red, which he used for transportation around the field. Other officials had different colors and numbers. We stopped to chat a bit, and among other things he mentioned that it must make me feel very good to walk around and see the airplanes incorporating things that I had worked on early in the game. He then reached his arms up and said, "Come on down here and let me give you a good old Russian kiss, the kind my father used to give me." I felt a little embarrassed, but leaned down and he bussed me on the cheek, and it was a warm feeling to have him want to do that.

Another pleasant incident occurred one day when Dorothy and I were resting in the camper. Kelly Viets drove up with a gentleman by the name of Jones who had seen him in the mini-museum and asked how to get in touch with us. He was none other than our good old friend, Jonesy, now famed Dr. Robert T. Jones of NASA. During his first years with the NACA in the 1930s Jonesy had helped my projects by making computations on the tricycle gear, two-control operation, and our lateral control program. Later he introduced the sweptback wing and delta wing concepts, which permitted airplanes to fly faster and closer to Mach 1 than they could with straight wings. This concept is now used on most jet airplanes. In recent years Jones had been proposing a skewed or oblique wing concept, involving a straight wing with a pivot at the fuselage that allows the wing to be held perpendicular to the fuselage during take-off and landing and skewed to put one wing tip well forward and the other well aft during cruising flight. The unsymmetrical appearance gives one a shock at first, but his computations show that it should be definitely advantageous to ordinary transport jets flying under but close to the speed of sound and also to supersonic aircraft. To test the flying and handling characteristics, NASA had Burt Rutan construct a 38-foot span model with his fiberglass and plastic methods, and we all saw a NASA pilot demonstrate it in flight at the EAA meet in Oshkosh in the summer of 1982.

In 1971 Jones was awarded the degree of doctor of science by the University of Colorado. In 1976, commemorating his sixty-fifth birthday, NASA published the collected works of Robert T. Jones, over one thousand pages long. He is a remarkable man, and I feel privileged that we wrote a couple of the early reports together. His interests are broad, involving astronomy, making telescopes, the fluid mechanics of the heart, and the making of violins, among other things. His work has been well recognized and he has received a large number of awards for it, including the Smithsonian Institution's Langley Medal and the Prandtl Ring Award, the German Aeronautics Society's highest honor in fluid dynamics. He is also an honorary fellow of the American Institute of Aeronautics and Astronautics and has been elected to the National Academy of Sciences. He is still active at NASA Ames, and in 1977 he wrote me a letter saying, "Just yesterday I took delivery on Ercoupe #1601-N94378." And he has been flying it for the last ten years.

Since the time that Kelly Viets brought him to see us at our camper several years ago, Jonesy has been holding a forum at the EAA fly-in each summer, and we have managed to get in a number of good visits.

In 1982 Jonesy and five other NASA research workers were honored at the open-air theater in the woods near our camp. I happened to encounter the group as I was going to another meeting and walking through the NASA quarters. Incidentally, NASA has put on a large exhibit at each meeting over the last several years. Jonesy stopped me and insisted that I go along with them, and so I got a good front seat at the theater in the woods with the NASA group to be honored. Each had a chance to speak of his work, and when Jonesy got up he spent the first good portion of it telling about my activity, telling about our early work together, and stating that I should have been one of those being honored. Of course by that time the NACA had become NASA, and the NASA officials did not even know that I existed.

During the years that I have been attending the fly-ins each summer, there have been many excellent and innovative designs constructed by the home builders. Outstanding among them in the early 1970s were Jim Bede's BD-5, which was both propeller-driven and jet-driven. Since that time Burt Rutan's designs, particularly the VariEze, LongEze, and Quickie, have dominated the field. Rutan always attends the meetings with a crew, and I have managed to get a visit with him of some kind each year.

My first contact with Rutan was in 1970 at an SAE meeting in Wichita where he gave a paper on his VariViggen. This was a two-place, 150-HP, all-metal airplane whose outstanding design feature was its canard, or horizontal-tail-first, arrangement—which had been inspired by the Swedish fighter plane named Viggen.

As was demonstrated later at the Experimental Aircraft Association's annual fly-in at Oshkosh, the VariViggen could be flown in turns with the longitudinal control full back and changed from one bank to the opposite and back again without difficulty, either with power on or power off, just as I had been able to do with the W-1 and later with the Ercoupe. With the canard arrangement, however, Burt had two advantages. First, he could get satisfactory flight characteristics with a wider range of center-of-gravity locations. Second, he could get his freedom from stalling by arranging for the canard not to have sufficient power to stall the main wing. Thus, although he had a limited longitudinal control, he did not have to call it a limited elevator travel, as I had done with my tail-aft arrangements.

In my experience, most pilots disliked greatly the idea of being limited in any way whatsoever. With hindsight, I could simply have used a small enough elevator to run out of control at the right point, and my arrangement would not have been thought of as limiting. In taking the easy way, I ignored the psychology of pilots.

When Rutan designed the VariViggen, he was working for Jim Bede as an engineer and test pilot, mainly on the BD-5, a little single-place pusher—only a few of which were ever produced. Later Burt struck out for himself and designed the VariEze, a sleek two-place tandem-pusher constructed out of fiberglass-reinforced plastic; like the VariViggen, the VariEze also had the canard design. Burt worked out a method of construction that was particularly well suited to home builders, for it did not require any of the large molds that had previously been necessary for fiberglass parts. His method was simply to cut out of suitable foam the form of wing or fuselage part desired, cover this part with suitable layers of fiberglass, some with the grain running mainly in certain directions, apply an epoxy resin, and allow it to cure at room temperature.

Burt's VariEze had excellent performance and made an immediate hit. He has since come out with an improved stretched-out model, called the LongEze, many of which have been built and are still flying. In fact, Rutan has designed a number of interesting canard airplanes, and his name is now one of the best known in the general aviation field. For the past several years he has been building and testing experimental prototypes for aircraft manufacturers, and now he is working with Beech on the *Starship*, a commuter airplane with canard configuration and composite structure. And of course he most recently was involved with his brother Dick and with a talented young woman named Jeana Yeager (no relation to Chuck) in designing an exceptionally interesting and highly refined airplane named the Voyager. In December 1986, this duo flew the Voyager around the world in one hop without refueling. That was quite a feat!

17.

Epilogue: Pilgrimage to Kitty Hawk

On December 17, 1978, Dorothy and I attended the celebration of the seventy-fifth anniversary of the Wright brothers' first flight at Kitty Hawk in 1903. The night before the big public celebration we attended a special anniversary dinner and were fortunate to sit opposite Paul Garber and his wife. I had known Paul, the curator of the Smithsonian's aeronautical exhibits, since the 1930s, and we had lots to talk about, including the recent opening of the National Air and Space Museum in Washington, D.C. In the early 1940s I had furnished him at his request with models of the W-1 and the Ercoupe airplanes for a Smithsonian exhibit. The models were made by a friend of mine, Morris Mountjoy, who had worked for me at ERCO.

The official ceremony at Kitty Hawk on the morning of the seventeenth took place on the grounds of the little National Park Service museum in the area of the first flight. It was a bright, sunshiny day, and we sat near Jean Thompson, widow of Floyd Thompson, who had come to work in the flight research section at NACA Langley in the mid-1920s, right after I had started at the lab. Thompson later

Panel in the National Air and Space Museum's Gallery of Flight Technology, Washington, D.C. It is a great honor to be included in such a group of significant air and space technologists, many of whom I knew quite well.

The National Air and Space Museum also honored me in its 1984 exhibit celebrating the three-hundredth anniversary of the first German immigrant to the United States.

Paying my respects at Kill Devil Hill on the occasion of the fiftieth anniversary of the Wrights' achievement in 1953 and the seventy-fifth anniversary in 1978.

advanced to the post of director of the NASA Langley Research Center (1960–68). During the ceremony I was recognized as being the only person who had attended all three of the main celebrations: the twenty-fifth anniversary in 1928, at which Orville Wright himself had dedicated the large granite boulder that was placed at the point where the first flight had started; the fiftieth anniversary in 1953, at which I represented private flying for the Aircraft Owners and Pilots Association (AOPA); and the seventy-fifth in 1978.

Following the morning ceremony there was a luncheon sponsored by the First Flight Society, which sponsored celebrations annually. A young man from California had built a replica of the Wrights' original airplane, and in the afternoon he attempted to fly it for the spectators. He made several attempts but did not succeed in getting it to lift above the ground, possibly because he had only a light breeze to fly against, whereas the Wright brothers had enjoyed a 25-MPH wind, which helped them substantially. At least this young man's attempt was better than the flight made at the fiftieth celebration, where a re-worked 1910 Curtiss Pusher flew around after the ceremony, no doubt causing the Wright brothers' ghosts to shake their fists.

Standing on the top of Kill Devil Hill and viewing the countryside all around, it was obvious to me that a great change had taken place since the twenty-fifth anniversary in 1928. At that time one saw largely sand with a little grass, the ocean on the east, Albemarle Sound on the west, and a few trees along the sound side. There was still no bridge across the sound from the mainland, and all traffic had to cross the sound by boat. The little town of Kitty Hawk was just barely perceptible in, the trees about four miles north on the sound side, and the only other structure was a Coast Guard life-saving station on the ocean. A bridge was put across the sound about 1930, and now the area has become a recreation center with houses all around and a 12-mile stretch along the ocean all the way to Nags Head and the Cape Hatteras National Seashore covered with cottages and hotels and the accompanying stores and shops.

Standing there on top of Kill Devil Hill in 1978, I thought of the time when the Wright brothers were there—when it was just a gradually moving large sand dune, before the army engineers had anchored it by planting vegetation and later erecting a monument on top of it. I imagined the countless times over a period of four years during which Orville and Wilbur Wright had carried their gliders up the hill and made gliding attempts down it, always wisely staying fairly close to the surface so that their mishaps did not result in serious injury. They were marvelously clear thinkers.

The Wrights accomplished what no one before them had ever had the insight to recognize and tackle—not even the world's top scientists who had put their thoughts in that direction. They worked out a means of controlling an aircraft aerodynamically by deflecting the wing and tail surfaces themselves, as Wilbur had seen the birds do.

The most successful glider trials, those by Otto Lilienthal and Octave Chanute, had attained a certain element of control by moving the body fore and aft or sideways, thus changing the location of the center of gravity of the aircraft with respect to the center of lift. Successful flights of model aircraft had been made by Samuel P. Langley and others, but these had depended on the stability of the aircraft to maintain flight in the direction desired. To start a turn requiring a certain angle of bank, the Wrights twisted their wing surfaces so that one wing had more lift and the other wing less lift, tilting the airplane to the desired bank. Recovery from the turn was then made by twisting the wings in the opposite direction, but this did not always operate successfully. The extra lift required to raise the down wing entailed also a retarding force on that side, or induced drag, to use Max Munk's later phrase, which was sometimes great enough to retard the wing on that side, slow it down, and cause the lift for that reason not to increase. Thus the wing would not come up.

The Wright brothers appear to have been the first to have recognized this problem, and they ultimately solved it, after many disappointing trials, by incorporating also a rudder at the rear of the craft to overcome the tendency of the lower wing to hold back or, as we would say now, to overcome the adverse yawing moments. They hesitated to add another control item to their already complicated arrangement. The present relatively simple foot and hand controls had not yet been worked out, and they flew lying prone. Orville then had the idea of connecting the rudders directly to the wing-warping device, making in effect what we now call a two-control airplane out of it, with one longitudinal control and one for banking and turning. This for the first time solved the problem of controlled heavier-than-aircraft flight.

In their 1902 session at Kitty Hawk, they made hundreds of satisfactory glides, including turns and recoveries in both directions. The load-carrying performance and the control of the gliding flights having been accomplished, there remained only the problem of adding an engine and propeller system. They did a remarkable job in the efficiency they obtained from their first propeller installation, and, I mused, their first successful powered flights had been made just seventy-five years before, from the flat area down below.

It was interesting to me also that although the powered flight had to wait for the development of a light engine with sufficient power, the controllable glider that was the essence of the aircraft could have been made with the materials and tools available several hundred years before. How the experiments of those two young men have changed our world, our means of travel over both land and seas and now, with the aid of rockets, even to the moon and beyond!

Two years after the seventy-fifth anniversary, in 1980, Dorothy and I made a trip around the world in twenty airline flights and in a wide range of airplanes from the little ten-passenger Britten-

Norman Islander, which shuttled us about central Africa and New Zealand, to the giant Boeing 747 in which we crossed vast expanses of ocean while watching Hollywood movies. All in all, it was quite a trip, and one that illustrated the advance in transportation during our lifetime. Imagine, two eighty-year-old people traveling all the way around the world with ease and comfort in less than two months, and spending most of the time visiting or sightseeing. I got a little boost out of the fact that each of the airplanes on which we flew took off and landed on a tricycle gear.

I get the same good feeling of accomplishment whenever I see NASA's Space Shuttle, the world's most sophisticated aircraft, because it too has the same type of tricycle gear with steerable and castered nose wheel which I had designed back in the 1930s in order to make it easier for neophytes to take off and land. No doubt the shuttle pilots, as experienced as they are, also appreciate an easy landing when they are coming in to land at speeds well above the top cruising speed of any of our light airplanes.

I am now nearly ninety years old. I feel very fortunate to have been alive throughout the early ventures of atmospheric flight and to have been one of the multitude working to further them. My activities in aeronautics have enriched my life greatly, especially through the personal associations and friendships encountered along the way.

I hope and trust that our world's political environment will improve so that our future generations can enjoy our technical advances and not be destroyed by them. I expect that the political problems will be solved, however, and I would like to have a look at the conditions of life that will be existing a hundred years from now, then a thousand years from now, again ten thousand years from now, and beyond.

Appendix A
Chronological List of Fred E. Weick's Technical Notes and Reports and Other Articles, Published and Unpublished

The following abbreviations are used:

ASME	American Society of Mechanical Engineers
IAS	Institute of Aeronautical Sciences
NACA TN	National Advisory Committee for Aeronautics Technical Note
NACA TR	National Advisory Committee for Aeronautics Technical Report
SAE	Society of Automotive Engineers

Jan. 1925	Simplified propeller design for low-powered airplanes. NACA TN 212.
Sept. 1925	Propeller scale effect and body interference. NACA TN 225.
Sept. 15, 1925	Aircraft propeller design. Bureau of Aeronautics, Navy Dept. Spec. SP-5.
May 1926	Propeller design.

	Part 1. Practical application of the blade element theory. NACA TN 235
	Part 2. Extension of test data on a family of model propellers by means of the modified blade element theory. NACA TN 236
	Part 3. A simple system based on model propeller test data. NACA TN 237.
June 1926	Part 4. A simple method for determining the strength of propellers. NACA TN 238.
Aug. 1926	Navy propeller section characteristics as used in propeller design. NACA TN 244.
Sept. 1926	Comparison of the symmetrical section propeller characteristics with those of a standard Durand model. NACA TN 246.
Aug. 1927	Study of open jet wind-tunnel cones. NACA TN 260.
Jan. 1928	Full-scale drag tests on various parts of Sperry Messenger airplane. NACA TN 271.
Jan. 1928	The effect of the Sperry Messenger fuselage on the air flow at the propeller plane. NACA TN 274.
Jan. 1928	Determination of propeller deflection by means of static load tests on models. NACA TN 275.
Mar. 1928	A comparison of propeller and centrifugal fans for circulating air in a wind tunnel. NACA TN 281.
June 2, 1928	The twenty-foot propeller research tunnel of the National Advisory Committee for Aeronautics. NACA TR 300. Coauthored by Donald H. Wood.
June 18, 1928	Full-scale tests of wood propellers on a VE-7 airplane in the propeller research tunnel. NACA TR 301.
June 20, 1928	Full-scale tests on a thin metal propeller at various tip speeds. NACA TR 302.
July 1928	The drag of a J-5 radial air-cooled engine. NACA TN 292.
July 13, 1928	Full-scale wind-tunnel tests of a series of metal propellers on a VE-7 airplane. NACA TR 306.
Oct. 5, 1928	Drag and cooling with various forms of cowling for a "Whirlwind" radial air-cooled engine. Part 1. NACA TR 313. (Also issued as NACA TN 301.)
Nov. 1928	Drag and cooling with various forms of cowling for a "Whirlwind" engine in a cabin fuselage. NACA TN 301.
Nov. 17, 1928	The new NACA low drag cowling. *Aviation.*

Dec. 17, 1928	Drag and cooling with various forms of cowling for a "Whirlwind" radial air-cooled engine. Part 2. NACA TR 314.
Feb. 16, 1929	Recent NACA cowling developments. *Aviation.*
Mar. 12, 1929	Full-scale wind-tunnel tests with a series of propellers of different diameters on a single fuselage. NACA TR 339.
Mar. 18, 1929	Full-scale wind-tunnel tests on several metal propellers having different blade forms. NACA TR 340.
Mar. 20, 1929	The effect of reduction gearing on propeller-body interference as shown by full-scale wind-tunnel tests. NACA TR 338.
Mar. 25, 1929	Working charts for the selection of aluminum alloy propellers of a standard form to operate with various aircraft engines and bodies. NACA TR 350.
Sept. 1929	Tests of four racing type airfoils in the twenty-foot propeller research tunnel. NACA TN 317.
Sept. 1929	Full-scale investigation of the drag of a wing radiator. NACA TN 318.
Oct. 1929	The effect of the wings of single engine airplanes on propulsive efficiency as shown by full-scale wind tunnel tests. NACA TN 322. Coauthored by Donald H. Wood.
Nov. 1930	The present status of research on airplane spinning. *SAE Journal.* (Paper presented at SAE meeting, Chicago, IL, Aug. 26–28, 1930.)
Feb. 1931	The behavior of conventional airplanes in situations thought to lead to most crashes. NACA TN 363.
Aug. 27, 1931	The characteristics of a Clark Y wing model equipped with several forms of low-drag fixed slots. NACA TR 407. Coauthored by Carl J. Wenzinger.
Dec. 10, 1931	Wind-tunnel research comparing lateral control devices, particularly at high angles of attack. Part 1. Ordinary ailerons on rectangular wings. NACA TR 419. Coauthored by Carl J. Wenzinger.
Jan. 25, 1932	Preliminary investigation of modifications to conventional airplanes to give non-stalling and short-landing characteristics. NACA TR 418.
Feb. 5, 1932	Wind-tunnel research comparing lateral control devices, particularly at high angles of attack. Part 3. Ordinary ailerons rigged up 10 degrees when neutral. NACA TR 423. Coauthored by Carl J. Wenzinger.

Feb. 12, 1932	Wind-tunnel research comparing lateral control devices, particularly at high angles of attack. Part 2. Slotted ailerons and Frise ailerons. NACA TR 422. Coauthored by Richard W. Noyes.
Feb. 18, 1932	Wind-tunnel research comparing lateral control devices, particularly at high angles of attack. Part 4. Floating tip ailerons on rectangular wings. NACA TR 424. Coauthored by Thomas A. Harris.
Feb. 23, 1932	Wind-tunnel tests of a Clark Y wing with a narrow auxiliary airfoil in different positions. NACA TR 428. Coauthored by Millard J. Bamber.
Apr. 1932	Preliminary investigation of rolling moments obtained with spoilers on both slotted and plain wings. NACA TN 415.
Apr. 6, 1932	The effect of multiple fixed slots and a trailing edge flap on the lift and drag of a Clark Y airfoil. NACA TR 427. Coauthored by Joseph A. Shortal.
May 1932	Wind-tunnel tests of a Hall high-lift wing. NACA TN 417. Coauthored by Robert Sanders.
May 1932	Wind-tunnel tests of the Fowler variable-area wing. NACA TN 419.
May 1932	The aerodynamic characteristics of a model wing having a split flap deflected downward and moved to the rear. NACA TN 422.
June 13, 1932	Wind-tunnel research comparing lateral control devices, particularly at high angles of attack. Part 5. Spoilers and ailerons on rectangular wings. NACA TR 439. Coauthored by Joseph A. Shortal.
July 1932	Effect of length of Handley Page tip slots on the lateral-stability factor, damping in rolling. NACA TN 423.
July 12, 1932	Wind-tunnel research comparing lateral control devices, particularly at high angles of attack. Part 6. Skewed ailerons on rectangular wings. NACA TR 444. Coauthored by Thomas A. Harris.
Oct./Dec. 1932	Racing propellers for light airplanes. *ASME Transactions.* (Paper presented at ASME meeting, Baltimore, MD, May 12–14, 1931.)
Jan. 1933	Wind-tunnel research comparing lateral control devices, particularly at high angles of attack. Part 7. Handley Page tip and full-span slots with ailerons and spoilers. NACA TN 443. Coauthored by Carl J. Wenzinger.

Feb. 1933	Wind-tunnel research comparing lateral control devices, particularly at high angles of attack. Part 8. Straight and skewed ailerons on wings with rounded tips. NACA TN 445. Coauthored by Joseph A. Shortal.
Feb. 1933	The effect on lift, drag, and spinning characteristics of sharp leading edges on airplane wings. NACA TN 447. Coauthored by Nathan F. Scudder.
Feb. 1933	Wind-tunnel research comparing lateral control devices, particularly at high angles of attack. Part 9. Tapered wings with ordinary ailerons. NACA TN 449. Coauthored by Carl J. Wenzinger.
Mar. 1933	Wind-tunnel research comparing lateral control devices, particularly at high angles of attack. Part 10. Various control devices on a wing with a fixed auxiliary airfoil. NACA TN 451. Coauthored by Richard W. Noyes.
May 1933	Wind-tunnel research comparing lateral control devices, particularly at high angles of attack. Part 11. Various floating tip ailerons on both rectangular and tapered wings. NACA TN 458. Coauthored by Thomas A. Harris.
May 1933	Wind-tunnel tests on model wing with Fowler flap and specially developed leading-edge slot. NACA TN 459. Coauthored by Robert C. Platt.
June 1933	Aerodynamic tests of a low aspect ratio tapered wing with various flaps for use on tailless airplanes. NACA TN 463. Coauthored by Robert Sanders.
June 1933	Some factors regarding propellers for airships. (Paper presented at ASME meeting, Chicago, IL, June 26–27, 1933.) NACA library file code 4104/234.
June 10, 1933	Wind-tunnel tests on combinations of a wing with fixed auxiliary airfoils having various chords and profiles. NACA TR 472.
Aug. 1933	Present status of lateral-control devices for use with split flaps. Unpublished NACA report. NACA library file code 1136.3/48.
May 19, 1934	A flight investigation of the lateral control characteristics of short wide ailerons and various spoilers with different amounts of wing dihedral. NACA TR 494.
June 8, 1934	Wind-tunnel research comparing lateral control devices, particularly at high angles of attack. Part 12.

	Upper-surface ailerons on wings with split flaps. NACA TR 499. Coauthored by Carl J. Wenzinger.
July 1934	The W-1 airplane. *Aviation*.
July 23, 1934	Wind-tunnel research comparing lateral control devices, particularly at high angles of attack. Part 13. Auxiliary airfoils used as external ailerons. NACA TR 510. Coauthored by Richard W. Noyes.
Aug. 1934	Preliminary wind-tunnel and flight tests of a balanced split flap. Unpublished NACA report. NACA library file code 1135 Fairchild 22/1. Coauthored by Floyd L. Thompson.
Sept. 12, 1935	Outline of work on safeguards against stalling. Unpublished NACA report. NACA library file code 1104/207.
Oct. 21, 1935	Three-wheel landing gear for transport airplanes. Unpublished NACA report. NACA library file code 1151 Weick 1/1.
Nov. 1935	Development of the NACA slot-lip aileron. NACA TN 547. Coauthored by Joseph A. Shortal.
Jan. 1936	Wind-tunnel tests of wing flaps suitable for direct control of glide-path angle. NACA TN 552.
Jan. 29, 1936	Further developments with the W-1 airplane. *Aeroplane*.
Apr. 20, 1936	The effect of lateral controls in producing motion of an airplane as computed from wind-tunnel data. NACA TR 570. Coauthored by Robert T. Jones.
May 1936	Everyman's airplane: A development toward simpler flying. *SAE Transactions*. (Paper presented at SAE meeting, Detroit, MI, Jan. 13–17, 1936.)
Apr. 20, 1937	Resume and analysis of NACA lateral control research. NACA TR 605. Coauthored by Robert T. Jones.
Apr. 1939	Developing the ERCO airplane. *Aviation*.
June 1939	Composite wood and plastic propeller blades. *SAE Transactions*. (Paper presented at SAE meeting, Detroit, MI, Jan. 9–13, 1939.)
July 1940	Simpler flying. *Southern Flight*.
Dec. 1941	Development of the Ercoupe, an airplane for simplified private flying. *SAE Transactions*. (Paper presented at SAE meeting, Washington, D.C., Mar. 13–14, 1941.)
Feb. 1944	What kind of airplane will you fly tomorrow? *Southern Flight*.

Oct. 1944	Four years of simpler flying with the Ercoupe. (Paper presented at SAE meeting, Los Angeles, CA, Oct. 5–7, 1947.) NACA library file code 1001 ERCO Ercoupe/1.
Nov. 19, 1948	Investigation of high lift device arrangements particularly suitable for personal aircraft. Progress report 1 (Aug. 5–Nov. 19, 1948), NACA contract NAw-5641, Texas A&M College Research Foundation, Personal Aircraft Research Center. Coauthored by L. E. Flanagan, Jr.
Dec. 1948	An analysis of personal airplane power plant failures during 1947 with some suggested remedies. Research report 4, Texas A&M College, Engineering Experiment Station.
Feb. 27, 1949	Investigation of high lift device arrangements particularly suitable for personal aircraft. Progress report 2 (Nov. 20, 1948–Feb. 27, 1949), NACA contract NAw-5641, Texas A&M College Research Foundation, Personal Aircraft Research Center.
Mar. 7, 1949	An analysis of personal aircraft power plant failures during 1947 with some suggested remedies. *Aviation Week*.
Sept. 1951	An analytical investigation of effect of high-lift flaps on take-off of light airplanes. NACA TN 2404. Coauthored by L. E. Flanagan, Jr., and H. H. Cherry.
May 1953	Investigation of lateral control near the stall: Flight investigation with a light high-wing monoplane tested with various amounts of washout and various lengths of leading-edge slot. NACA TN 2948. Coauthored by Maurice S. Sevelson, James G. McClure, and Marion D. Flanagan.
June 1956	Investigation of lateral control near the stall: Flight tests with high-wing and low-wing monoplanes of various configurations. NACA TN 3676. Coauthored by H. Norman Abrahamson.
June 1956	Investigation of lateral control near the stall: Analysis for required longitudinal trim characteristics and discussion of design variables. NACA TN 3677. Coauthored by H. Norman Abrahamson.
1957	*Handbook on Aerial Application in Agriculture Short Course Office, A&M College of Texas, College Station, Texas.*

Nov. 1959	Present and near-future use of aircraft in agriculture. *IAS Journal.* (Paper presented at IAS meeting, Wichita, KS, Nov. 2–4, 1959.)
1960	Design philosophy of agricultural airplanes. *Quarterly Journal of the European Agricultural Aviation Centre.*
Dec. 1960	Simplified propeller design for low-powered airplanes. *Sport Aviation.* Reprint of NACA TN 212, Jan. 1925.
Jan. 1975	Thoughts on mush-stall-spin accidents and how to avoid them. *Sport Aviation.*
Sept. 1982	On airspeed control. *Sport Aviation.*

Appendix B
Patents Issued to Fred E. Weick

Jan. 26, 1932	1,842,466	Propeller. (Filed Feb. 6, 1929.)
Mar. 1, 1932	1,848,037	Airplane. (Filed Feb. 16, 1931.)
July 10, 1934	1,965,622	Method of Making Propeller Blades. (Filed Apr. 8, 1925.)
Mar. 17, 1936	2,034,218	Lateral Control for Airplanes. (Filed Nov. 21, 1934.)
Apr. 7, 1936	2,036,905	Airplane Wing. (Filed Dec. 2, 1932.)
Mar. 8, 1938	2,110,516	Airplane. (Filed Jan. 18, 1934.)
Oct. 3, 1939	2,174,542	Retractable Lateral Control Aileron. (File date unknown.)
Apr. 22, 1941	2,239,475	Balancing Aircraft Control System. (Filed July 24, 1937.)
May 12, 1970	3,511,455	Retractable Landing Gear System for Aircraft. (Filed 23 May 1968.)

Notes

Chapter 2

1. The Fokker T-2 flown by Kelly and McCready is among the permanent exhibits of the National Air and Space Museum in Washington, D.C.

Chapter 4

1. The co-author of this book, Dr. James Hansen, wants the reader to know that the author of all of the above reports was yours truly, Fred Weick. There is a complete bibliography of my technical reports and other articles at the end of this book.

Chapter 5

1. Because its speed range was so extensive, the Monomail needed a variable-pitch propeller, a design not yet available. Fixed-pitch propellers could not match the plane's high speed and take-off requirements. Equally

important were its high costs relative to already available equipment. The Monomail cost almost as much as a Ford Trimotor.

2. The stenographic records of these committee meetings are preserved in the archives of the United Technologies Corporation, East Hartford, Connecticut.

3. During World War II, Berlin would also become somewhat infamous for his idea to design a mass-produced fighter, the General Motors XP-75.

4. Later Tom Hamilton was made president of United Aircraft Export Corporation, whose main offices he set up in Paris, France!

Chapter 6

1. After my book had been out for four or five years, McGraw-Hill suggested I revise it to bring it up to date. This was really necessary because so much progress had been made in controllable-pitch propellers and in measuring the variable stresses during propeller operation. I did not feel that I had the time, but said that I would do it if I could get someone to help me. In 1935 I made such an arrangement with Langley's David Biermann, a Purdue graduate who had been working on propellers in the 20-foot propeller research tunnel. We worked together on the revision of the first few chapters, but this arrangement ended when Biermann got married. He later left Langley to become the chief engineer and then the president of the Hartzel Propeller Company. In 1943 I made the same arrangement with a fellow, Bill Green, who did propeller design work under me at ERCO, but the same thing happened: we got through three or four chapters before he became engrossed with a young lady and soon married. That was the end of the revisions, and I never did go back to it again.

There was an urgent need for a new propeller textbook, though, and a little later, in 1944, Professor Wilbur C. Nelson of the University of Michigan did write a small book that brought most of the material up to date. The title of Nelson's book was *Airplane Propeller Principles;* it was published by Wiley in New York City.

2. A few years later, while vacationing in Michigan, I attended a glider meet near the town of Frankfort, where there were 400-foot-high bluffs overlooking Lake Michigan. With the usual west wind, the conditions were very favorable there for ridge soaring. The gliders took off by winch tow from the beach below the bluff, and when they got about halfway up the elevation of the bluff, they would cast off and soar very nicely. A contestant by the name of Stan Smith had a two-place glider there called the *City of Utica,* and he needed an observer to record endurance and altitude data. Although a number of people wanted the job, Smith gave it to me. While we were soaring above the ridge, there were about a dozen gliders soaring

back and forth. Smith managed to get the *City of Utica* up to a little more than a thousand feet, and from there it was easy to stay aloft for the required hour or more.

Chapter 7

1. The Stout Skycar is among the rare vintage airplanes at the National Air and Space Museum's Silver Hill (Md.) facility.

2. The engine failure, we discovered later, was caused merely by the ignition switch clicking off. We had placed the ignition switch on the left wall of the cockpit, with the brake lever near the wall and somewhat ahead of it. NACA pilots had noticed that the switch was in a bad position, but we had not yet changed it. While using the brake on a previous landing, I must have brushed against the switch and put it right on the center of its motion so it could slip off in either direction. Then during the flight it must have merely slipped off due to vibration. It did not take us long after that to change the switch's location.

3. On our drive back to Virginia from Buffalo, Wenzinger and I stopped in Bradford, Pennsylvania, to see the Piper plant. Unfortunately, this was on a Saturday afternoon, and there was only one lady at the plant, making some seat upholstery. We saw the little factory but did not stop to look up any members of the Piper family. I had hoped to talk to them about their trying out the tricycle gear but was too timid to chase them down at home on a weekend.

Later that same day, we stopped at the airport at Butler, Pennsylvania, to see C. Gilbert Taylor, who was then just about half finished with the construction of his first Taylorcraft airplane. He was not interested in the possible application of the tricycle gear, however, because he had all he could do to get his Taylorcraft out as it was. Anyway, I don't think that I convinced him that the tricycle gear was worth having.

Chapter 8

1. Even now, half a century later, I feel confident in saying that I have never seen a tricycle gear on a production airplane that was as effective in making a wide variety of landings, both easily and safely, as that of the W-1 and W-1A. Our plane's nose wheel was far out ahead; the gear had 12 inches of shock absorber and was designed much stronger than it needed to be. We could afford to go overboard in this direction because with the W-1's pusher arrangement, the plane's balance was helped by a little extra weight in the nose. And with the 18 inches of shock-absorber

travel for the rear wheels, safe landings on smooth surfaces could be made, as long as the vertical velocity was not in excess of about 20 feet per second, almost regardless of the manner in which the airplane was brought to the ground. With the wing-tip clearance made possible by our high wing arrangement and 5 degrees of dihedral, we made satisfactory landings while still turning with a 30-degree bank; the airplane merely straightened out by itself.

With a tractor arrangement, it was almost impossible to get the full potential of the gear. To achieve the effective wheel base one would have had to put the nose wheel out in front of the propeller, and this could not be done structurally.

2. The CAA, superseding the Bureau of Air Commerce, was established by the Civil Aeronautics Act of 1938 (Public Law 706, 75th Cong., 3rd sess., passed June 23, 1938).

3. The first published article on the "ERCO Airplane," as it was then called, was in the April 1939 issue of *Aviation* magazine.

4. Two other articles that covered aspects of the Ercoupe's early development were John C. A. Watkins, "The Phenomental Flivver," *Popular Aviation* (April 1941); and Wolfgang Langewiesche, "Making the Airplane Behave," *Harper's Magazine* (May 1942). Articles such as this helped the Ercoupe to become quite well known in a relatively short time.

5. A few years earlier the dean of engineering at RPI had invited me to start an aeronautical engineering department at his school, but I had declined. By 1941 Dr. Paul Hemke, who had problems with Dr. Max Munk while working at NACA Langley back in 1926 and 1927, was the dean of engineering, and Andrew J. Fairbanks, whom I had also known at Langley Field in the 1920s and whom I had visited at the Consolidated plant in Buffalo in 1929, was teaching aeronautical courses there.

Incidentally, in the late 1930s, the dean of engineering at Ohio State University had also invited me to start an aeronautical engineering department at his school; I declined but recommended Fairbanks for the job. Fairbanks did teach in Columbus for a while.

Chapter 9

1. These distributors were Oliver Parks, Parks Aircraft Sales and Service, St. Louis, Missouri; R. E. McCaughn, Aviation Enterprises Ltd., Houston, Texas (who later started Trans-Texas Airways); Douglas Robinson and H. O. Nelson, Tucson Arizona; C. C. Moseley and Otis D. McKenzie, Grand Central Airport, Glendale, California; E. M. Anderson, Anderson Air Activities, Milwaukee, Wisconsin; W. J. Waddell and G. H. Shepner, Waddell Aviation Company, Detroit, Michigan; Cody Laird and Gus Lazar,

Southeastern Air Services, Inc., Atlanta, Georgia; W. E. Schmidt, Wilkes-Barre, Pennsylvania; Merrill Christopherson, Provo Flying Service, Provo, Utah; John R. Keefe, Safeways Aircraft, Miami, Florida; W. D. Tipton, W. E. Mainville, and Lester Scythe, Baltimore, Maryland; Ralph Stemmens, Connecticut Aviation Company, Hartford, Connecticut; R. C. Davis, Union Motor Company, Little Rock, Arkansas; G. H. Kensinger, Memphis, Tennessee; L. W. Mack, Jr., and Willard Bridgman, Aero Enterprises, Inc., Denver, Colorado; George Patterson, Cincinnati, Ohio; and J. Wade Stewart, Parkersburg Flying Service, Parkersburg, West Virginia.

2. For a period of time in the mid-1940s, Secretary of Commerce Wallace had me on pins and needles: showing a strong personal interest in aviation he decided to learn to fly, and he picked the Ercoupe as the airplane in which to do it. Wallace's decision to learn to fly in the Ercoupe could become fine publicity for it, of course, but there was also the opposite potential. This became more and more apparent as daily reports of Wallace's progress as a pilot appeared in the newspapers. One newspaper story said, for example, that after soloing for the first time Wallace had invited a couple of friends out to Washington National Airport to watch him take off and land. The secretary of commerce took off all right and flew around a while practicing his flying, but when he landed and taxied up to the terminal, there were no friends to greet him. He had landed not at Washington National but at the Baltimore airport! This news did nothing to prop up my confidence. It turned out all right in the end, though, for I heard nothing worse than this item.

3. OMNI, which is the abbreviation for omnidirectional range, is a system of radio navigation developed largely by the CAA in the late 1940s in which any bearing relative to a special radio transmitter on the ground could be chosen and flown by an airplane pilot. VOR refers to the very high frequency Omnirange. I had an opportunity to test the new Omnirange system in 1949 after moving from ERCO to Texas A&M. A company by the name of Narco had been given a consignment to develop the receiving instrument portion of the Omnirange system that would be mounted in the airplane, and after initial experiments, the company had sent me one of its prototypes to try out. I put the receiver in the four-place Navion airplane that our college administration was using to transport people to and from the various branches of the state college system. I made many tests at various altitudes with the Narco Omnirange receiver, both locally and on trips around Texas. This was after the CAA had Omnirange ground stations operating at Houston, Dallas, and San Antonio.

By and large, the operation of the Omnirange unit was satisfactory, and soon Narco came out with a small set for private flyers, which the company called the Homer. I obtained one of these and put it in my personal Ercoupe. The operation of this unit was not entirely satisfactory, and a year or so later, Narco came out with a new unit named the Superhomer, which the company also gave me free of charge in replacement for the first one. This unit worked satisfactorily for several years. The Omnirange or VOR system eventually became, of course, the standard system and one of the basic aids to navigation throughout the world.

4. In January 1950 Dr. Jenkins coauthored *The Combat Criterion in Naval Aviation*, a report issued by the Committee on Aviation Psychology, Bureau of Medicine and Surgery, National Research Council.

Chapter 10

1. After removing their Ercoupe's rudder pedals, the CAA mechanics either threw them away or put them in a place that no one could ever find them again. In 1948 John Geisse of the CAA asked me if I could find a set of pedals, because he wanted to use them in some tests with his crosswind-type landing gear on an Ercoupe. I managed to find a pair for him, though it wasn't easy. Howard Ailer of Long Island, New York, was setting up an airplane rental business modeled after the Hertz Rent-a-Car system, with bases at various places. Ailer had ordered five Ercoupes to be delivered serially, the first one with rudder pedals, because he had figured that the general run of pilots would want them. After possessing the first plane for a couple of weeks, though, Ailer and his people began flying it without pedals. He then ordered the rest of the five as two-control airplanes.

2. Speaking of the 99's, their first all-woman transcontinental air race (later known as the Powderpuff Derby) was held in June 1950. Thirty-six planes were entered and were flown by everything from youngsters to grandmothers. The oldest was the now well-known Marian Hart, then fifty-nine years old. Standard production airplanes were used, and each one was handicapped against a given cruising speed. The race was 2,460 miles long with a number of specified overnight stops. Twenty-six airplanes finished the race without being disqualified for some reason or other, and there were no injuries. This gave a good indication of the safety of lightplane flying by that time. Two of the planes were Ercoupes, one flown by Barbara Ward, a magazine writer. In an article about the race Ms. Ward stated, "75 HP, 130 gallons of gas and a picture that designer Fred Weick drew on an engineer's drawing board took me across the continent in 24.46 flying hours." Thus my work was recognized.

3. Glenn L. Martin established the Minta Martin Aeronautical Student Fund in 1954 in honor of his mother, who had just died. I had known Glenn Martin since the summer of 1926 when he was good enough to spend the best part of an afternoon showing me, a young engineer from NACA, through his plant, which was then in Cleveland. Both Dorothy and I had met and visited with his mother, Mrs. Minta Martin, at an informal piano

recital at the Bellevue Hotel in Baltimore sponsored by a good friend of mine, Frank Schenuit, owner of the Schenuit Rubber Company. (Schenuit furnished tires for light airplanes at about half the price that was charged by the large rubber companies. A World War I seaplane pilot, he owned a Loening amphibian and a twin-engine Grumman Widgeon, which he gave me some rides in.)

4. Besides Piper, Horner, and myself, the membership of this NACA committee included Lawrence D. Bell, chairman; Jack K. Northrop, vice-chairman; Robert E. Gross of the Lockheed Aircraft Corporation; C. Bedell Monro of Pennsylvania-Central Airlines; and W. A. Patterson of United Airlines.

Chapter 11

1. At that time DeHaven's most recent publications on the subject were "Causes of Injury in Lightplane Accidents," *Aero Digest* (March 1, 1944); and "Crash Research from the Point of View of Cabin Design," *Aeronautical Engineering Review* (June 1946).

2. In the late 1970s Otto Koppen visited me at my home in Vero Beach. He was in Florida to get some refresher time in a new airplane that he had bought a little while before for his own use. And what do you suppose this designer of the Skyfarer and the Helioplane, then approaching eighty years old, had bought for his own use? A hot, snappy little Grumman American Yankee.

3. After we finished working on the Ag-1, DeHaven took me home with him to his house about 70 miles away in Connecticut. The next day, Saturday, he rented a Luscombe airplane and flew me to Boston to see Otto Koppen's Helioplane. This episode is mentioned previously in this chapter.

Chapter 13

1. The all-movable tail had a full-span tab that acted as a flap and worked with the main surface as it was moved for higher lift. This arrangement, which today is called a stabilator, had an advantage over the usual stabilizer-elevator arrangement in which the elevator worked opposite to the stabilizer. With the stabilator, a somewhat smaller overall horizontal surface could be used.

2. It was at about this time that Bill Barnhouse, one of the Texas A & M engineers who had come to work with me at Piper, left Vero Beach for Snow's operation at Olney. Barnhouse had started with us at the Piper Aircraft Development Center right after his graduation from Texas A & M in aeronautical engineering in the spring of 1958. He had spent some time in

military service and had done some work as an aerial applicator pilot before starting his courses at Texas A & M. Bill's first job with us at Piper had been on the structural design of the early PA-25, and in this connection he had worked well with his former professor, Ben Hamner, who, as I have mentioned before, was our consultant on structures. After leaving for Olney in 1962, Barnhouse returned to us in 1966. He later became head of our experimental flight testing, a position that he held until after I retired in 1969. Later he was in charge of engineering at Vero Beach, and several years ago he left Piper and became a very successful consultant.

Chapter 14

1. The number of FAA regions had been cut down to four during the Eisenhower administration as an economy move. During the Kennedy administration, the country would again be broken up into smaller FAA units and our FAA headquarters would be moved to Atlanta, Georgia. Some of our contacts with the FAA could even be handled at a branch office in Miami. However, we still had to get every engineering item and every production item approved by a government inspector, directly or indirectly.

In early 1968, Piper would obtain FAA approval to establish a "delegation-option-authorization," or DOA, system that gave certain selected and qualified employees the authority to approve certain items, such as flying qualities and production methods. When making their inspections, these persons would be actual government representatives. In my opinion, these individuals would always take their responsibilities very seriously and be at least as rigorous as the government inspectors themselves. The DOA system had been established in the Lock Haven plant a few years earlier than at Vero Beach.

Chapter 15

1. Most accidents of this nature occur when VFR pilots fly into clouds, but the loss of the horizon can occur on a clear night also. In his book *Flying Safely*, Richard Collins, editor of *Flying* magazine, writes: "A lot of factors influence the risk involved in night VFR. The most important one is the simple fact that you can't see in the dark. This reduces night flying to instrument flying except on a clear night with a substantial moon and when flying over large lighted metropolitan areas in good weather. Even if a pilot thinks he is flying VFR and is licensed only for VFR, survival depends on information from the instrument panel when it is really dark out."

Index

Big Spring airfields, Tex., 202
Blériot, Louis, 4
Blériot monoplane, 7, 8
blind flying, 247–248, 368–369
Blume, Luke, 358
Boeing Aircraft Co., xiii, 42, 44, 85, 98,
    162, 192, 196, 211, 213
Boeing aircraft: B-15, 159, 162–163;
    B-17, 163, 284; B-29, 195, 196; 40B,
    100, 101ill.; Monomail, 90, 425–426;
    PW-9, 120; 747, 415; 314-A Clipper,
    70; 247, 95; XB-15, 162–163; XPB-1,
    192–193
Boeing, William, 86, 102
Bollinger, Lynn, 251–252
Bolling Field, D.C., 43
Boob, Bob, 314ill.
Boots, Ed, 16
Boreman, Art, 206ill., 207
boundary-layer control, 282–283
Brazos River Valley, Tex., 281, 284–285
Breguet 14 airplane, 20, 21
Bridgeman, Leonard, 170
Bristol engine, 69
Britten-Norman Islander airplane,
    414–415
Brock, Billy, 94
Brown, Earl, 365
Brown, Rose "Aunt Rose," 36–37, 74
Brukner, Clayton, 23
Brush, Ed, 242, 255ill.
Brussels airport, Belgium, 169
Bryan Aircraft Inc., 367
Bryant, Farris, 339
Burbank Field, Calif., 97, 99ill., 103,
    107, 108, 237
Burden, Bill, 206ill.
Bureau of Aeronautics, U.S. Navy, 35,
    36, 37, 38, 40, 41, 43, 44, 45, 46, 47,
    56, 59, 60, 77, 88, 98, 115, 196, 416
Bureau of Air Commerce, 137, 139, 144,
    147, 150, 153, 160, 161, 181, 428
Bureau of Safety Investigation, Civil
    Aeronautics Board, 248
Burgess, Herschel, 245
Burkhalter, Billy Ray, 378, 381
Burroughs, Asa, 272
Byrd, Richard E., 77, 79

Caldwell, Frank, 37, 45, 97, 98, 109
California Institute of Technology, 103,
    149, 188, 397
Cambridge University, 57
Canadian Curtiss Jenny, 29, 30
canards, 5, 389, 408, 409
Carden, Norman F. "Skip," 399

Carroll, Thomas, 49, 83ill., 104ill.
Caudill, William W., 244
Cessna Aircraft Company, 98, 160,
    211–212, 241, 304, 324, 327, 328–
    329, 340, 374, 375
Cessna aircraft: 291, 328, 340, 341;
    Ag-Husky, 327; Ag-Truck, 327; Ag-
    Wagon, 327; Airmaster, 160, 162;
    Family Car of the Air, 211–212;
    305-A monoplane, 291
Cessna, Clyde, 279
Chamberlain, Clarence D., 77
Chamberlain, Walter, 12
Chanute, Octave, 20, 27, 413
Checkerboard Field, Ill., 13, 16–18, 22,
    23, 27, 28, 30, 31, 103
Cherry, H. H., 422
Chesapeake Aircraft Co., 131
Chester, Art, 80
Chicago Air Races, 1930, 146
Chicago, Ill., 3, 4, 5, 10, 11, 12, 13, 16,
    18, 21, 22, 28
Chris-Craft, 370–373
Church, Harry V., 8, 12
Cicero Field, Ill., 4, 7, 8
Cierva autogiro, 170
City of Utica glider, 426–427
Civil Aeromedical Research Institute,
    Oklahoma City, Ok., 312
Civil Aeronautics Act of 1938, 428
Civil Aeronautics Administration
    (CAA), 253–254, 257, 260, 262–263,
    264, 265, 270, 271, 272, 274, 283, 286,
    287, 289, 291, 299, 306, 309, 331, 333,
    334, 429, 430
Civil Aeronautics Authority (CAA), 44,
    181, 182, 183, 191, 201, 206, 207, 208,
    209, 211, 221, 250, 428
Civil Aeronautics Board (CAB), 249, 250
Civil Air Patrol, 195
Civil Service Commission, 146–147
Clark, Virginius E., 86
Clark Y airfoil, see airfoils
Clearing, Ill., 5
"Cloud Hopper," 258, 258ill., 259
Coli, Francois, 77, 79–80
Collbohm, F. R., 149
College Park airport, Md., 44, 177, 179
Collier Trophy, Robert J., 68, 396
Collins, Leighton, 179, 394
Collins, Richard, 432
composite materials, 341–344, 367
"compreg," 166, 172, 195
compressibility effects, 46
Conrad, Max, 339
Consolidated Aircraft Corp., 86, 428

440   *Index*

Verville, Alfred, 26
Verville airplanes: AT Trainer, 120, 122–123; R-2 Racer, 26, 45
Vest Field, Co., 388–389
Victor Company (RCA), 41
Victory, John F., 39, 137
Vidal, Eugene L., 137
Viets, Kelly, 403, 406
Volkswagon camper "wind tunnel," 395
von Karman, Theodore, 103, 104ill., 113ill., 188, 397
Von Rosenberg, C. W., 254, 263–264, 272, 274
VOR station (very high frequency omnirange), 209–211, 247, 299, 306, 368, 369, 429–430
Vought Aircraft Co., 43, 85
Vought, Chance, 43, 68, 95, 96
Vought VE-7 airplane, 40, 63, 64, 66, 417
Voyager, xiii, 409
VTOL (vertical takeoff and landing) aircraft, 232
Vultee, Gerald, 68, 105, 107

Waco airplane, 254, 285
Wagner, Rube, 18, 22
Waggy, Ted, 183, 186
Waldorf Astoria Hotel, New York City, 68–69
Wallace, Dwane, 160–162, 211, 212
Wallace, Henry A., 206ill., 207, 209, 429
Ward, Barbara, 430
Warner, Edward P., 56, 80, 110, 142, 150, 162–163
Warner engines, see engines, aircraft
Washington National Airport, 429
Washington (S.S.), 172
Watts, Henry C., 37, 166–167, 172
Wayne County Airport, Mich., 160–161
Weaver Aircraft Co., 23
Weaver, Buck, 23
Wegerer, Josef, 87ill., 89–90
Weick, Donald Victor, 61–62, 80, 91, 98, 132ill., 217, 218, 230ill., 230–231, 242
Weick, Dorothy Church, viii, 11ill., 12, 21, 30, 31, 36, 42, 45, 47, 48, 61, 73, 76, 86, 96, 103, 108, 109, 110, 114, 115, 116, 135, 136, 187, 199ill., 205, 230ill., 231, 236, 237, 242, 244, 291, 315, 320, 387–388, 394, 395, 399, 401, 403, 404, 406, 410, 414–415, 430
Weick, Elizabeth Jane "Betsey," 91, 100, 132ill., 229–230, 230ill., 231, 232, 242

Weick, Herb, 204
Weick, Richard F., "Dick," 230ill., 231–232, 242, 245ill.
Wells, Les, 194, 205, 231
Wenzinger, Carl, 129ill., 135, 145, 155, 418, 419, 420, 421, 424
Wes-Tex Aircraft Sales, 315
White House, 36, 43
White touring car, 16
Willard Hotel, Washington, 80
Williams, Alford, 26, 45, 96, 118
Williamson, Ed, 206ill., 207
Wilson, Ernest, 86
Wilson, Eugene E., 60, 98, 108, 109
Windecker Eagle airplane, 367
Windecker Research Inc., 366–367
Windler, Ray, 62ill., 63
windshield design in W-1, 134
wind tunnels: at NACA LANGLEY, atmospheric (NACA No. 1), 40, 50, 112, 114, 116–117, 126, 130, 135; 11-inch high-speed, 84; full-scale, 112, 127, 130, 137, 139, 148, 150, 159, 162–163, 418; propeller research, x, 46–47, 50, 50ill., 51ill., 52–67, 54ill., 55ill., 58ill., 62ill., 65ill., 78, 112, 119, 417, 418, 426; spin, 114, 169; variable-density, 40, 50, 52ill., 112, 165, 242; at STANFORD UNIVERSITY, 40; at TEXAS A&M, 243, 253, 292
Wing, George, 279–280
wing warping, 413–414
Wittman, Steve, 402
Wittman Tailwind, 402
W-1 airplane, x–xi, xiii, 126–158, 129ill., 134ill., 138ill., 159, 165, 173, 175, 197, 228, 255, 401, 410, 421, 424
W-1A airplane, 144–158, 148ill., 159, 174, 250, 424
Wood, Donald H., 62, 62ill., 64, 65ill., 66, 72, 112, 162, 417, 418
Woods, Bob, 196
Wooster, Stanton, 47, 77–79
Workentin, Herman S., 260
World Cruisers (Douglas), 42–43
World War I, 12, 13, 16, 81, 132, 149, 155, 339
World War II, 89, 150, 163, 167, 172, 192–214, 226, 229, 238, 273, 299, 302, 304, 326, 339, 396, 400, 403, 426
Wright brothers, 3, 7, 20, 403, 410, 412, 413–414
Wright Co., 4, 6
Wright engines, see engines, aircraft
Wright Field, Ohio, 97, 162
Wright Flyer, 3, 412

Photo Credits